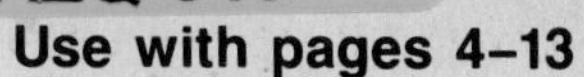

Name

Using Globes

Use the picture of the globe below to complete the activities on this page. For help, you can refer to pages 4–13 in your textbook.

1. Underline the name of the hemisphere shown on the globe.
   - a. Northern
   - b. Southern
   - c. Eastern
   - d. Western

2. Underline the name of each continent in this hemisphere. Then label the continents on the globe.
   - a. North America
   - b. Antarctica
   - c. South America
   - d. Europe
   - e. Asia
   - f. Africa

3. Underline the name of the continent that is entirely in the Northern Hemisphere.
   - a. South America
   - b. Africa
   - c. North America
   - d. Asia

4. Underline the name of the imaginary line that separates the Eastern Hemisphere from the Western Hemisphere. Then find it on the globe and label it.
   - a. prime meridian
   - b. equator

5. Underline the name of each ocean in this hemisphere. Then label the oceans on the globe.
   - a. Atlantic Ocean
   - b. Pacific Ocean
   - c. Arctic Ocean
   - d. Indian Ocean

6. Underline the name of the ocean that is entirely in the Northern Hemisphere.
   - a. Atlantic Ocean
   - b. Pacific Ocean
   - c. Arctic Ocean
   - d. Indian Ocean

Name

Distance and Direction on a Map

Use the map of Madagascar and the map scale below to answer the questions. For help, you can refer to pages 4–13 in your textbook.

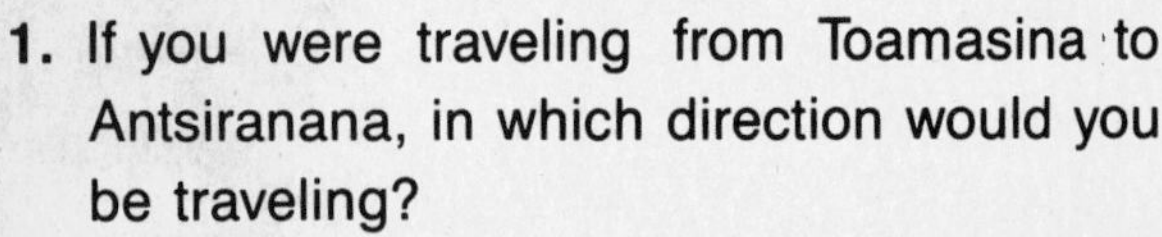

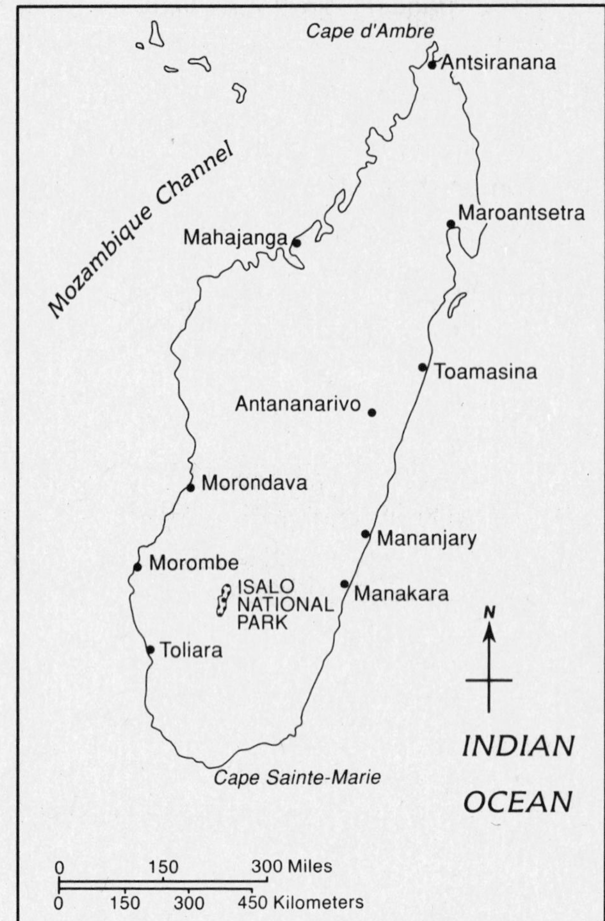

1. If you were traveling from Toamasina to Antsiranana, in which direction would you be traveling?

   ____

2. About how many miles is it from Toamasina to Maroantsetra?

   ____

3. Suppose you wanted to go from Antananarivo to Morondava. In which direction would you be traveling?

   ____

4. About how many kilometers is it from Antananarivo to Morondava?

   ____

5. About how many miles long is the island of Madagascar?

   ____

6. About how many kilometers is it from Morombe to the Indian Ocean by the shortest route?

   ____

7. About how many miles long is Isalo National Park?

   ____

8. In which part of Madagascar is Isalo National Park located?

   northern southern eastern western

Using Map Symbols

Study the map of Japan and the map key below. Then put an X next to each sentence that makes a true statement according to the information on the map. For help, you can refer to pages 4–13 in your textbook.

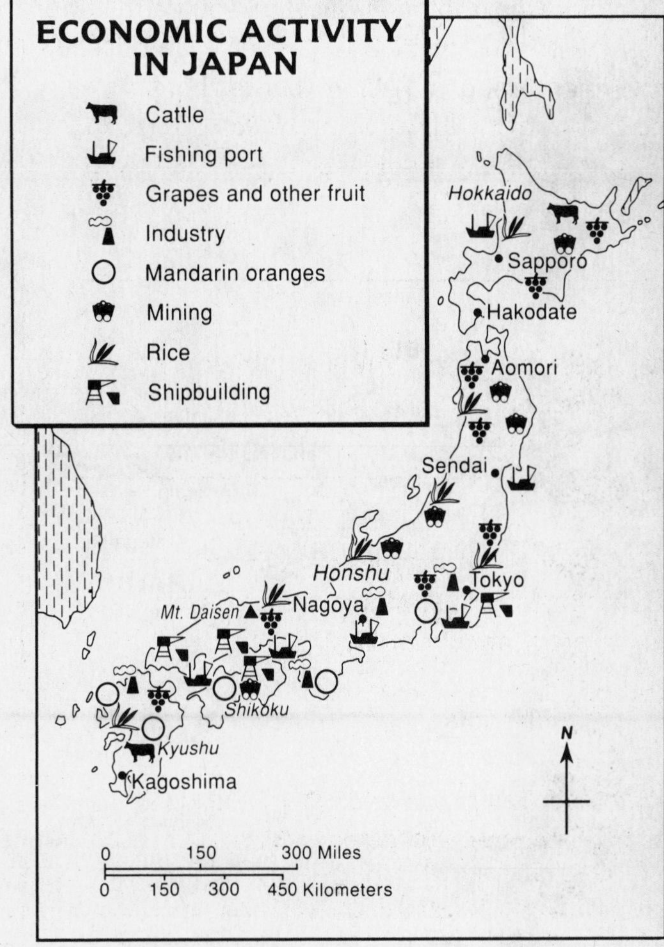

_____ **1.** The major economic activity near the city of Sendai is shipbuilding.

_____ **2.** Most of Japan's industry is located on the island of Honshu.

_____ **3.** Fruit production is the only economic activity on the island of Kyushu.

_____ **4.** Mt. Daisen is northeast of the city of Kagoshima.

_____ **5.** Sapporo is about 150 miles north of Aomori.

_____ **6.** The main cattle raising areas are on the islands of Hokkaido in the south and Kyushu in the north.

_____ **7.** The two main crops grown on the island of Hokkaido are fruits and rice.

_____ **8.** Mandarin oranges are grown mostly in the southern half of Japan.

_____ **9.** This map could help you figure out the locations of the most popular tourist attractions in Japan.

_____ **10.** This map helps you to understand where most of Japan's major economic activities are located.

Name Use with pages 4–13

Using Map Symbols

Put and **X** next to each question you can answer based on information on the map. Then use the space provided to answer each question you marked with an X. For help, you can refer to pages 4–13 in your textbook.

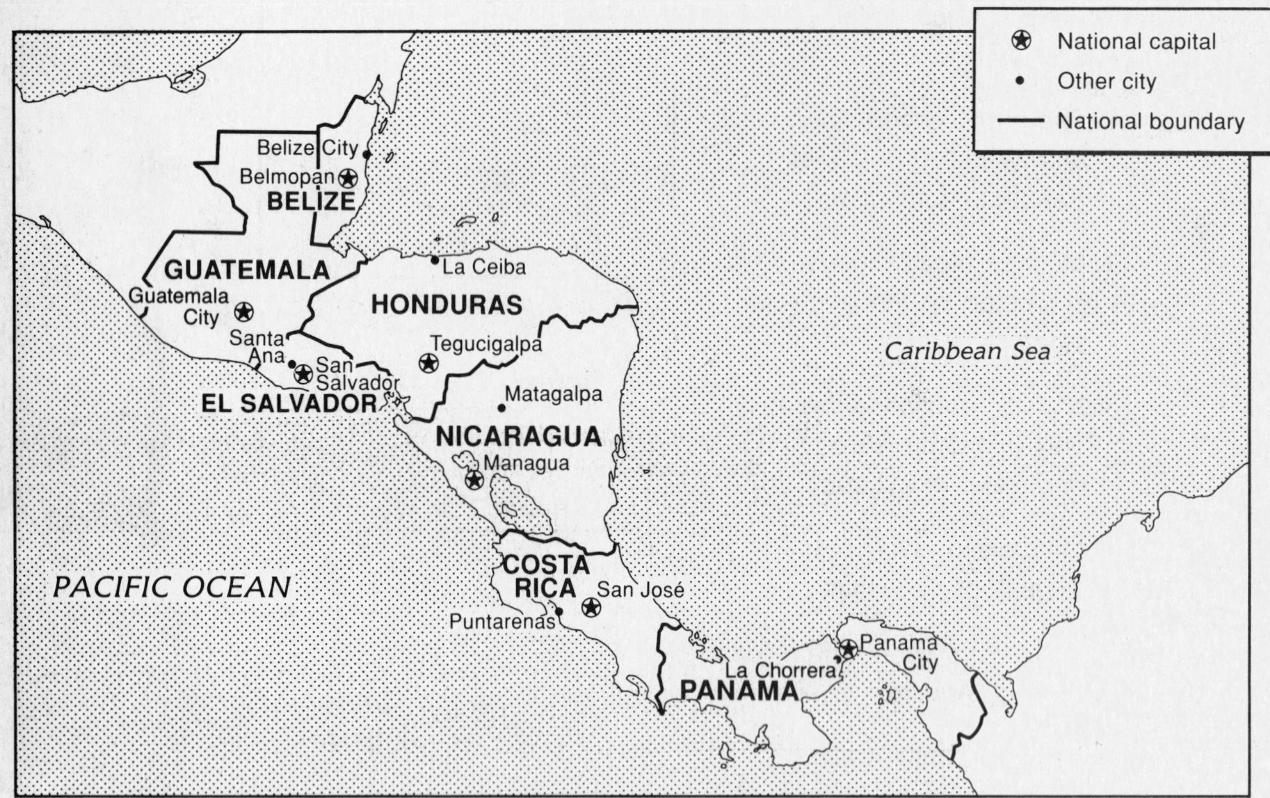

_____ **1.** Which country has no mountains, hills, or plateaus? __________

_____ **2.** Which country has the most people per square mile? __________

_____ **3.** What is the capital of Nicaragua? __________

_____ **4.** Which countries border Costa Rica? __________

_____ **5.** Which country is the most mountainous? __________

_____ **6.** How many countries make up Central America? __________

_____ **7.** What crops are grown in Honduras? __________

_____ **8.** What is the average temperature in San Salvador for the month of July? _____

Name Use with pages 4–13

Touring Paris

Use the map of Paris below to complete the activities on this page. For help, you can refer to pages 4–13 in your textbook.

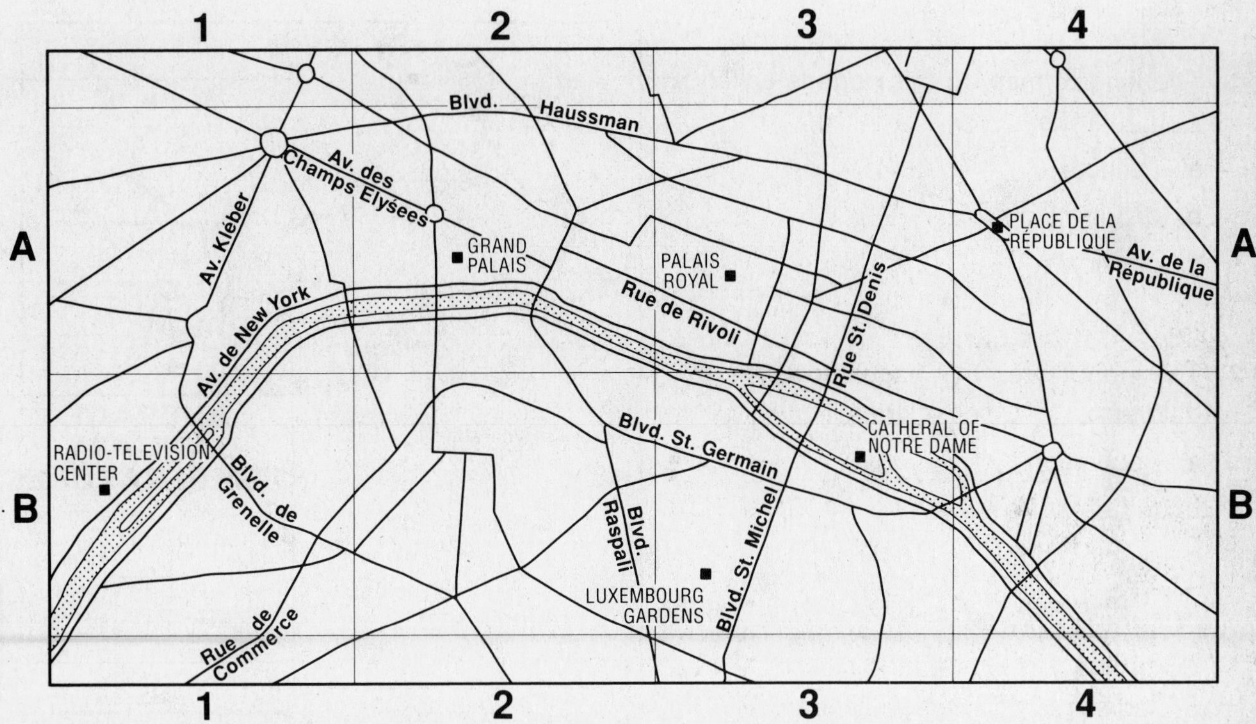

1. Suppose you and your family were planning a trip to Paris. Listed below are the places you intend to visit. Find and circle each place on the map. Then write the number and letter of the square in which it is shown on the map.

Cathedral of Notre Dame: ____________ Grand Palais: ____________

Radio-Television Center: ____________ Luxembourg Gardens: ____________

Place de la Republique: ____________ Palais Royal: ____________

2. Use the map to plan a visit to each place in Paris listed above. Use a colored pencil to draw a line on the map showing the route you would take. Your route should require as little travel as possible. Then, in the space provided, list the places you would visit in the order shown on your route.

Stop 1: ____________ Stop 4: ____________

Stop 2: ____________ Stop 5: ____________

Stop 3: ____________ Stop 6: ____________

Name Use with pages 4–13

Using a Distribution Map

Draw a line under the word or phrase that best completes each sentence. For help, you can refer to pages 4–13 in your textbook.

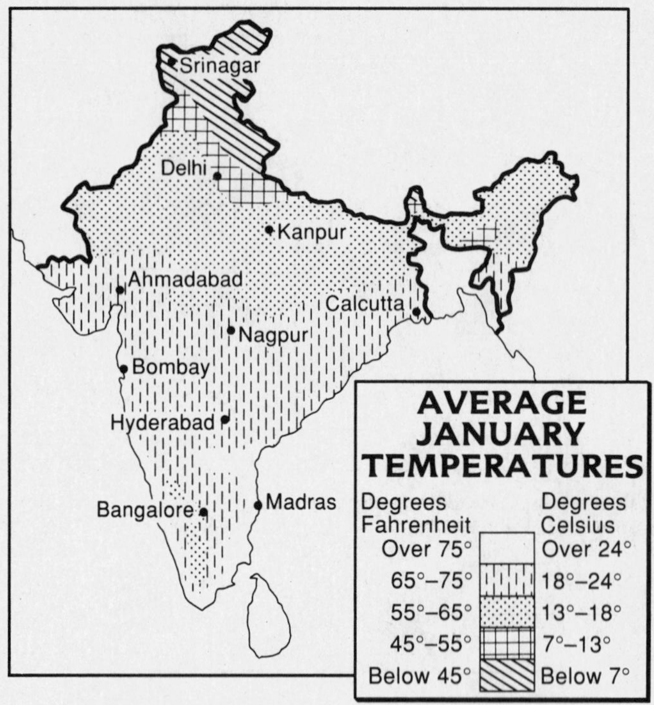

1. The kind of map on this page is called a ______ map.

a. political

b. distribution

c. physical

2. The map key on this page shows different ______ categories.

a. population

b. temperature

c. precipitation

3. According to the map, the city of Srinagar has an average January temperature of ______.

a. below 45°F.

b. 45°F. to 55°F.

c. over 24°C

4. According to the map, it is colder in ______ than in Calcutta during January.

a. Madras

b. Hyderabad

c. Delhi

5. According to the map, the coolest part of India during January is in the ______ part of the country.

a. far northern

b. southern

c. southeastern

6. According to the map, the southeastern coast of India has an average January temperature of ______.

a. over 24°C

b. 13°C to 18°C

c. below 7°C

7. According to the map, the average January temperature in Kanpur is ______ the average January temperature in your community.

a. higher than

b. lower than

c. about the same as

8. The symbol for temperatures between 65°F. and 75°F. is ______.

a.  **b.**  **c.** 

Name

Using Maps

Use the map on this page to complete the activities below. For help, you can refer to pages 38–44 in your textbook.

1. Locate and label the following regions of the United States and Canada.

   Pacific Mountains
   Appalachian Highlands
   Canadian Shield
   Coastal Plains
   Interior Plains
   Arctic Islands
   Rocky Mountains

2. Name and describe the region of the United States in which you live.

   ____

   ____

3. Name and describe the region you would most like to visit.

   ____

   ____

Name Use with pages 45–49

Resources of the United States and Canada

Study the table on this page. Then answer the questions below. For help, you can refer to pages 45–49 in your textbook.

PRODUCTS FROM NORTH AMERICAN RESOURCES

Products	United States	Canada
most important crops	corn, soybeans, wheat	barley, oats, wheat
most valuable mineral products	petroleum, natural gas, coal	petroleum, natural gas, uranium, zinc
amount of lumber produced each year	37,153,000,000 board feet	21,136,000,000 board feet
percent of electricity from hydroelectric power	5 percent	70 percent

1. a. According to the table, which crop is an important product in both countries?

   ____

   b. What natural resource makes an abundance of this crop possible?

   ____

2. a. According to the table, which country produces more lumber per year?

   ____

   b. What natural resource makes this product possible?

   ____

3. Which two mineral products are valuable to both the United States and Canada?

   ____

   ____

4. Which country uses hydroelectric power as its main source of electricity?

   ____

5. What are three reasons that the United States and Canada are lands of abundance?

   ____

   ____

   ____

Name Use with pages 50–51

Using Latitude and Longitude

Chen and his family took a trip around the world. In the chart at the bottom of the page are the latitudes and longitudes near ten of the cities they visited. Put a dot on the map to show the approximate location of each city. Then label the city according to the letter in the chart. Finally, connect the dots with a line to show the route that Chen and his family took. For help, you can refer to pages 50–51 in your textbook.

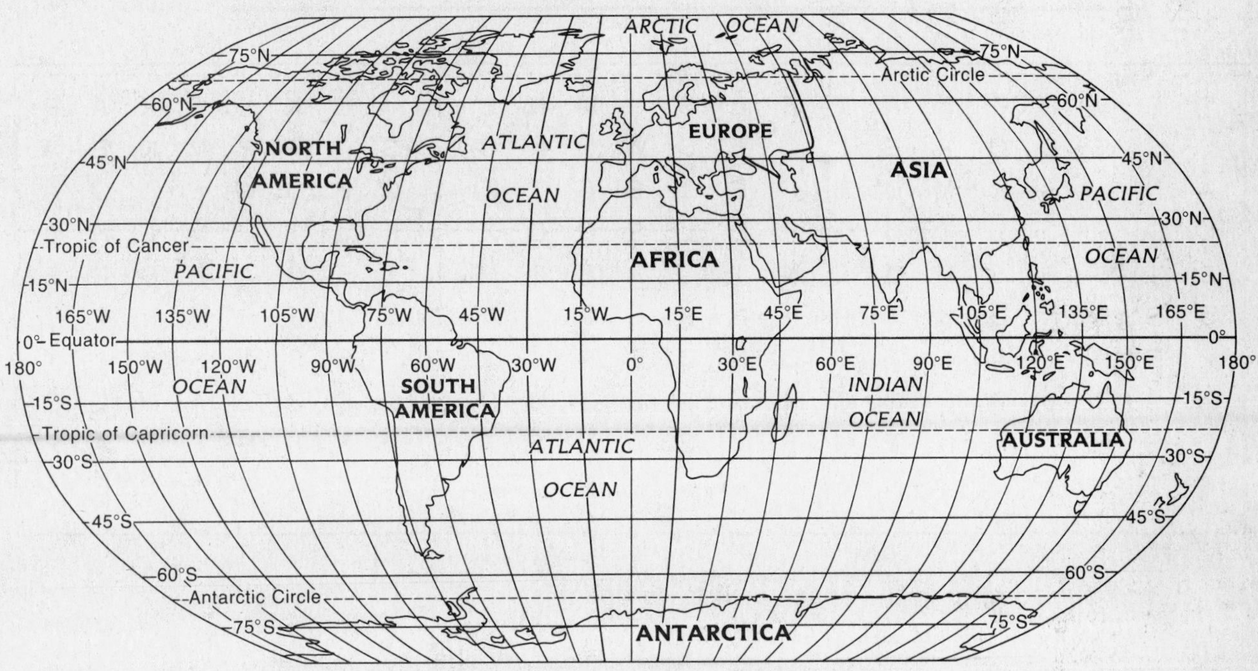

Los Angeles, California	35°N, 118°W	A
Denver, Colorado	40°N, 105°W	B
Brasília, Brazil	16°S, 48°W	C
Dakar, Senegal	15°N, 16°W	D
London, England	52°N, 0°	E
Cairo, Egypt	30°N, 30°E	F
Bombay, India	19°N, 73°E	G
Bangkok, Thailand	13°N, 100°E	H
Sydney, Australia	27°S, 150°E	I
Honolulu, Hawaii	20°N, 155°W	J

Name _______________ Use with pages 52–53

Using New Words

Find each of the terms in the box hidden among the letters that follow. Draw a circle around each term you find. The words may be read forward, backward, up, down, or diagonally. For help, you can refer to the lessons in Chapter 1 in your textbook.

hydroelectric power	permafrost	erosion	population density
Continental Divide	temperate	arable	timberline

T	E	M	P	E	R	A	T	E	D	S	N	M	N	E	T	V	O	X	L	E	K	A	P
C	S	E	C	Q	A	E	L	O	E	D	W	Q	K	C	Q	S	T	R	P	M	N	E	S
A	N	I	S	H	Y	D	R	O	E	L	E	C	T	R	I	C	P	O	W	E	R	O	A
C	O	P	Z	D	T	U	S	P	D	L	E	Q	C	X	O	E	J	I	U	M	L	R	L
D	I	B	P	S	N	O	E	N	I	L	R	E	B	M	I	T	E	G	A	F	R	R	E
J	S	E	D	O	K	T	R	K	B	R	O	P	D	V	T	Z	A	F	R	M	E	L	U
P	O	P	U	L	A	T	I	O	N	D	E	N	S	I	T	Y	R	S	I	F	B	I	K
A	R	T	U	R	O	Q	E	J	K	L	S	T	R	D	Q	O	C	O	Z	A	M	L	O
D	E	N	L	M	D	T	U	S	V	E	W	N	E	T	S	O	X	L	R	E	I	A	P
O	E	D	I	V	I	D	L	A	T	N	E	N	I	T	N	O	C	A	N	T	O	R	K

Write each circled term in the space next to its definition.

_______________ **1.** an imaginary line that separates rivers flowing eastward and westward across the land

_______________ **2.** the gradual wearing down of the earth's surface by water and wind

_______________ **3.** neither too hot nor too cold

_______________ **4.** the elevation above which trees cannot grow

_______________ **5.** good for farming

_______________ **6.** people per square mile in a given land area

_______________ **7.** a layer of soil that is permanently frozen

_______________ **8.** electricity generated by the force of rapidly moving water

A Look at Ethnic Groups

Read what Sadie Frowne wrote upon arriving in the United States in 1902. Then answer the questions. For help, you can refer to pages 55–59 in your textbook.

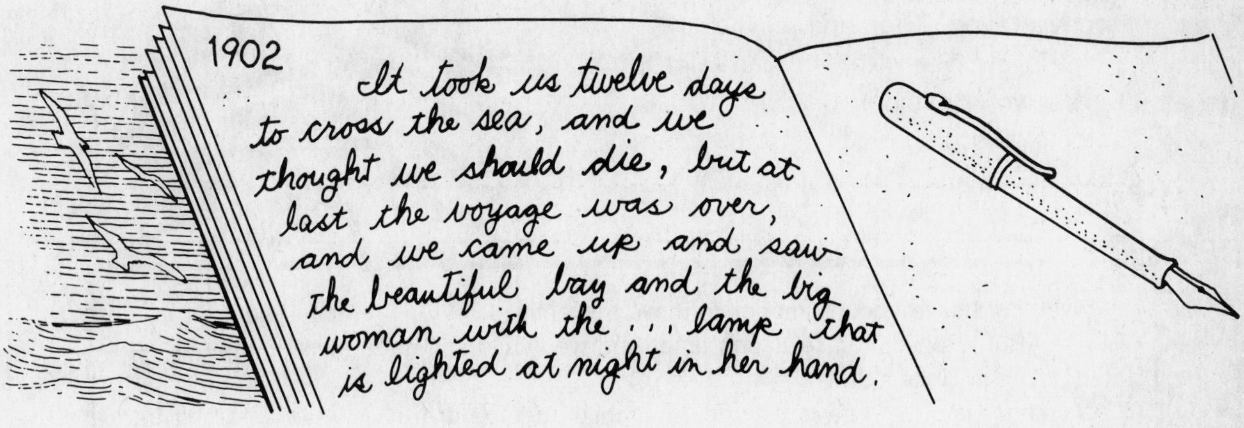

1. Sadie Frowne mentioned a "big woman with the . . . lamp." To whom or what was she referring? ______

2. Sadie Frowne was one of the many Europeans who came to the United States in 1902. From which European countries have many immigrants come to the United States?

______

3. How has the pattern of immigration changed since the early 1900s?

______

______

4. Why have people continued to immigrate to the United States?

______

______

5. What are two problems that most ethnic groups have faced at some time in their history? ______ ______

6. How have members of ethnic groups been protected against these problems?

______

______

______

Name Use with pages 60–61

Immigrating to the United States

Mr. and Mrs. Slavin want to move to the United States. In the conversation below they are trying to decide how best to make the move. Read the conversation. Then answer the questions that follow. For help, you can refer to pages 60–61 in your textbook.

"We could save enough money to move the entire family all at once," said Mr. Slavin. "But that would take a long time. And we would still need more money to get started in the United States."

"Another way would be to wait until the children have grown up," said Mrs. Slavin. "Then we could move to the United States by ourselves. The children could follow if they wanted to. But that would be many years from now. And besides, I want the children to have the advantages of growing up in the United States."

"Perhaps it would be best if I went to the United States by myself and sent for you and the children later," said Mr. Slavin. "I could get a good job and find a place to live. Then in a year or two you and the children could come. When you arrive, everything would be ready. We would miss each other, but in the end we would all be together in our new country. What do you think?"

1. According to the conversation, what was Mr. and Mrs. Slavin's goal?

a. to take a vacation in the United States
b. to move their family to the United States
c. to save money
d. to get an education

2. Which three of the following alternatives did Mr. and Mrs. Slavin consider?

a. Have the entire family move together.

b. Have everyone in the family but Mr. Slavin move.

c. Wait until the children grow up before moving.

d. Have Mr. Slavin move first and send for the family later.

3. How do you think Mrs. Slavin answered the question that Mr. Slavin asked at the end of their conversation? Explain why you think she answered the way she did.

____

____

____

Name ______________________ Use with pages 62–65

Earning a Living in the United States

Use the table below to answer the first three questions on this page. For help, you can refer to pages 62–65 in your textbook.

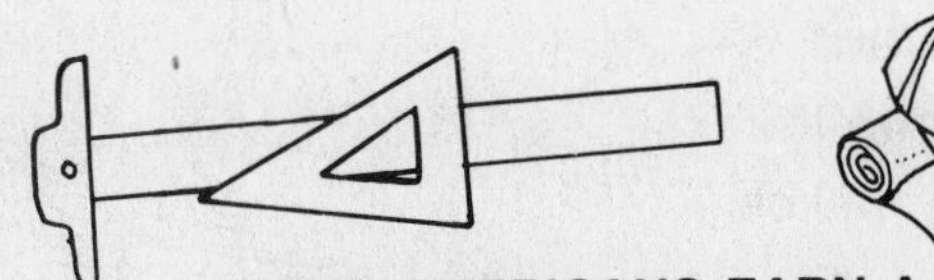

HOW AMERICANS EARN A LIVING

Type of Job	Number of Workers	Percentage of Workers
Services	72,638,000	72%
Manufacturing	19,424,000	19%
Construction	4,661,000	4%
Agriculture	3,750,000	4%
Mining	969,000	1%

1. According to the table, in which type of job do most people work?

____

What percent of the people in the United States have these types of jobs?

____

2. In which type of job do the fewest people work?

____

3. About how many people have jobs in agriculture?

____

How can this relatively small number of people supply food for the nation?

____

____

____

____

4. If you worked in a factory, what type of job would you have?

____

About how many people in the United States have these types of jobs?

____

5. What kind of economic system does the United States have?

____

What is an important part of this system?

____

6. How does the developed economy of the United States help provide a comfortable way of life for many Americans?

____

____

____

____

Name Use with pages 66–69

The Federal Government

Use the pictures on the right to complete the activities on this page. For help, you can refer to pages 66–69 in your textbook.

1. a. Draw a line to the picture that shows the branch of federal government that makes the laws of the nation.

   b. Which two houses make up this branch?

   ____

   ____

2. a. Draw a line to the picture that shows the branch of government that is responsible for carrying out the laws of the United States.

   b. What is the title of the person who heads this branch of government?

   ____

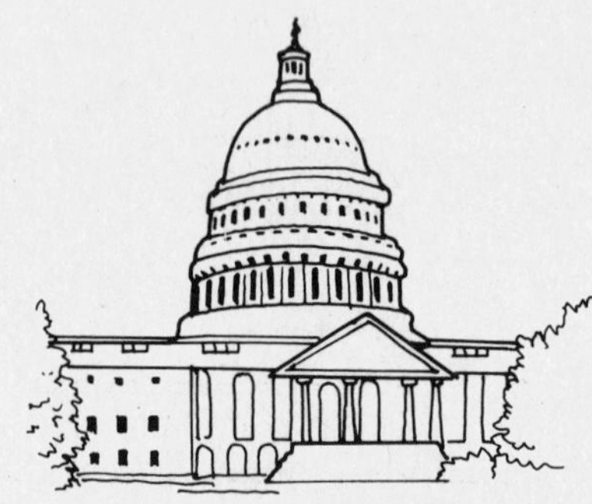

3. a. Draw a line to the picture that shows the branch of government that interprets the nation's laws.

   b. What court is at the head of this branch of government?

   ____

4. How is a system of checks and balances built into the system of federal government in the United States? ______________________________

   ____

   ____

5. How are state governments organized? ______________________________

   ____

   ____

Freedom and the Arts

Use the pictures to answer the questions on this page. For help, you can refer to pages 70–73 in your textbook.

1. Which freedom are these artists exercising?

____

2. How has this freedom affected the arts in the United States?

____

3. Suppose you could participate in one of the events illustrated above. Which one would you choose? _______________

4. Which freedom would you be exercising when you choose? _______________

5. Do you think freedom of expression and freedom of choice are important? Explain your ideas. _______________

Name Use with pages 78–79

Using New Words

Write the letter of the term that matches each description below. For help, you can refer to the lessons in Chapter 2 in your textbook.

a. freedom of expression	**f.** free enterprise	**k.** capitalism	**p.** republic
b. checks and balances	**g.** judicial branch	**l.** technology	**q.** export
c. legislative branch	**h.** discrimination	**m.** prejudice	**r.** import
d. developed economy	**i.** federal system	**n.** immigrants	
e. executive branch	**j.** megalopolis	**o.** democracy	

_____ **1.** an unfavorable opinion of a group that is formed unfairly

_____ **2.** the branch of goverment that makes the nation's laws

_____ **3.** the unfair treatment of a person or group by another person or group

_____ **4.** an area of cities and suburbs that is so crowded it looks like one vast city

_____ **5.** the branch of government that interprets the nation's laws

_____ **6.** an economic system in which businesses are owned by individuals or groups rather than by the government

_____ **7.** people who move to a country other than the one where they were born

_____ **8.** the freedom to own property and run a business free of government control

_____ **9.** any item sold to another nation

_____ **10.** an economy that has many different economic activities

_____ **11.** the methods, tools, and machinery used to meet human needs

_____ **12.** a government in which decisions are made by citizens

_____ **13.** a democracy where voters elect officials to represent them in government

_____ **14.** an item bought from another nation

_____ **15.** a government system where each branch limits the powers of the others

_____ **16.** a system of government that divides power between the national government and local governments

_____ **17.** the branch of government responsible for carrying out the laws

_____ **18.** the freedom to express any idea or opinion

Name _______________ Use with pages 81–83

Thinking About Canadian Culture

Read the following statements carefully. If a statement is true, write **True** after it. If a statement is false, write **False** after it. Then, in the space provided, write the reasons for your answers. For help, you can refer to pages 81–83 in your textbook.

1. The picture above shows an Inuit making a traditional soapstone sculpture. The Inuit were one of the first peoples to settle in the land that is now called Canada.

____

____

2. Today the Inuit are the largest cultural group in Canada.

____

____

3. Because Canada was colonized mainly by people from Great Britain, its official language is English. _______________

____

____

4. In the 1960s some French Canadians wanted to break away from Canada.

____

____

5. Some Canadians worry that the United States may be a threat to their way of life.

____

____

____

Name **Use with pages 86–88**

Writing About Canada's Economy

A letter like the one below might have been written by a miner at the Polaris Mine. Read the letter. Then complete the following exercises. For help, you can refer to pages 86–88 in your textbook.

Dear Jed,
Polaris is about the coldest place on earth. I keep my car running 24 hours a day for fear that it won't start again if I turn it off. Half the time it's so cold the tires freeze!
I used to think winters in Toronto were cold. But not after this.
Your frosty pal,
Ben

1. What is the writer describing?

____

____

2. Why is it so cold at Polaris?

____

____

3. Because of its location, the Polaris Mine is expensive to run. Why is it profitable?

____

____

4. Besides iron ore, what are two other minerals that help make mining Canada's most important industry?

____

5. List two other natural resources important for Canada's economy.

a. ______________________________

____

b. ______________________________

____

6. a. What is acid rain and how is it harmful to the environment?

____

____

____

b. How might the problem of acid rain strain relations between Canada and the United States?

____

____

Finding Information in a Library

Suppose you are writing a report about Canada. You need to check some facts in the library. Draw a line from the information you want to the picture that shows where you might find it. In the space provided, give a reason for your answer. For help, you can refer to page 89 in your textbook.

1. You want to check the location of each of Canada's provinces.

____

____

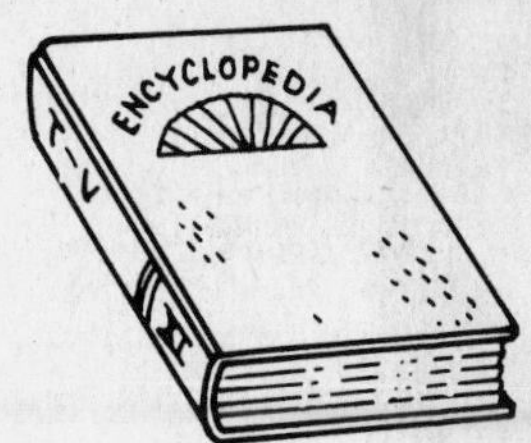

2. You need to find out what the word *separatism* means and how to spell it.

____

____

3. You want to check the most recent population figures for Canada's largest cities.

____

____

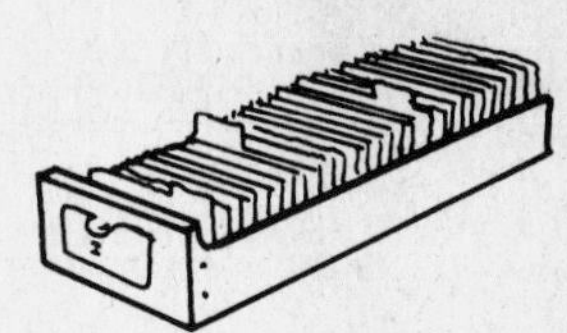

4. You need to find some information about Canada's economy.

____

____

5. You need to find a book on the Inuit.

____

____

Name _______________ Use with pages 90–92

A Look at Canada's Government

Complete the activities below. For help, you can refer to pages 90–92 in your textbook.

1. The picture shows Queen Elizabeth II of Great Britain signing the Constitution Act, which gave Canada full independence from British rule. In what year did the signing take place?

____

2. What role does the British monarch play in Canada's government today?

____

____

3. In the picture the man looking on is former Prime Minister Pierre Trudeau of Canada. What part does the prime minister play in the national government of Canada?

____

____

4. Which branches of the Canadian government does the prime minister head?

____

5. What is Canada's national legislative branch called? _______________________

6. What two houses make up the Canadian legislative branch?

____

7. How are these two houses different? _______________________

____

____

8. What must the Canadian prime minister do if he or she loses support of the majority of the members of Parliament? _______________________

Art and Recreation in Canada

Use the pictures on the right to complete the activities on this page. For help, you can refer to pages 93–95 in your textbook.

1. a. Draw a line to the picture that shows one of Canada's artistic traditions.

   b. What is a favorite topic among Canada's many artists?

   ____

   ____

2. a. Draw a line to the picture that shows one way Canadians might express their interest in ethnic identity.

   b. Why are Canadians interested in ethnic identity?

   ____

   ____

3. a. Draw a line to the picture that shows Canada's national sport.

   b. What other sports event draws thousands of spectators to Alberta every year?

   ____

Name Use with pages 96–97

Using New Words

Use the terms in the box to complete the crossword puzzle below. For help, you can refer to the lessons in Chapter 3 in your textbook.

Commonwealth of Nations	fossil fuels	monarchy	mosaic
parliamentary democracy	separatism	province	
prime minister	acid rain	cabinet	

1 2 3 4 5 6 7 8 9 10

Across

2. coal, petroleum, and natural gas (2 words)
6. a system of government with a national legislature called parliament (2 words)
7. a group of independent nations once ruled by Great Britain (3 words)
9. a governmental body made up of the prime minister and about 30 members from the House of Commons
10. a self-governing area within a nation

Down

1. the leader of the political party that has a majority of members in the House of Commons (2 words)
3. a movement to break away from a country in order to preserve a particular culture
4. a pattern or picture made up of many small pieces of stone or glass
5. a government headed by a hereditary ruler, such as a king or a queen
8. rain mixed with chemicals from burning coal and other fuels (2 words)

Using Maps

Use the map on this page to complete the activities below. For help, you can refer to pages 107–110 in your textbook.

1. a. Locate and label the following land areas.

Central America

Caribbean Islands

South America

Mexico

b. Which region do these land areas form?

____

2. a. Locate and label the following rivers. Then trace each river and its tributaries in blue.

Amazon Orinoco

Paraná Paraguay

b. Which of these rivers forms one of the world's largest river systems?

____

3. a. Locate and label the Andes mountains. Then color them brown.

b. How would you describe the climate in these mountains?

____

____

____

4. a. Locate and label Lake Titicaca.

b. What is the area around Lake Titicaca called?

____

Name Use with pages 111–114

Climate and Resources in Latin America

Use the picture to answer the first question below. Then answer the following questions. For help, you can refer to pages 111–114 in your textbook.

1. In which of Latin America's three climate zones would you find snow-capped mountain peaks?

____

Mount Aconcagua

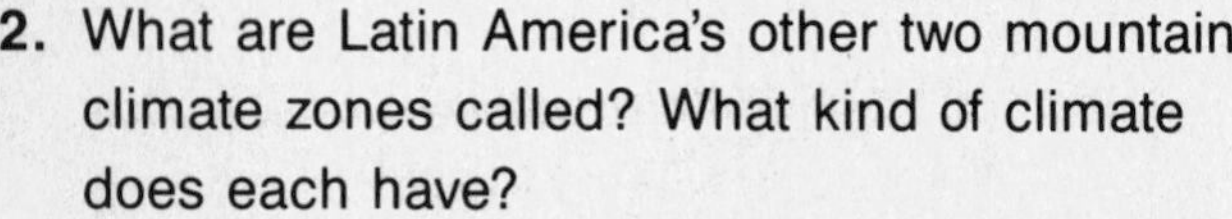

2. What are Latin America's other two mountain climate zones called? What kind of climate does each have?

name_______________________________

climate_______________________________

name_______________________________

climate_______________________________

3. Why is it surprising that Latin America's mountainous areas have three climate zones? _______________________________

4. What two places in Latin America hold world records for rainfall?

   a. World's driest place: _______________________________

   b. World's largest rainy area: _______________________________

5. What natural resource is found in the rain forest of the Amazon River Valley?

____

6. What are three other important natural resources found in Latin America?

____

7. Why are many of these resources said to be "nature's jealously hidden treasures"?

____

Relating Latitude, Elevation, and Climate

The following statements are based on information in the chart. Read the statements carefully. If a statement is true, write **True** after it. If a statement is false, write **False** after it. Then, in the space provided, write the reasons for your answer. For help, you can refer to page 115 in your textbook.

City and Country	Latitude	Approximate Elevation (ft.)
Mexico City, Mexico	21°N	7,500
Pueblo, Mexico	21°N	7,500
Bogotá, Colombia	5°N	8,500
Buenaventura, Colombia	5°N	500
Quito, Ecuador	equator	15,500
Guayaquil, Ecuador	2°S	sea level

1. You would expect the climate of Mexico City and Pueblo to be similar.

____

2. Despite the fact that Bogotá is near the equator, you would expect it to have a cold climate. ______________________________

____

3. Because Quito and Guayaquil are both near the equator, you would expect them to have hot climates. ______________________________

____

____

4. If you were planning to visit Mexico City and then Bogotá, you would expect to encounter cool climates in both cities. ______________________________

____

5. The climates of Bogotá and Buenaventura are quite different from each other. ______________

____

____

Name ______ Use with pages 116–117

Using New Words

Put an **X** next to each statement that gives correct information about the term in boldface type. For help, you can refer to the lessons in Chapter 4 in your textbook.

1. archipelago

______ **a.** An archipelago is a group of islands.

______ **b.** The Caribbean archipelagos are part of Latin America's mountain system.

______ **c.** Latin America's mountain system is known as an archipelago.

______ **d.** The Caribbean Islands are made up of small archipelagos.

2. rain forest

______ **a.** Much of North America is covered by rain forest.

______ **b.** A rain forest is a dense tropical forest.

______ **c.** Most of Latin America's trees grow in the rain forest of the Amazon River Valley.

______ **d.** The rain forests of Latin America are located in the climate zone known as tierra fría.

3. altiplano

______ **a.** The Andes mountains are sometimes called the altiplano.

______ **b.** The altiplano is a high, cold, flat area between two mountain ranges in Bolivia and Peru.

______ **c.** Many people live in the altiplano area of the Andes mountains.

______ **d.** Lake Titicaca is on the altiplano.

4. river system

______ **a.** A river system is the land drained by a major river and its tributaries.

______ **b.** South America doesn't have any large river systems.

______ **c.** The Amazon is one of the world's greatest river systems.

______ **d.** The Andean altiplano is Latin America's second-largest river system.

Name Use with pages 119–122

The Origins of Mexico's Culture

Answer the following questions. For help, you can refer to pages 119–122 in your textbook.

1. The picture above shows the ancient city of Tenochtitlán. Who built the city and where did they build it? ____________________

2. The Spanish explorer Hernando Cortés thought Tenochtitlán was "the most beautiful city in the world." If he felt this way, why did he destroy it? ____________________

3. How did the Spanish conquest of Mexico change the culture and way of life of its people? ____________________

4. What is the ancestry of the Mexican people today? ____________________

5. Why are most present-day Mexicans Roman Catholic? ____________________

Name Use with pages 123–125

A Look at Mexico's Economy

Use the graph below to answer the first two questions on this page. Then answer the following questions. For help, you can refer to pages 123–125 in your textbook.

1. a. According to the graph, what percent of Mexicans work in the agriculture, forestry, and fishing industries?

____

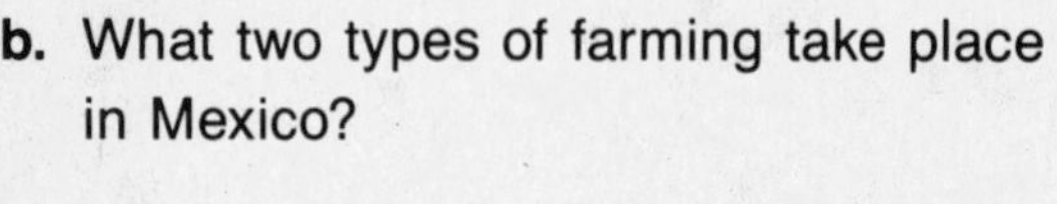

b. What two types of farming take place in Mexico?

____

____

HOW PEOPLE EARN A LIVING IN MEXICO

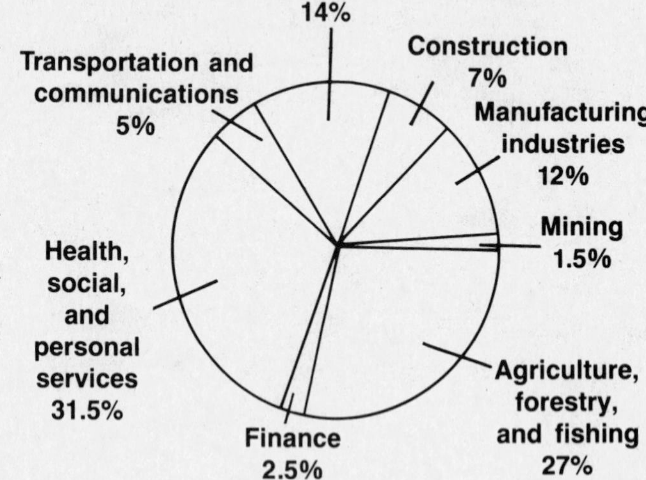

2. a. According to the graph, what percent of Mexicans work in manufacturing industries?

____

b. In which city is most of Mexico's industry located? ______________________________

3. What is one reason that Mexico is only partly industrialized?

____

____

____

4. How did the discovery of large petroleum deposits in Mexico in the 1970s affect Mexico's economy? ______________________________

____

____

5. How has Mexico's population affected the country's economic growth?

____

____

____

Name ____________________ Use with pages 126–127

Is It Accurate?

The paragraph below is from a book titled *Latin America and Canada*. The book was published in 1987. Read the paragraph. Then answer the questions that follow. For help, you can refer to pages 126–127 in your textbook.

> Mexico's largest city is its capital, Mexico City. There the nation's roads, railroads, and telephone and telegraph lines all come together. It is the center of Mexico's political, economic, and cultural life. Mexico City is the most important manufacturing center in the country. It is home to about 20 percent of the nation's population, with over 9 million people. By the year 2000, it will probably be the world's largest city.
>
> *by John Jarolimek, recognized authority on social studies, author of several books and articles on teaching and learning social studies, professor at the University of Washington; published by Macmillan*

1. What is the source of the information above? ____________________

2. Is the author an expert or well-informed on the topic? How do you know?

____

____

3. Does the author have anything to gain by giving inaccurate information on the topic?

   yes   no

4. Is the information current? How do you know? ____________________

____

____

5. What are two sources you might check to determine the accuracy of the information?

____

____

6. Do you think the information is probably accurate? How can you tell? ____________________

____

____

____

Name _______________ Use with pages 128–130

Mexico's Government

Use the terms in the box to complete the diagram of Mexico's government. Then answer the questions that follow. For help, you can refer to pages 128–130 in your textbook.

Chamber of Deputies	Senate	Supreme Court	President

EXECUTIVE BRANCH **LEGISLATIVE BRANCH** **JUDICIAL BRANCH**

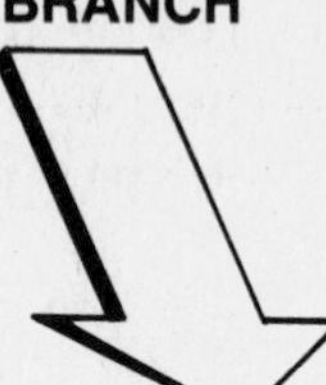

1. According to its constitution, what kind of government does Mexico have?

2. What are two powers that the President of Mexico has that the President of the United States does not have?

3. For what is the Chamber of Deputies responsible?

4. For what is the Senate responsible?

5. Why was only one strong political party, the PRI, formed in Mexico?

6. Why do critics of the PRI feel it is time for a change?

Name   Use with pages 131–133

Art, Culture, and Recreation in Mexico

The pictures below show two features of Mexican culture. Write a caption for each picture. Explain what is shown and how the picture illustrates the combining of Indian and Spanish cultures. Then answer the question that follows. For help, you can refer to pages 131–133 in your textbook.

1. ______________________________

2. ______________________________

3. How and why has the Mexican government supported traditional Mexican crafts?

____

Name _______________ Use with pages 138–139

Using New Words

Write the letter of the term that matches each definition. For help, you can refer to the lessons in Chapter 5 in your textbook.

a. subsistence farming	**e.** mestizo	**h.** petrochemical
b. developing economy	**f.** mural	**i.** civilization
c. commercial farming	**g.** extended family	**j.** campesino
d. metropolitan area		

______ **1.** a Mexican village farmer with a small plot of land and a very low income

______ **2.** a chemical that is made from petroleum

______ **3.** a culture that has developed systems of government, religion, and learning

______ **4.** farming in which just enough food is grown to feed the families of the farmers

______ **5.** a work of art on a building wall

______ **6.** a Mexican of mixed Indian and Spanish ancestry

______ **7.** a family that contains, in addition to parents and their children, other family members

______ **8.** large-scale farming in which crops are sold and exported

______ **9.** a national economy that is only partly industrialized

______ **10.** an area that includes a large city and its surrounding suburbs and towns

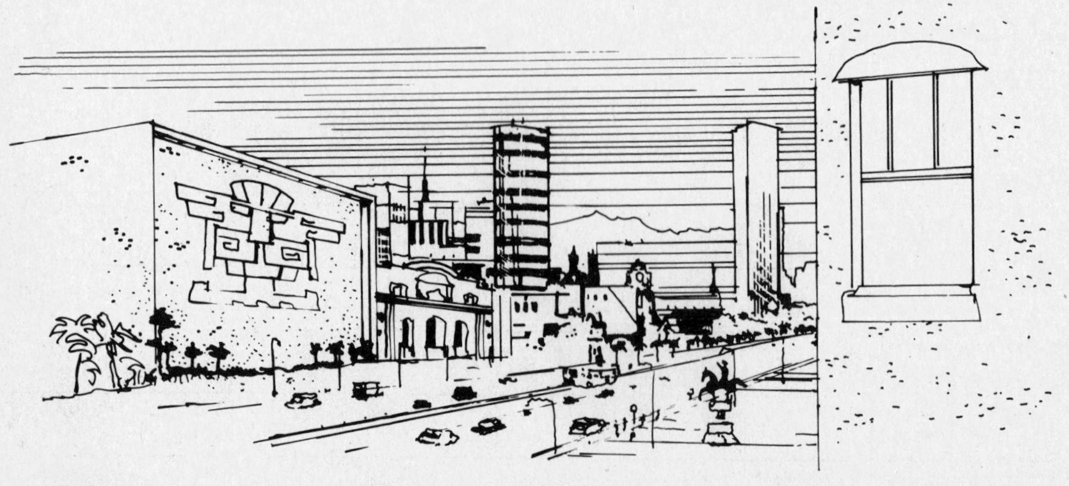

Name

Use with pages 141–144

The Origins of Latin American Cultures

Use the pictures on the right to complete the activities on this page. For help, you can refer to pages 141–144 in your textbook.

1. a. Draw a line to the picture that shows something made by the first people to live in Central America.

   b. Which three areas in Central America did these people settle?

   ____

   ____

   ____

Enslaved Africans brought to the Caribbean Islands

2. a. Draw a line to the picture that shows the second stream of people to come to Central America and the Caribbean.

   b. Which four European countries gained control of the Caribbean Islands?

   __________ __________

   __________ __________

Spanish settlers landing on a Caribbean island

3. a. Draw a line to the picture that shows the third stream of people to come to Latin America.

   b. Why did these people come to Central America and the Caribbean Islands?

   ____

   ____

   ____

Mayan sculpture

4. What makes each of the Caribbean Islands unique? ______________________

____

Name Use with pages 145–147

ECONOMY: Central America and the Caribbean

Use the bar graph below to complete the exercises on this page. For help, you can refer to pages 145–147 in your textbook.

MAIN EXPORTS OF THIRTEEN CENTRAL AMERICAN AND CARIBBEAN COUNTRIES

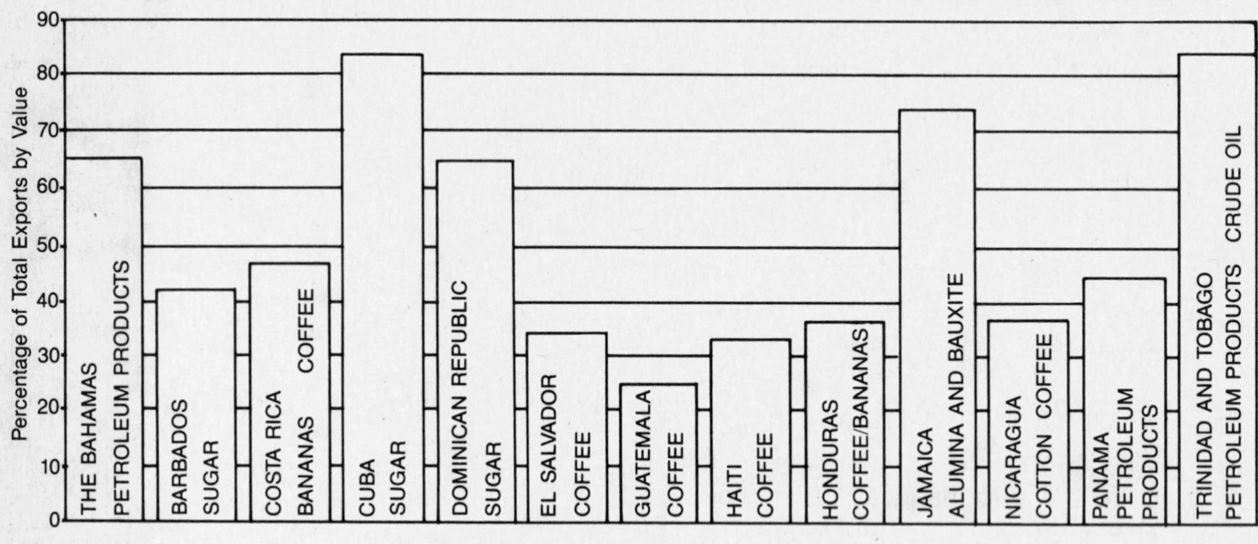

1. List the countries that export mineral products.

______________________ ______________________

______________________ ______________________

2. List the countries that export mainly agricultural products. Put an * next to those countries that depend heavily on a single crop.

______________ ______________ ______________

______________ ______________ ______________

______________ ______________ ______________

3. Why is it risky for a nation to depend heavily on one crop for its income?

____

____

4. Why are most manufacturing jobs in Central America and the Caribbean countries related to agricultural products instead of mineral products?

____

____

Name ______________________ Use with page 148

The Pan-American Highway

The map below shows the Pan-American Highway system. Study the map. Then answer the questions that follow. For help, you can refer to page 148 in your textbook.

1. According to the map, at which three cities in the United States does the Pan-American Highway begin?

____

____

____

2. To which major city do each of these routes lead?

____

3. If you traveled on the Pan-American Highway from Mexico City to Managua, Nicaragua, which three major cities would you pass through?

____

____

____

4. Trace one route you could take from Managua to Brasília in red. Trace a second route you could take in blue. ______________________

5. Why is the Pan-American Highway system of great importance to the economies of Latin America and South America? ______________________

____

____

GOVERNMENT: Central America and the Caribbean

Complete the map by writing phrases from the box in the spaces provided on the map. Each space should have a separate phrase. For help, you can refer to pages 149–151 in your textbook.

commonwealth	part of Britain
overseas area	part of France
dictatorship	part of the United States
colony	independent nation

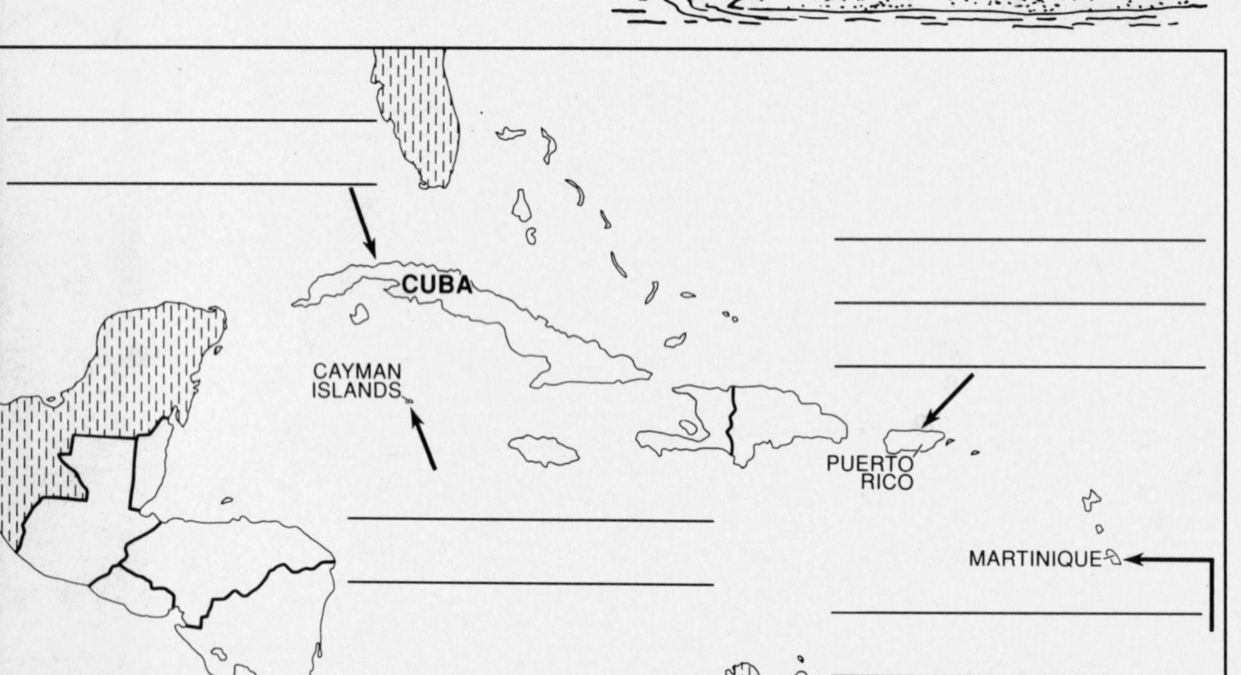

Why does the United States closely watch the events that take place in the Caribbean?

Name ______ Use with pages 154–155

Arts and Recreation in Latin America

Use the pictures below to complete the activities on this page. For help, you can refer to pages 154–155 in your textbook.

1. a. What kind of musical instrument are the people in the picture playing?

   ______

   b. On which Caribbean Island was this musical instrument developed?

   ______

   c. What kind of music are the musicians probably playing? ______

   d. What is the origin of calypso music? ______

   ______

   ______

2. a. Which popular sport is being played in the picture?

   ______

   b. In which Caribbean and Central American nations is this sport played most frequently?

   ______

   ______

   c. What is remarkable about the Dominican Republic's contribution to this sport?

   ______

   ______

   ______

   d. What other sport is a favorite in this part of the world? ______

Name Use with pages 148–149

Using New Words

Use the code to spell the words in the left column. Then write the number of each word next to its definition in the right column. For help, you can refer to the lessons in Chapter 6 of your textbook.

CODE

a = 26	g = 23	m = 20	s = 17	y = 14
b = 1	h = 4	n = 7	t = 10	z = 13
c = 25	i = 22	o = 19	u = 16	
d = 2	j = 5	p = 8	v = 11	
e = 24	k = 21	q = 18	w = 15	
f = 3	l = 6	r = 9	x = 12	

1. 20 26 9 19 19 7 ______________________

2. 25 26 6 14 8 17 19 ______________________

3. 25 19 20 20 19 7 15 24 26 6 10 4 ______________________

4. 17 24 25 10 ______________________

5. 2 22 25 10 26 10 19 9 ______________________

6. 8 6 26 7 10 26 10 22 19 7 ______________________

7. 19 7 24-25 9 19 8 24 25 19 7 19 20 14 ______________________

______ **a.** a style of music developed in the Caribbean by African slaves

______ **b.** a descendant of enslaved Africans who escaped from the Spanish in the Caribbean

______ **c.** a religious group that is outside the mainstream of large, organized religion

______ **d.** a ruler who has total control over a country

______ **e.** a large farm that grows crops for sale

______ **f.** a self-governing territory

______ **g.** an economy that depends on a single crop for income

Name Use with pages 159–161

Some Ethnic Groups in South America

Use the map to complete the activities on this page. For help, you can refer to pages 159–161 in your textbook.

1. Shade and list the two countries in which much of the population is European or of European ancestry.

____

____

2. Put a star in and list each of the three countries whose population includes many Indians.

____

____

____

3. Outline and list each of the four countries in which the population consists mainly of mestizos.

____

____

____

____

4. Name and briefly describe South America's best-known mestizo group.

____

____

5. Briefly explain how the ethnic mix of South America affects its culture.

____

____

____

Name Use with pages 162–163

Is It Fact or Opinion?

You might read statements similar to the ones below in an article about the Incas. Decide if each statement is a fact, a value judgment, or a reasoned opinion. Circle your choice. Then explain your answer. For help, you can refer to pages 162–163 in your textbook.

1. The Incas are the most interesting people to have lived in South America.

   fact value judgment reasoned opinion

   explanation: ______________________________

   ____

2. By the middle of the 1400s, the Incan empire had expanded to occupy more than 2,500 miles (4,200 km) along the western coast of South America.

   fact value judgment reasoned opinion

   explanation: ______________________________

   ____

3. The Incas built a vast network of roads to link the provinces of their large empire.

   fact value judgment reasoned opinion

   explanation: ______________________________

   ____

4. The Incan people must have been very creative since they made so many beautiful works of art.

   fact value judgment reasoned opinion

   explanation: ______________________________

   ____

5. Because so much of the private and public lives of the Incas revolved around religious practices, priests and other religious leaders must have had great authority.

   fact value judgment reasoned opinion

   explanation: ______________________________

   ____

6. Today the Incan ruins are the most interesting things to see in Peru.

   fact value judgment reasoned opinion

   explanation: ______________________________

   ____

Name ____________________

Looking at the Products of South America

Use the pictures below to complete the activities on this page. For help, you can refer to pages 164–167 in your textbook.

1. a. Which South American country is the leading exporter of this product?

____

b. What cash crop is grown in Colombia and Brazil?

____

2. a. In which part of South America might these animals be raised?

____

b. What two crops are also grown in this area?

______________________________ ______________________________

3. a. From which South American country might these leather goods have come?

____

b. What do most South American manufacturers process?

____

____

4. a. Which South American country used this major resource to help its economic development?

____

b. Why was basing its economy on this one product risky?

____

Name Use with pages 170–171

A Look at the Dictatorship of Juan Perón

The headline and article below are from *The New York Times,* September 20, 1955. Read the article and answer the questions that follow. For help, you can refer to pages 170–171 in your textbook.

PERÓN'S REGIME IS OVERTHROWN; JUNTA WILL MEET WITH REBELS; CROWDS HAIL FALL OF DICTATOR

BUENOS AIRES, Tuesday, Sept. 20–The Government of President Juan D. Perón fell last night.

A four-man junta of army generals assumed command of the forces that had fought unsuccessfully to keep General Perón in power. He had been master of Argentina since Oct. 17, 1945, and its President for nine years. . . .

The junta quickly entered into negotiations to end the four-day civil war. Army and Navy units had joined in the rebellion and forced the resignation of the President, the Cabinet and other authorities. . . .

There was no news about the whereabouts of President Perón tonight. Some reports had him in . . . the Paraguayan Embassy in Buenos Aires.

1. According to the article, who was Juan Perón and what happened to him?

2. According to the headline, how did Argentinians feel about the fall of Perón's dictatorship?

3. According to the article, how long had Perón been president of Argentina?

4. How did Perón maintain power in Argentina?

5. At the same time Eva Perón encouraged workers to give money to government programs, what did Juan Perón do?

6. Who ruled Argentina after Perón's death?

Name Use with pages 172–173

A Look at South American Traditions

Use the pictures on the right to complete the activities on this page. For help, you can refer to pages 172–173 in your textbook.

1. a. Draw a line to the picture that shows one of South America's famous poets.

b. What are some of the topics most often described by South American poets?

____

____

Carnaval in Rio de Janeiro

2. a. Draw a line to the picture that shows one of South America's most famous celebrations.

b. What national dance is featured at this celebration?

____

c. What is the origin of this dance?

____

____

João Nuñes de Oliveira

3. a. Draw a line to the picture that shows one of South America's most famous soccer players.

b. What are some other popular sports in South America?

____

____

Pablo Neruda

Name ______ **Use with pages 174–175**

Using New Words

Complete each of the exercises below. For help, you can refer to the lessons in Chapter 7 in your textbook.

1. Put an **X** next to each statement that correctly describes a gaucho.

______ **a.** A gaucho is a member of one of South America's best-known mestizo groups.

______ **b.** A gaucho is a cowhand who roams the pampas herding cattle.

______ **c.** A gaucho is a farmer who lives high in the Andes.

2. Put an **X** next to each statement that correctly describes a caudillo.

______ **a.** A caudillo is a South American mestizo group.

______ **b.** A caudillo is a local South American military leader.

______ **c.** A caudillo may become powerful enough to form an army.

3. Put an **X** next to each statement that correctly describes junta.

______ **a.** A junta is a group of military officers that run a country.

______ **b.** Junta is the name of a South American dictator.

______ **c.** A junta is a South American farmer.

4. Put an **X** next to each statement that correctly uses the word coup.

______ **a.** A coup is the sudden overthrow of a government.

______ **b.** Enemies of Juan Perón overthrew him in a coup.

______ **c.** Perón's wife helped him by forming a coup.

5. Put an **X** next to each statement that correctly uses the term per capita income.

______ **a.** The average yearly income for each person in a country is called per capita income.

______ **b.** Taxes are called per capita income in some countries.

______ **c.** Venezuela's per capita income rose when oil was discovered there.

Name

Using Maps

Use the map on this page to complete the activities below. For help, you can refer to pages 183–187 and the atlas on page 629 in your textbook.

1. Locate and label the following bodies of water.

   Atlantic Ocean
   English Channel
   Mediterranean Sea
   North Sea
   Baltic Sea

2. Locate and label the following peninsulas. Then color each one as indicated.
   a. Jutland Peninsula—brown
   b. Scandinavian Peninsula—red
   c. Italian Peninsula—green
   d. Balkan Peninsula—blue
   e. Iberian Peninsula—yellow

3. Locate and label the following islands.

   British Isles
   Sardinia
   Corsica
   Sicily

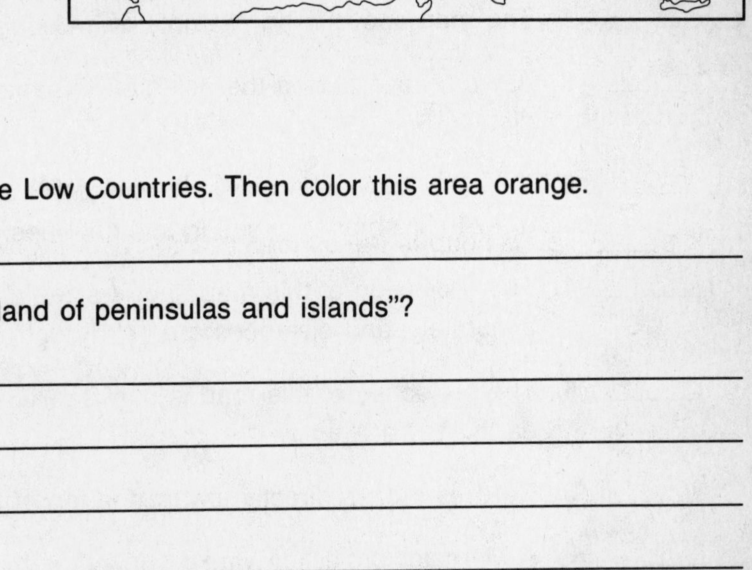

4. List the countries that make up the Low Countries. Then color this area orange.

____

5. Why is Western Europe called "a land of peninsulas and islands"?

____

____

____

____

____

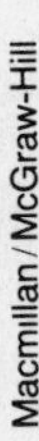

Name _______________ Use with pages 188–189

Understanding Map Projections

The map below is called a Robinson projection. Put an **X** next to each sentence that makes a true statement about the map. For help, you can refer to pages 188–189 in your textbook.

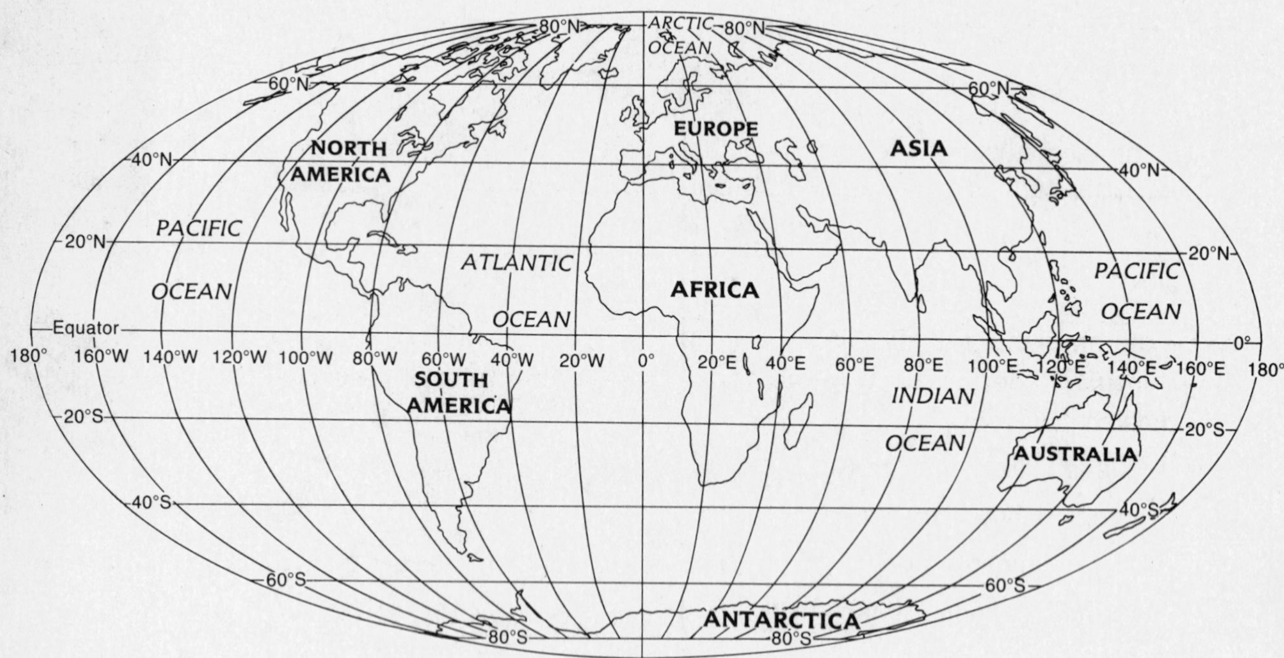

______ **1.** The map above is an example of an equal-area projection.

______ **2.** As you move toward the poles on this map, distances and shapes become distorted.

______ **3.** This kind of map is useful to navigators of ships because they can use it to draw their ships' courses in straight lines.

______ **4.** The projection of this map shows sizes and shapes of continents fairly accurately, and distances are nearly correct.

______ **5.** The projection of this map is useful for comparing different places on the earth.

______ **6.** North is always directly toward the top of this map.

______ **7.** A Mercator projection would show the shapes of the continents more accurately than they are shown on this map.

______ **8.** On this map all the lines of longitude are curved except the prime meridian.

Name

Writing About Western Europe

Use the space provided to answer the questions in each box. Arrange your answers in paragraphs. Your paragraphs will be a summary of important ideas from the lesson. For help, you can refer to pages 192–197 in your textbook.

- Which factors cause the mild climate of the Atlantic coast of Europe?
- What kind of climate does the northern part of Western Europe have? Why?
- What kind of climate does the southern part of Western Europe have? Why?

- What happened to most of the forests that once covered Western Europe?
- What threatens the forests that are left?
- What makes Western Europe a good region for growing crops?
- Why are Western Europe's rivers and waterways important?

Name ______

Using New Words

Complete each of the activities below. For help, you can refer to the lessons in Chapter 8 in your textbook.

1. Put an **X** next to each statement that correctly uses the word *landlocked*.

   ______ **a.** A landlocked country is one that is surrounded by water on three sides.

   ______ **b.** A landlocked country is one that is entirely surrounded by land.

   ______ **c.** Luxembourg, Switzerland, and Austria are the three landlocked countries of Western Europe.

   ______ **d.** Good inland waterways are of little use to a landlocked country.

   ______ **e.** Great Britain is a landlocked country.

   ______ **f.** The Rhine River begins in the landlocked country of Switzerland.

2. Put an **X** next to each statement that correctly uses the word *fjord*.

   ______ **a.** A fjord is a deep, narrow inlet of the sea between high cliffs.

   ______ **b.** The western coast of Norway is a good place to see a fjord.

   ______ **c.** A fjord is a large lake formed by retreating glaciers.

   ______ **d.** The landlocked countries of Western Europe are good places to see a fjord.

   ______ **e.** A fjord is often located far from the sea.

   ______ **f.** A fjord must be located along the coast of a country.

3. Write a sentence containing both the words *fjord* and *landlocked*.

____

____

Name ______ Use with pages 201–203

The People Who Came to the British Isles

Use the sentences in the box to complete the time line. Then answer the questions that follow. For help, you can refer to pages 201–203 in your textbook.

Stonehenge was built.
The Celts came to the British Isles.
The Romans invaded the British Isles.
The Anglo-Saxons invaded Britain.
The Normans invaded England.

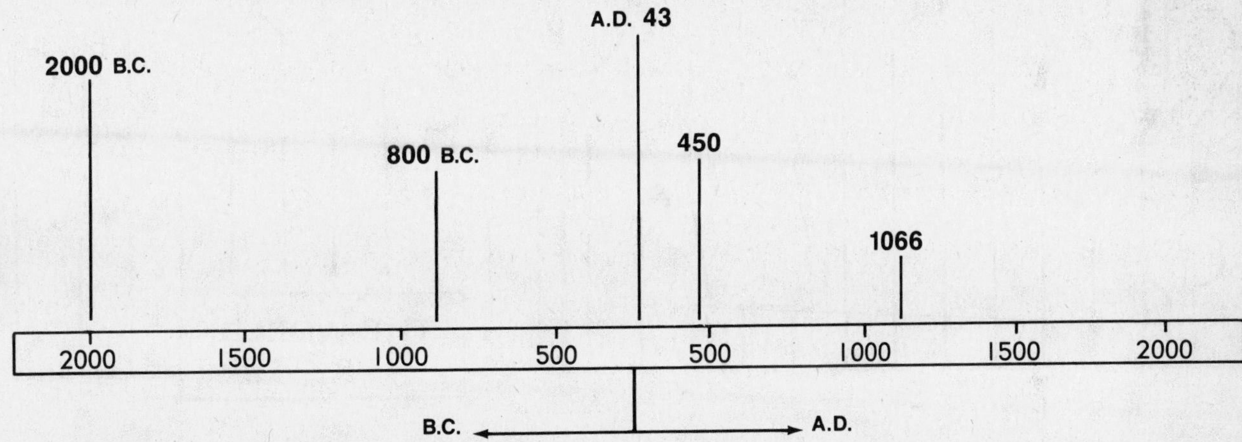

1. Who built Stonehenge?

______

______

2. According to the time line, about how long after Stonehenge was built did the Celts invade the British Isles?

______

3. About how long were the Celts in the British Isles before the Romans invaded?

______

4. Who were the Anglo-Saxons?

______

______

5. Where did the Normans come from?

______

______

6. Today where do the largest groups of newcomers to Great Britain come from?

______

______

______

Name

Use with pages 204–205

Reading Time Zone Maps

Use the time zone map below to complete the sentences. For help, you can refer to pages 204–205 in your textbook.

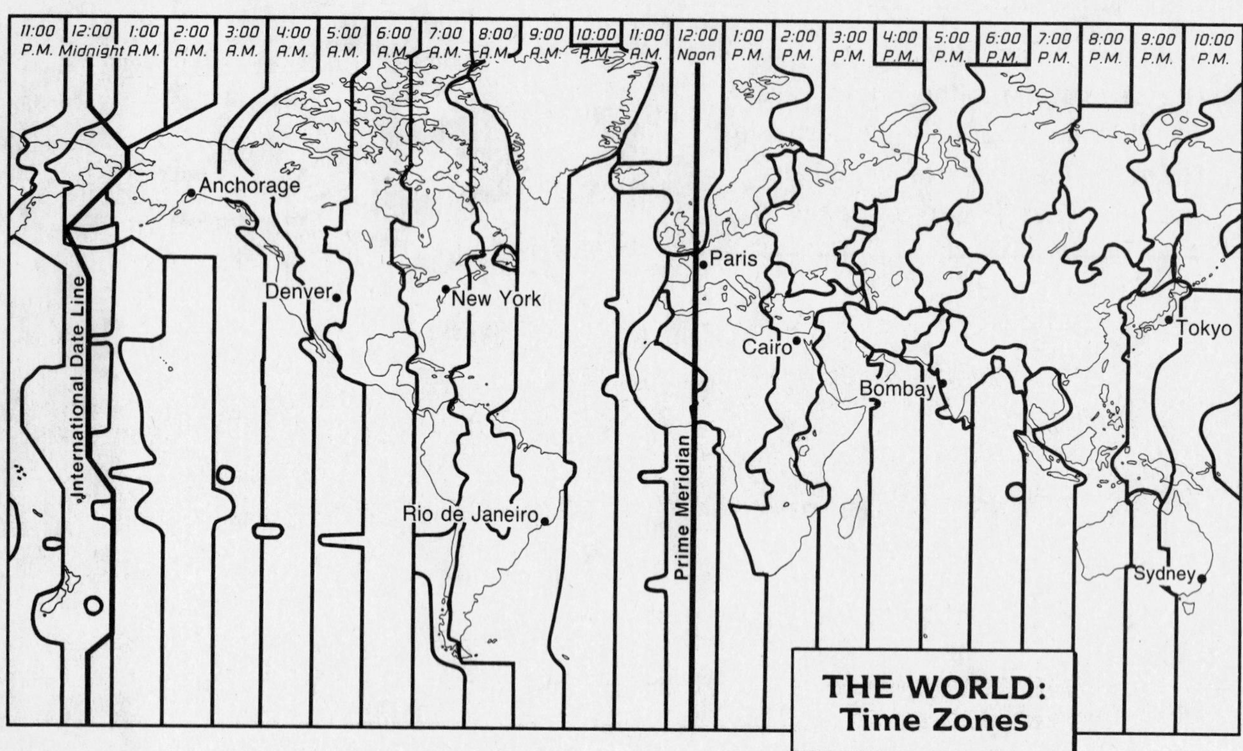

1. The line that marks the boundary between one day and the next is called the

____.

2. If you travel east across this line, today becomes _______________________.

3. If you travel west across this line, today becomes _______________________.

4. If you were traveling east from New York to Bombay, you would pass through __________ time zones.

5. When it is noon on Monday in Paris, it is ______________ on ______________ in Denver.

6. When it is 6:00 A.M. on Wednesday in Anchorage, it is ____________ on ____________ in Sydney.

Name Use with pages 206–208

Taking a Look at the British Economy

Answer the following questions. For help, you can refer to pages 206–208 in your textbook.

1. The picture above shows the inside of a British factory during the Industrial Revolution. How did factories like this change the way things were produced?

____

____

____

2. How did the economies of Great Britain and the Republic of Ireland differ during the Industrial Revolution? ____

____

____

3. How has the economy of Great Britain changed since the days of the Industrial Revolution? ____

____

____

4. What economic problems does Britain face today? ____

____

____

5. Which newly discovered natural resources in Great Britain are likely to be the key to Britain's economic future? ____

Name Use with pages 209–211

The Government of Great Britain

Answer the questions below. For help, you can refer to pages 209–211 in your textbook.

1. The picture shows King John of England signing the Magna Carta. In which year did the signing take place?

____

2. What was the Magna Carta?

____

____

____

3. What role does the monarch play in Britain's government today?

____

____

4. How does the British constitution differ from most other constitutions in the world today? ______________________________

____

____

5. What are the names of the two houses that make up the British Parliament?

______________________________ ______________________________

6. What is the title of the person who heads the Parliament? ______________________________

7. Who becomes the prime minister? ______________________________

____

8. How has the British system of government influenced other democracies in the world?

____

Name Use with pages 228–229

People in the Arts and in Sports

Each picture below shows a person who has contributed to the arts or sports of France and the Low Countries. Draw a line from each picture to its correct description. Then complete each description with the correct word or words. For help, you can refer to pages 228–229 in your textbook.

1.

Claude Monet

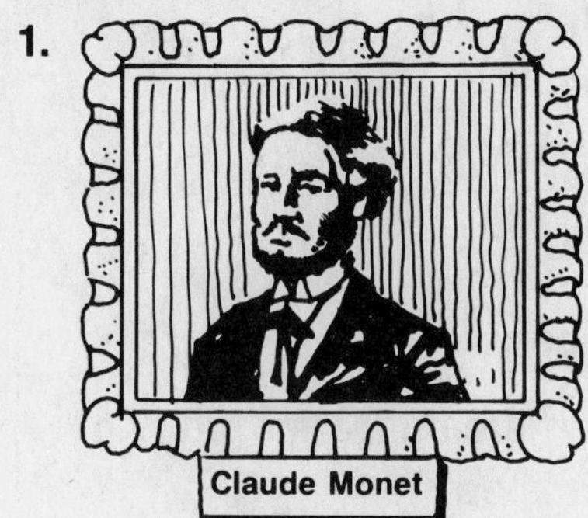

He is one of the Belgian painters who helped to invent new ways to show light in paintings. He is known as one of the ______________________.

2.

Jan Van Eyck

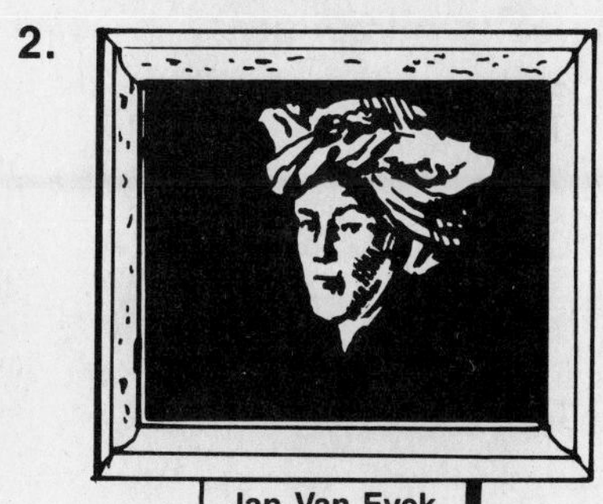

He is a Dutch painter who lived during the late 1800s. In 1988 his painting of ______________ sold for almost $40 million.

3.

Eddy Merckx

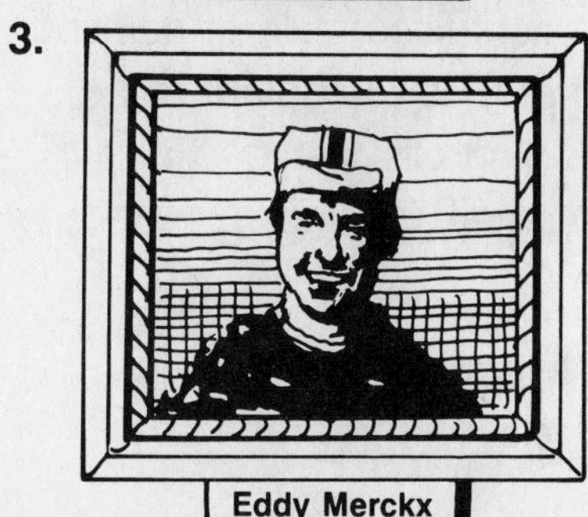

He is a famous French painter of the late nineteenth century. He helped to develop a style of painting known as ______________ .

4. 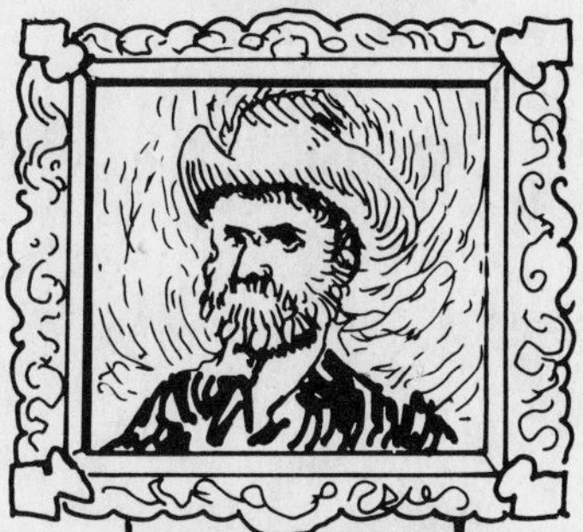

Vincent Van Gogh

He has been a Belgian contender in the Tour de France. He has won this famous bicycle race __________ times.

Name

Using New Words

Use the words in the box to complete the crossword puzzle below. For help, you can refer to the lessons in Chapter 10 in your textbook.

Tour de France	vineyard	polder
Impressionism	European Community	canal
guest worker	premier	dike

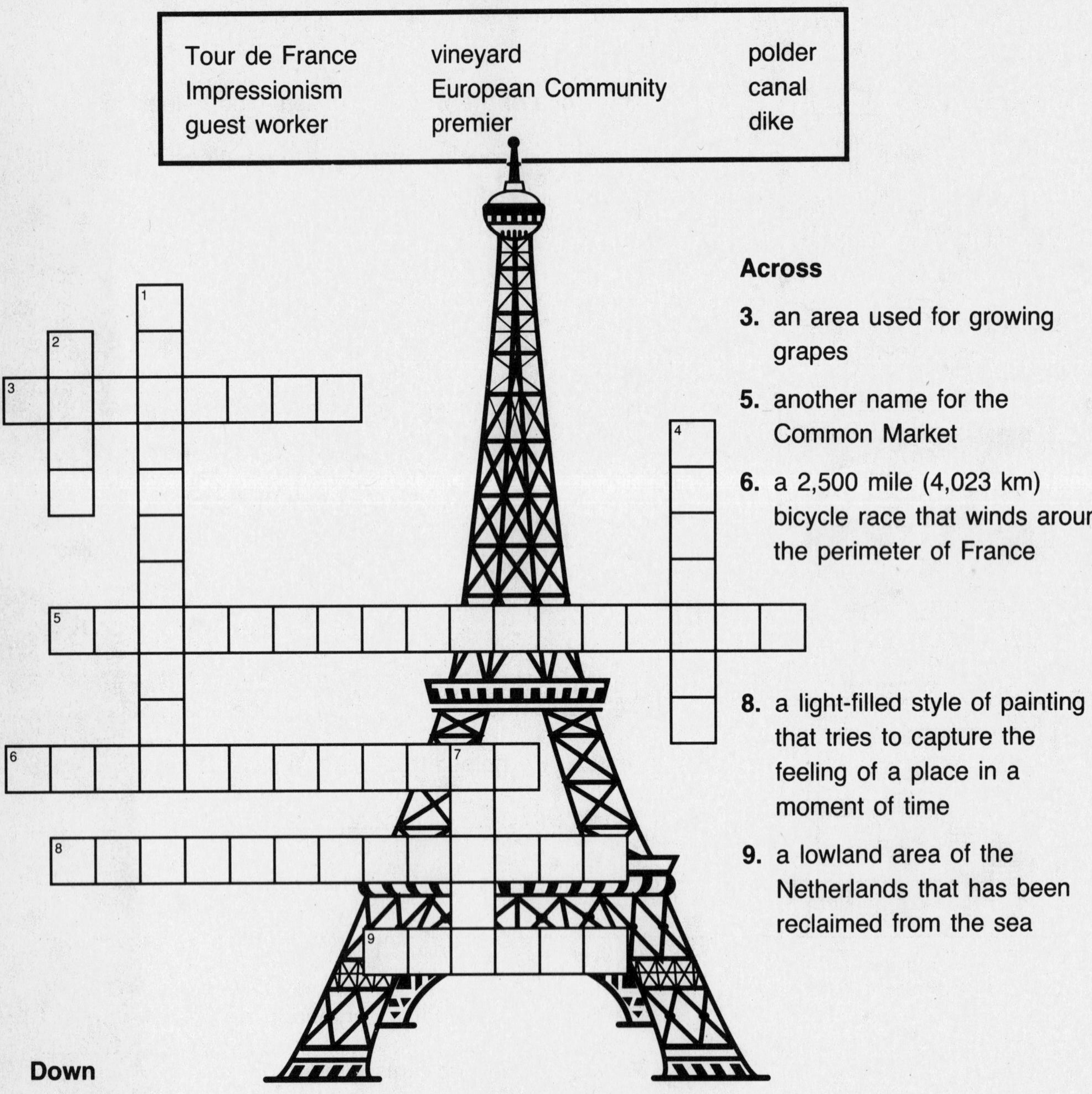

Across

3. an area used for growing grapes

5. another name for the Common Market

6. a 2,500 mile (4,023 km) bicycle race that winds around the perimeter of France

8. a light-filled style of painting that tries to capture the feeling of a place in a moment of time

9. a lowland area of the Netherlands that has been reclaimed from the sea

Down

1. an immigrant who has moved to France in search of work

2. a huge wall built to keep water away from the land

4. what the prime minister is called in France

7. a waterway that is dug for boat travel

Taking a Look at Central Europe

Follow the directions and answer the questions below. For help, you can refer to pages 233–236 in your textbook.

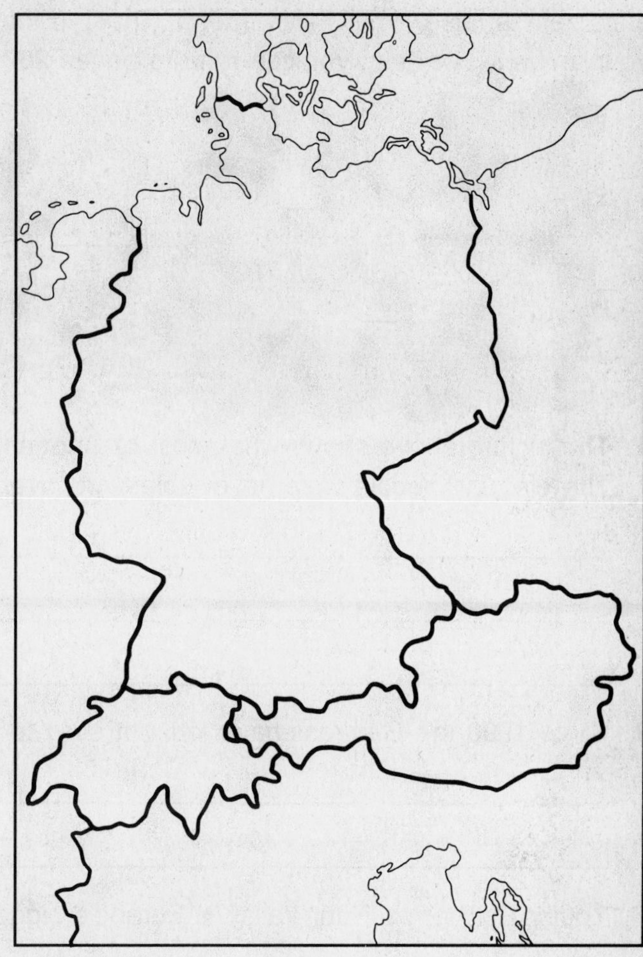

1. Locate and label the following countries on the map.
   Germany
   Switzerland
   Austria

2. Locate the Alps and color them green.

3. a. Locate and label the largest city in Central Europe.

   b. Why was this city once a divided city? ______________

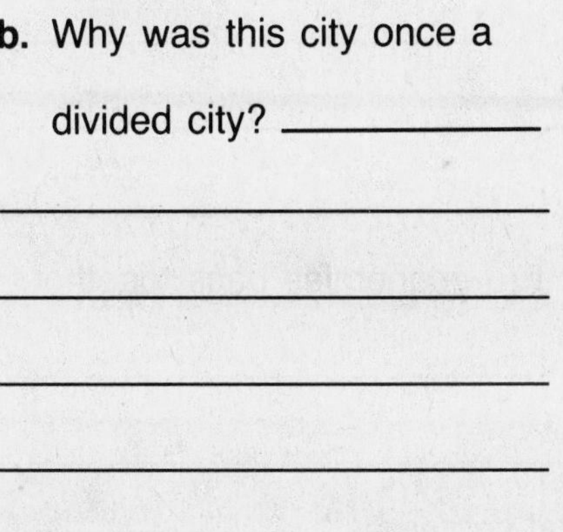

4. How and when did reunification come about in Germany?

5. a. Locate and label the capital of Austria.

   b. Do most Austrians live in cities, such as the capital, or in rural areas?

6. What two characteristics are common for most people of Central Europe?

Name Use with pages 237–239

Thinking About Central Europe's Economy

Read the following statements carefully. If a statement is true, write **True** after it. If a statement is false, write **False** after it. Then, in the space provided, write the reasons for your answer. For help, you can refer to pages 237–239 in your textbook.

1. The picture above shows what most of Germany looked like at the end of World War II. The German people were never able to recover from such devastation.

____

____

____

2. Since 1990 the Germans have found it easy to bring their two economies back together.

____

____

3. Today Germany's Ruhr Valley is Europe's biggest industrial center.

____

____

4. The Swiss and Austrian peoples have low standards of living because their countries have few natural resources and little arable land.

____

____

____

5. Air and water pollution are a serious problem for the countries of Central Europe.

____

____

Name Use with pages 240–241

The Governments of Central Europe

Use the table to answer questions 1 to 4. Then answer the question that follows. For help, you can refer to pages 240–241 in your textbook.

CENTRAL EUROPEAN GOVERNMENTS

Part of Government	Germany	Austria	Switzerland
two-house legislature	Bundestag	Nationalrat	Federal Assembly
head of state	president	president	president
head of government	chancellor	chancellor	Federal Council
local division of government	lander	province	canton

1. According to the table, how are the Bundestag, Nationalrat, and Federal Assembly similar?

2. What is the head of state in each of the countries called?

3. What is the difference between the head of government in Switzerland and the head of government in Austria and Germany?

4. a. How are lander, provinces, and cantons alike?

   b. In which country is pure democracy at work in its local division of government? Describe how it works.

5. Why is the city of Geneva, Switzerland, the headquarters of many world organizations?

Name Use with pages 242–243

Identifying a Biased Statement

Read each of the passages. Then follow the directions and answer the questions. For help, you can refer to pages 242–243 in your textbook.

Passage A

The Ruhr Valley is one of the largest industrial centers in Europe. Production from the region's factories has helped to make Germany one of the leading industrial nations of the world. But not without a price. The Ruhr is also one of the most polluted areas in Europe. Germany is taking steps to curb the pollution, but it will take time, money, and a serious commitment to solve the problem without seriously damaging Germany's economy.

Passage B

A heavy blanket of smog hangs over the entire Ruhr Valley. It is one of the most horrifying sights you can imagine. The greedy corporations responsible for the pollution care only about profits, not about the health of the nation's people. The German government must put an end to this national disgrace. Pollution generated by the region's industries must be stopped at once, no matter what the cost.

1. Recall the definition of bias. Write it here. ____________________

____

2. Underline any loaded or emotionally charged words or phrases in either passage. Underline any words or phrases that are exaggerations.

3. Which passage presents only one side of the issue? passage A passage B

4. Which passage presents a one-sided view or impression about the pollution problem in the Ruhr Valley? passage A passage B

5. Which passage do you think is a biased statement? passage A passage B

6. State the bias. ____________________

____

____

Name Use with pages 244–245

Arts and Recreation in Central Europe

Use the pictures on the right to complete the exercises below. For help, you can refer to pages 244–245 in your textbook.

1. a. Draw a line to the picture that shows one way Central Europe celebrates its musical heritage.

b. Who are three well-known composers from Central Europe whose music is celebrated in this way?

____

____

____

2. a. Draw a line to the picture that shows one way Central Europeans enjoy the outdoors.

b. What are three other popular outdoor sports in Central Europe?

____

____

____

3. a. Draw a line to the picture that shows one way Central Europeans celebrate the harvest

b. What are some of the things people do at festivals?

____

____

____

Name Use with pages 246–247

Using New Words

Follow the directions to find each hidden term. Then write the definition of the term on the line below the letters. For help, you can refer to the lessons in Chapter 11 in your textbook.

1. Cross out the letters b, o, r, s, u
   s d u i b a o l e r c t ______________________

   ____

2. Cross out the letters d, g, i, s
   d c s h i a n i c e g l l o r ______________________

   ____

3. Cross out the letters b, i, o, s
   s n b e o s u t i r a i l ______________________

   ____

4. Cross out the letters a, c, k, r, s
   s p o a l l c u r a t i r o k n s ______________________

   ____

5. Cross out the letters d, g, i, m
   i h g o l d o c d a u s m t ______________________

   ____

   ____

6. Cross out the letters b, k, d, h, l
   r l e u d n i f k i c h a t i b o n ______________________

   ____

   ____

7. Cross out the letters d, h, k, s, u
   s c a d n u t h o n k u ______________________

   ____

Name

Use with pages 249–252

The Southern European Countries

Answer the questions and complete the activities below. For help, you can refer to pages 249–252 in your textbook.

1. On the map below locate and label the following countries.

   Italy

   Spain

   Greece

   Portugal

2. What is this region called?

   ____

   ____

3. On the map below locate and label the following cities.

   Barcelona

   Rome

   Athens

4. From which of these cities did the ancient Romans once rule?

   ____

5. On the map below shade in the countries where most of the people belong to the Roman Catholic Church. List them below.

   ____

6. To which religion do most of the people in the remaining country belong?

   ____

7. Outline each of the three countries where languages based on Latin are spoken. List them below.

   ____

   ____

   ____

8. Which Southern European country has a language that is written in a different alphabet from those of the other three?

   ____

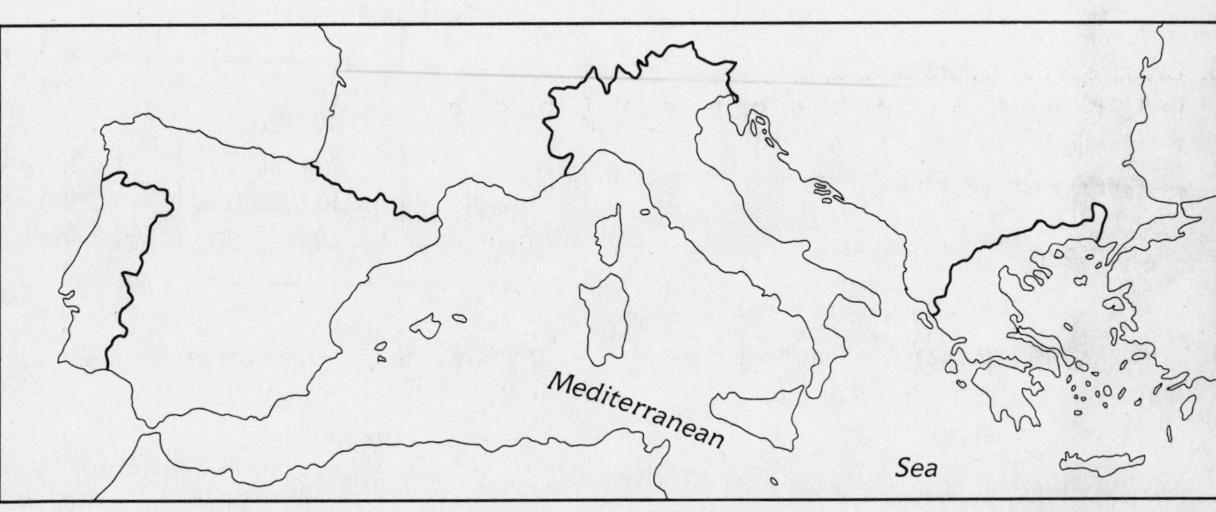

Name Use with page 253

Reading Graphs and Charts

Study the bar graph and the chart below. Then answer the questions that follow. For help, you can refer to page 253 in your textbook.

1. a. What does the bar graph show?

____

____

b. What does the horizontal axis of the graph show?

____

c. What does the vertical axis show?

____

d. According to the graph, which Southern European country has the largest area?

____

AREA OF THE FOUR MAIN COUNTRIES OF SOUTHERN EUROPE

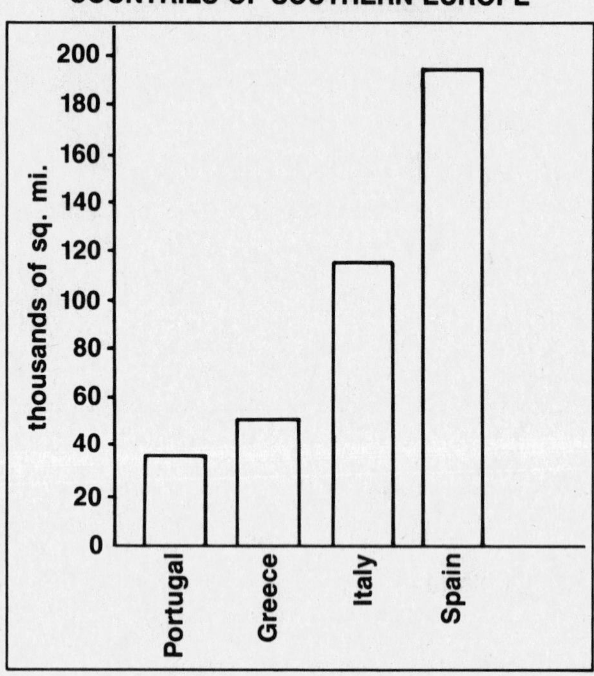

Source: World Almanac, 1989

2. a. According to the title, what does the chart show?

____

____

____

b. According to the chart, which country has the smallest area?

____

c. Does this country also have the smallest population? If not, which country does?

____

____

POPULATION AND AREA OF THE FOUR MAIN COUNTRIES OF SOUTHERN EUROPE

country	population	area (sq. mi.)
Greece	10,048,000	51,146
Italy	57,439,000	116,303
Portugal	10,240,000	36,390
Spain	39,784,000	194,896

3. If you wanted to compare information at a glance, would you use a chart or a bar graph? Circle your answer.

chart bar graph

4. If you wanted to know actual figures, would you look at a chart or a bar graph? Circle your answer.

chart bar graph

Name Use with pages 254–256

Writing About Southern Europe's Economy

The travel brochure below tells about some of the things you might see and do in Southern Europe. Complete the brochure by filling in the blanks. For help, you can refer to pages 254–256 in your textbook.

Explore the Wonders of Southern Europe

Bask in the sun along the beautiful ________ shore. Take a side trip to the village of Marbella on the ________ coast. While in Athens, wander through the ancient remains of the ________. Explore the ancient Forum on your visit to ________. Everywhere you go you will see the splendid architecture of ________, ________, ________, and ________.

As you travel through the countryside, you you will pass by the small farms that grow some of the sweetest ________ and ________ in the world. Other crops produced in the region include ________, ________, ________, and ________.

In ________ you can take a tour of the ________ assembly lines.

Every year more than one ________ cars are assembled here. Some of the finest leather goods in the world are made in factories in ________, ________, and ________.

If you arrived in Southern Europe by ship, the ship you were on may have been built by one of the shipping ________ that make the Greek island of ________ their home. Greek shipowners control the largest ________ ________ in the world.

Name Use with pages 257–260

Thinking About Today's Governments

Answer the questions below. For help, you can refer to pages 257–260 in your textbook.

1. a. What kind of government does this country have?

____

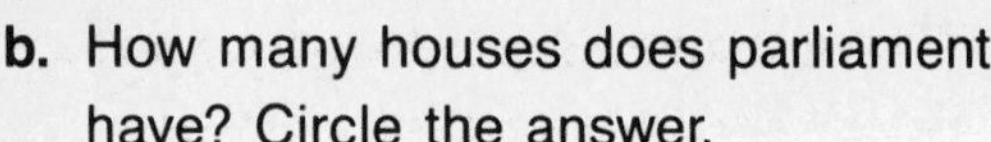

b. How many houses does parliament have? Circle the answer.

one two

c. What is the head of government called?

____

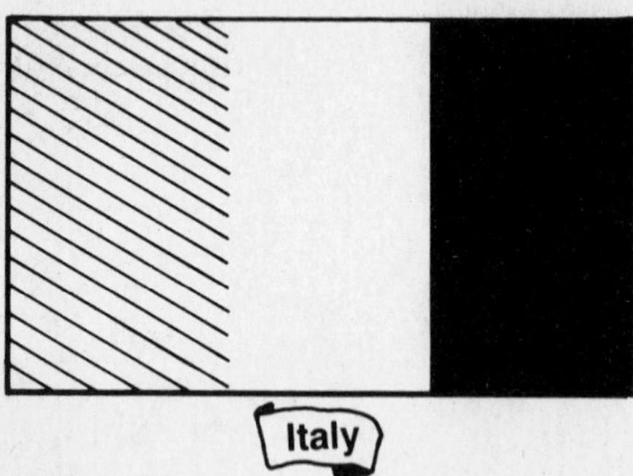

2. a. What kind of government does this country have?

____

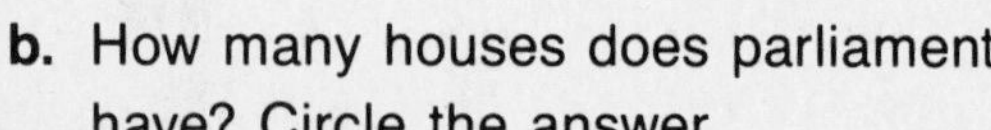

b. How many houses does parliament have? Circle the answer.

one two

c. Who runs the government from day to day?

____

3. a. What kind of government does this country have?

____

b. How many houses does parliament have? Circle the answer.

one two

c. Who shares executive power?

____

4. a. What kind of government does this country have?

____

b. How many houses does parliament have? Circle the answer.

one two

c. Who is head of state?

____

Name ________________ Use with pages 261–263

The Heritage of Southern Europe

Use the maps on the right to complete the activities below. For help, you can refer to pages 261–263 in your textbook.

1. a. Draw a line to the map of the country where the world's oldest dramas were written.

   b. What are the names of three poets who wrote these plays?

   ____

   ____

   ____

2. a. Draw a line to the map of the country where the Renaissance began.

   b. What was the goal of the artists of this period?

   ____

   ____

   c. Which Renaissance artist painted the inside of the Sistine Chapel?

   ____

3. a. Draw a line to the map of the country in which famous pilgrimages have been made for almost 2,000 years.

   b. What does this pilgrimage celebrate?

   ____

   ____

Name ______ Use with pages 268–269

Learning New Words

Look at the box containing the Morse Code. The Morse Code uses dots and dashes to stand for the letters of the alphabet. Use the code to figure out the words that follow. For help, you can refer to the lessons in Chapter 12 in your textbook.

A	B	C	D	E	F	G	H	I
•—	—•••	—•—•	—••	•	••—•	——•	••••	••
J	**K**	**L**	**M**	**N**	**O**	**P**	**Q**	**R**
•———	—•—	•—••	——	—•	———	•——•	——•—	•—•
S	**T**	**U**	**V**	**W**	**X**	**Y**	**Z**	
•••	—	••—	•••—	•——	—••—	—•——	——••	

______ **1.** ______________________
••• •• • ••• — •—

______ **2.** ______________________
•—• • —• •— •• ••• ••• •— —• —•—• •

______ **3.** ______________________
— • •—• •—• ——— •—• •• ••• ——

______ **4.** ______________________
•— ••— — ——— —• ——— —— —•——

______ **5.** ______________________
—•—• ——— •— •—•• •• — •• ——— —•

______ **6.** ______________________
•——• •• •—•• ——• •—• •• —— •— ——• •

Match the definitions below with the words above. Write the letter of each definition on the line before the appropriate word.

a. a period of great activity in the arts beginning in the 1300s and 1400s

b. a temporary union between different political parties that agree to work together for a common purpose

c. the right of self-government

d. a period of rest taken during the middle of the afternoon

e. a journey that people make to a sacred place

f. the use of violence and the threat of violence to frighten people

Name   Use with pages 271–273

The People of Scandinavia

Look at the picture and bar graph, then answer the questions. For help, you can refer to pages 271–273 in your textbook.

1. The picture shows a Viking warrior. Who were the Vikings?

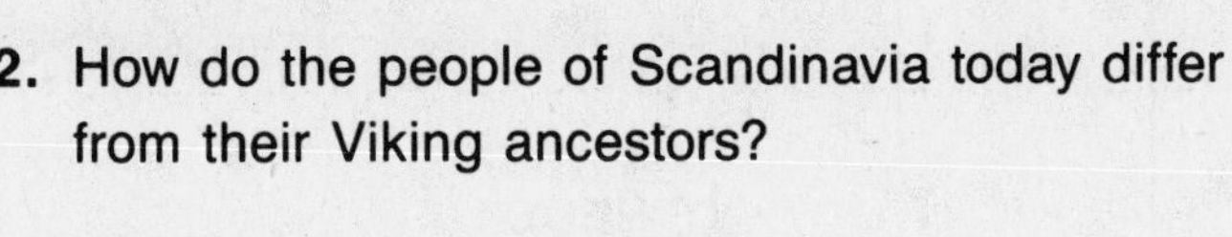

2. How do the people of Scandinavia today differ from their Viking ancestors?

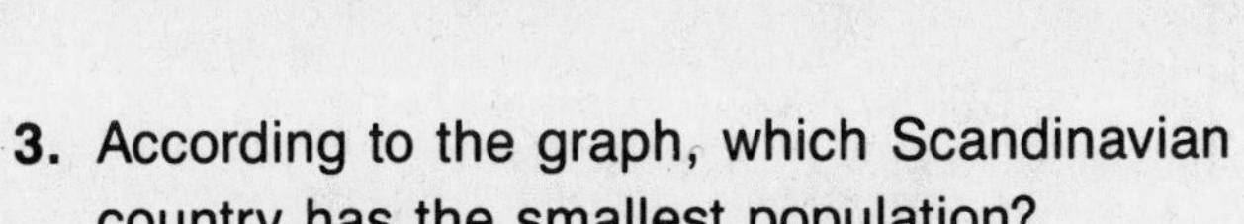

3. According to the graph, which Scandinavian country has the smallest population?

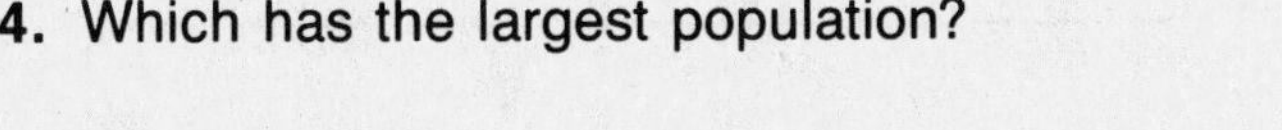

4. Which has the largest population?

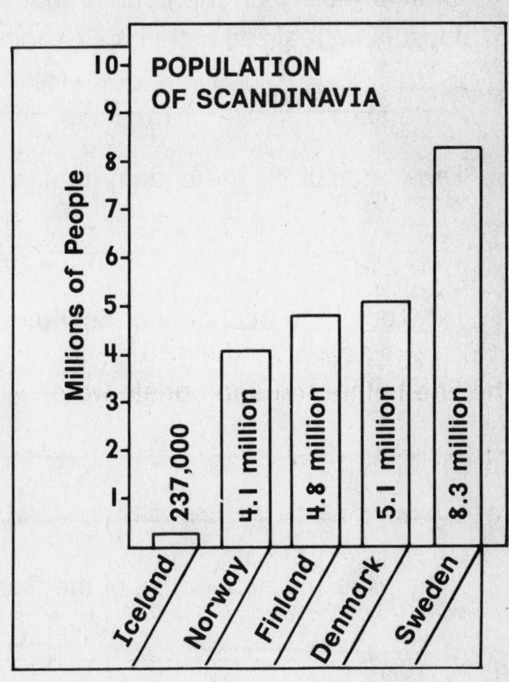

5. How is the size of Scandinavia's population an advantage?

6. What ties the Scandinavian people together?

Name _______________ Use with pages 274–276

The Resources and Economy of Scandinavia

Use the map to complete the first five activities. Then answer the questions that follow. For help, you can refer to pages 274–276 in your textbook.

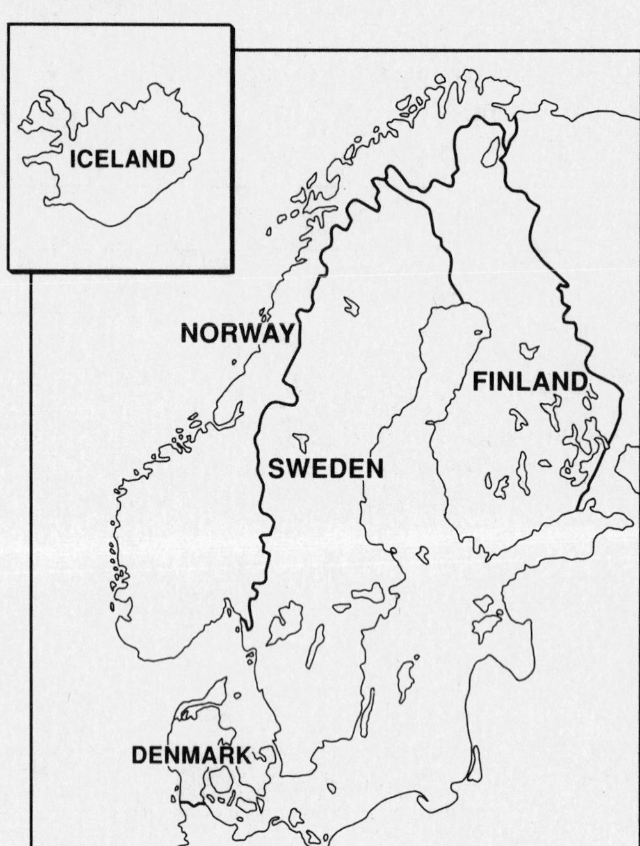

1. Draw a fish on the two countries where the fishing industry has played an important role in the economy.

____

2. Draw an oil barrel on the country that has Western Europe's largest fields of offshore oil and natural gas.

____

3. Draw a tree on the two countries that have for hundreds of years based their economies on their huge forests.

____

4. Draw a factory on the country that is the most industrialized nation in Scandinavia.

____

5. Draw a chair on the country that is renowned for its furniture, glassware, and toys.

____

6. How does the economy of Scandinavia today differ from the economy of the past?

____

____

____

7. Why have the economies of the Scandinavian countries prospered?

____

____

____

Taking a Look at Scandinavian Governments

Answer the questions below. For help, you can refer to pages 277–279 in your textbook.

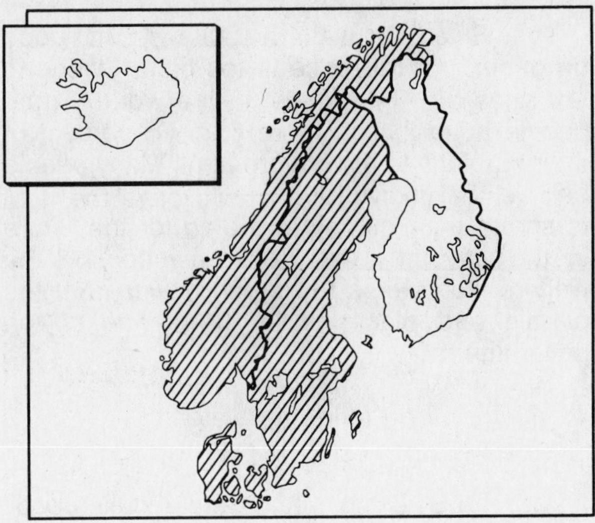

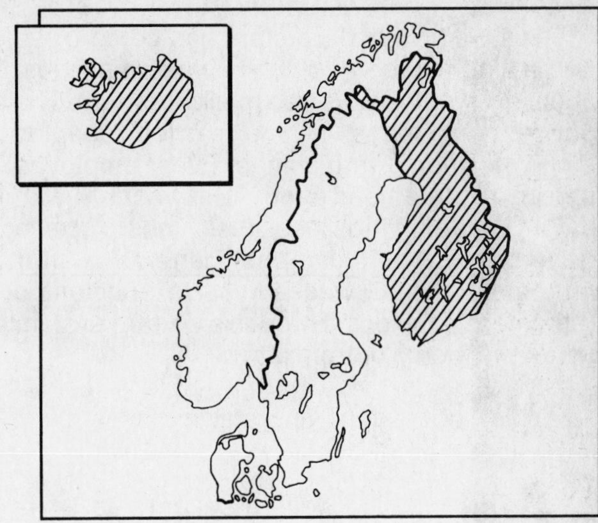

1. What form of government do these countries have?

____

2. How many houses make up the legislature in each of these countries?

____

3. Who elects the head of the executive branch of government?

____

4. What is the head of government called?

____

5. What form of government do these countries have?

____

6. How do the governments of these countries differ from those of Sweden, Norway, and Denmark?

____

____

7. How are the governments of these countries like those of Sweden, Norway, and Denmark?

____

____

8. Why are the taxes in the Scandinavian countries so high? _______________

____

____

Name

Use with pages 280–281

Recognizing Point of View

Read the passages below. Then read the questions that follow and underline the answer to each question. For help, you can refer to pages 280–281 in your textbook.

The Swedish welfare state has come close to creating the ideal society. For example, just about everyone enjoys free medical service. The government loans newly married couples money for home furnishings. Every employed person is guaranteed a four-week vacation with pay. Swedes who lose their jobs receive generous unemployment benefits. After retirement most Swedes receive substantial retirement pensions. Sweden's welfare system takes the worry out of living.

1. Which of the following statements is a fact?
   - **a.** The Swedish welfare system has come close to creating an ideal society.
   - **b.** Just about everyone receives free medical service.
   - **c.** Sweden's welfare system takes the worry out of living.
2. What information does the writer leave out?
   - **a.** The Swedes pay the highest taxes in the world.
   - **b.** After retirement, most Swedes receive substantial retirement pensions.
   - **c.** Most Swedes receive free medical services.
3. What is the writer's point of view?

____

____

The Swedish welfare state looks good on paper, but the price is too high. Sweden's tax rates are the highest in the world. Some people have to pay more than 75 percent of their earnings to the government. Many people believe that individuals should have the right to spend their money and plan for the future in the way they see fit. In my opinion the welfare state takes too much power from the people and places it in the hands of the government.

4. Which of the following statements is a fact?
   - **a.** The Swedish welfare state looks good on paper, but the price is too high.
   - **b.** Sweden's tax rates are the highest in the world.
   - **c.** People have the right to spend their money and plan for the future in the way they see fit.
5. What information does the writer leave out?
   - **a.** The Swedish government ensures the well-being of its citizens.
   - **b.** Sweden's taxes are the highest in the world.
   - **c.** Sweden's welfare state is very expensive.
6. What is the writer's point of view?

____

____

Name

Arts and Recreation in Scandinavia

Complete the activities below. For help, you can refer to pages 282–283 in your textbook. The excerpt below is from the Poem entitled "Voluspa" on page 1, *Poems of the Elder Edda,* translated by Patricia Terry.

Then all the gods
  Met to give judgment,
The holy gods
  Took counsel together;
They named night
  and the waning moon,
They gave names
  To morning and midday,
Afternoon and evening,
  Ordered time by years.

1. The verse above is from an ancient **Edda.** What were Eddas and what did they tell about? ______________________________

____

2. What are the ancient **sagas** of Iceland and what do they tell about?

____

____

3. List three modern Scandinavian writers who have carried on this long tradition of storytelling. Tell what each wrote about.

WRITER	WROTE ABOUT
______________	______________
	______________
	______________
______________	______________
	______________
______________	______________
	______________
	______________

Name Use with pages 284–285

Thinking About New Words

Answer each question in the space provided. For help, you can refer to the lessons in Chapter 13 in your textbook.

1. What is a **diversified economy**? ______________________________

   ____

   Why do most Scandinavian countries now have diversified economies? ______________

   ____

   ____

   ____

2. Almost 200 years ago, Sweden created a special officer called an **ombudsman**. What does an ombudsman do? ______________________________

   ____

   ____

   ____

   ____

3. What is the difference between a Viking **Edda** and an Icelandic **saga**? What does each tell about? ______________________________

   ____

   ____

   ____

4. If you lived in Scandinavia, you might do business through a **cooperative**. What is a cooperative? ______________________________

   ____

   How does a retail cooperative help consumers? ______________________________

   ____

   ____

   ____

Name   Use with pages 293–297

Using Maps

Use the map on this page to complete the exercises below. For help, you can refer to pages 293–297 in your textbook.

1. Locate and label the Ural Mountains. These mountains mark the boundary between which two continents?

   ____

2. Locate and label these rivers. Then trace the rivers in blue.

   Volga River   Danube River

3. Locate and label the West Siberian Plain. What feature of its environment would make the West Siberian Plain an unpleasant place to live?

   ____

   ____

4. Locate and label Central Asia. Color the area brown. Why is Central Asia so dry?

   ____

   ____

   ____

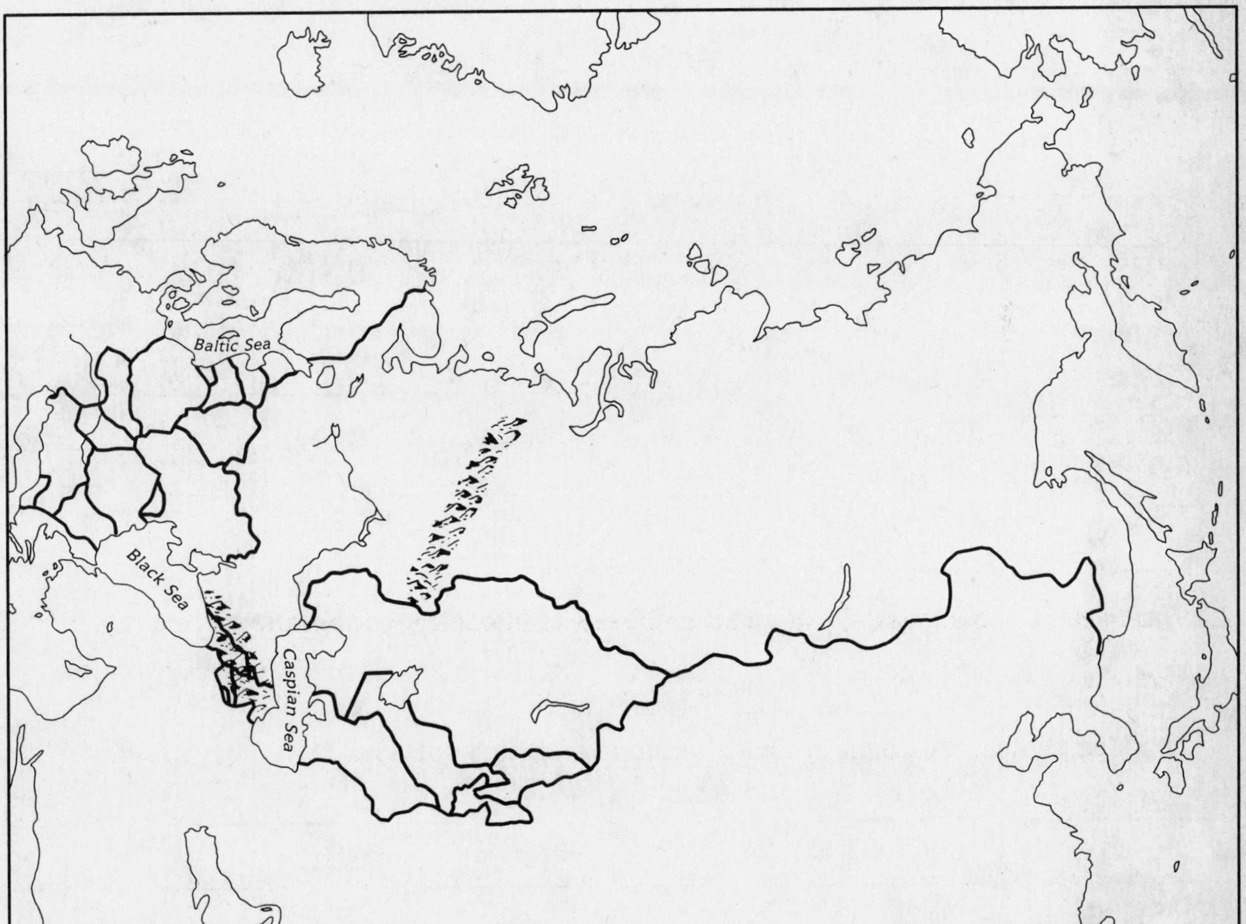

Baltic Sea

Black Sea

Caspian Sea

Identifying Climates and Natural Resources

Study the pictures at the right. On the line beneath each picture write the letter of the place or places from the column at the left where you might find this scene. You may use a letter more than once or not at all. For help, you can refer to pages 298–300 in your textbook.

a. Romania

b. Siberia

c. steppes

d. Poland

e. taiga

f. Ukraine

g. Russia

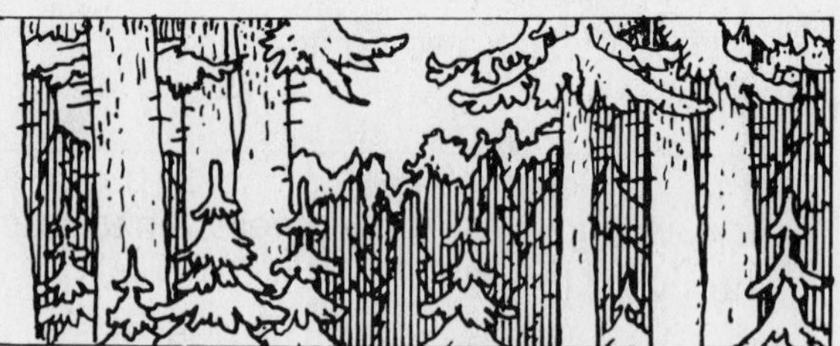

Describe the two climate zones in Eastern Europe and Northern Asia.

Name ____________________ Use with page 301

Reading Climographs

Study the climograph below. Then answer the questions. For help, you can refer to page 301 in your textbook.

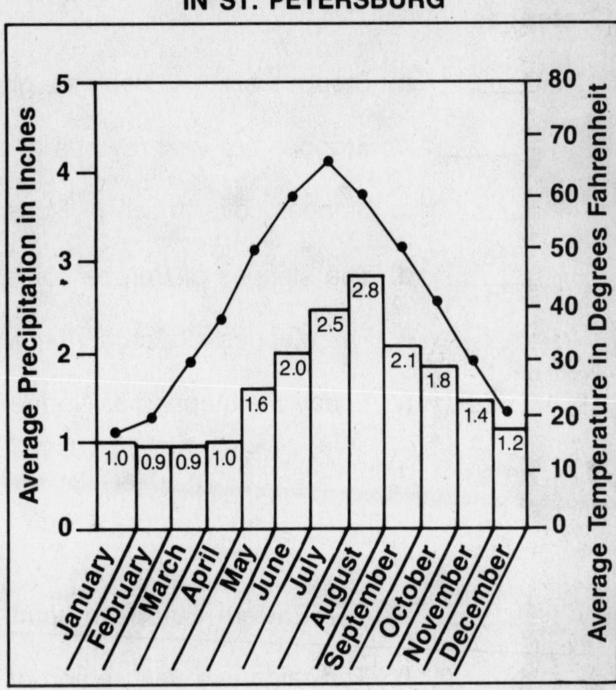

1. a. What does the bar graph of the climograph show?

   ____

   ____

   b. What does the line graph show?

   ____

   ____

2. a. During which month is there the most precipitation?

   ____

   b. What is the average temperature during this month?

   ____

3. a. During which two months is there the least precipitation?

   ____

   b. Which of the two months is generally cooler?

   ____

4. a. Suppose you were to visit St. Petersburg in July. How would you describe the weather?

   ____

   b. During which month do you think St. Petersburg has the most favorable weather? Why?

   ____

   ____

Name Use with pages 302–303

Thinking About New Words

Put an **X** next to each statement that gives correct information about the word in boldface type. Then complete the activity that follows. For help, you can refer to the lessons in Chapter 14 in your textbook.

1. steppes

______ **a.** Steppes are dry, treeless, grassy plains south of the taiga.

______ **b.** Steppes are vast regions of evergreen forests south of the tundra.

______ **c.** Steppes cover much of Russia, Ukraine, and parts of Eastern Europe.

______ **d.** The steppes of Europe contain some of the world's finest soil.

______ **e.** The steppes stretch all the way from Finland to the Pacific Ocean.

______ **f.** Today the steppes of Northern Asia are a major grain-growing area.

2. taiga

______ **a.** The Eastern European countries are covered mostly by taiga.

______ **b.** The taiga is a vast region of evergreen forests located south of the tundra.

______ **c.** The taiga is a dry, treeless, grassy plain located south of the steppes.

______ **d.** The taiga is one of the richest farming areas in the world.

______ **e.** The taiga stretches all the way from Finland to the Pacific Ocean.

______ **f.** Russia's vast regions of evergreen forests are located in the taiga.

Use the words *taiga* and *steppes* in a single sentence.

____

____

____

____

Name Use with pages 305–309

Taking a Look at Ethnic Groups

Read the following statements carefully. If a statement is true, write **True** after it. If a statement is false, write **False** after it. Then, in the space provided, write the reasons for your answer. For help, you can refer to pages 305–309 in your textbook.

1. Russia is part of a large country called the Soviet Union. ____________________

____

____

____

2. The largest ethnic groups in the region are the Uzbeks and Kazakhs.

____

____

____

3. The people of Russia and its neighboring countires are now free to worship as they please.

____

____

____

____

4. In Russia women make up an important part of the work force.

____

____

____

____

5. Even though there is no longer a Soviet Union in the region, education has changed little.

____

____

____

____

Name Use with pages 314–317

Economies of Russia and Its Neighbors

The headlines below might have been written about the economies of Russia and its neighbors. Answer the questions about each headline. For help, you can refer to pages 314–317 in your textbook.

Command Economy Slows Down

a. What is a command economy? ____________________

____

b. What problems did people in the Soviet Union face under their command economy?

____

____

____

Gorbachev Seeks Change

a. What did Gorbachev call his plan of reforms? ____________________

b. How was Boris Yeltsin's plan different? ____________________

____

____

Commonwealth of Independent States Faces Many Challenges

a. In about what year would this headline have been written? ____________________

b. Why was the Commonwealth of Independent States set up?

____

____

c. What were three economic challenges faced by the C.I.S.?

____

____

____

Name _______________ Use with pages 320–323

Using a Map

Use the map to complete the activities below. For help, you can refer to pages 320–323 in your textbook.

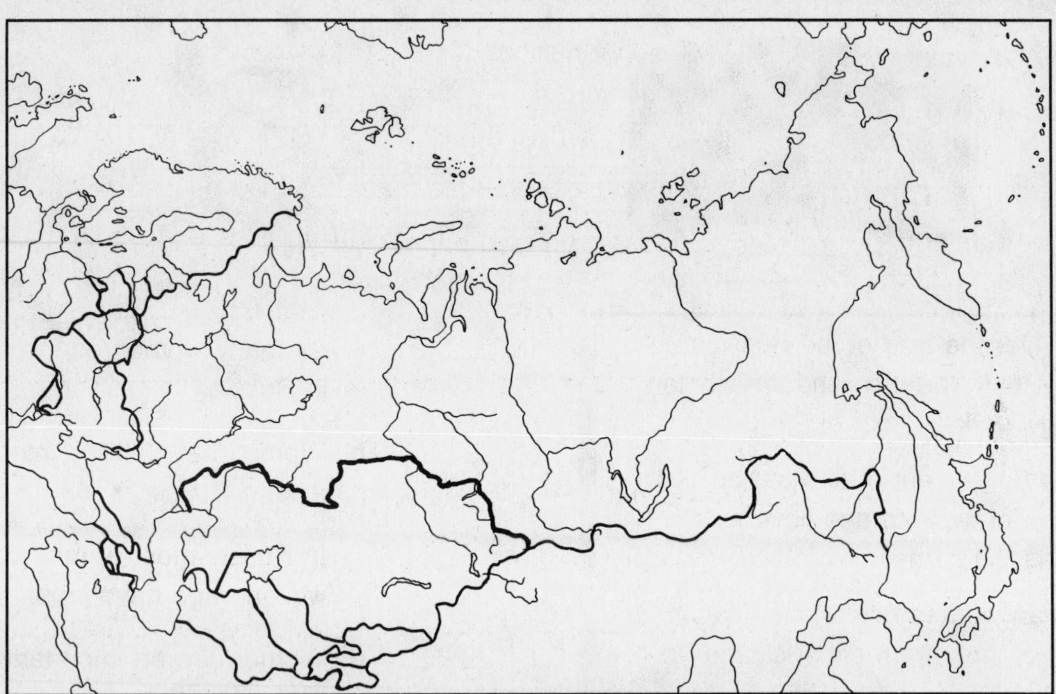

1. Which country took the Soviet Union's seat in the Security Council of the United Nations?

   ____

   Label the country and color it green.

2. In which country are C.I.S. headquarters located? _______________________
   Label it and color it brown.

3. The C.I.S. was started by Russia, Byelarus, and _______________________.
   Label the third country and color it purple.

4. Which was the first non-Slavic country to join the C.I.S.? _______________________
   Label it and color it yellow.

5. Label at least three other countries on the map.

6. What ideas of Lenin's were practiced in the Soviet Union until 1989?

   ____

   ____

Name Use with pages 324–325

Drawing Conclusions

Put an **X** next to each conclusion you can draw from information in each of the boxes. For help, you can refer to pages 324–325 in your textbook.

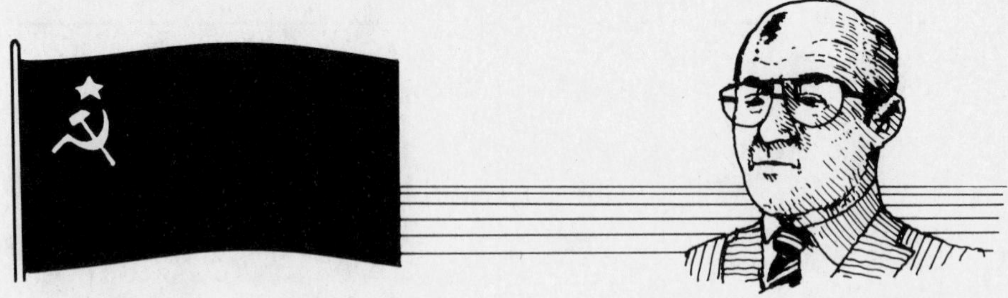

- Whatever the size of the Russian family, both the men and the women usually work.
- About 85 percent of all Russian women of working age have jobs outside the home.
- Russian women hold many different kinds of jobs, from street cleaner to judge.
- About 75 percent of all Russian physicians are women.

_____ **a.** As many women as men work in Russia.

_____ **b.** Women have all the important jobs in Russia.

_____ **c.** In Russia most women of working age have jobs.

_____ **d.** Women are an important part of the Russian work force.

- Before the Soviet Union became 15 independent countries, the government controlled almost all economic and government decisions.
- Today 15 independent countries are each working to create mixed or free-enterprise economies.
- The C.I.S., set up in 1991, is a loose organization of most of the countries that used to be bound together by the Soviet Union.
- Leaders in each of the 15 countries were elected by their people.

_____ **a.** Enormous changes have come to the economies and governments of Russia and its neighbors.

_____ **b.** The people of the former Soviet Union are glad they now have their own countries.

_____ **c.** The 15 countries of the former Soviet Union are working together to solve their problems.

_____ **d.** Russia, through the C.I.S., still dominates its neighbors.

Name Use with pages 326–327

Arts and Recreation in Russia

Label each picture with a phrase from the box. Then answer the questions that follow. For help, you can refer to pages 326–327 in your textbook.

the father of Russian literature	won Nobel Prize for Literature in the 1950s
great Russian novelist of the 1800s	composed *The Nutcracker*

______________________ ______________________

______________________ ______________________

1. In the past, what effect did the Soviet government have on the arts?

____

2. How did Mikhail Gorbachev's policy of glasnost affect the arts in the Soviet Union in the late 1980s? ______________________

Thinking About New Words

Write the letter of the term that matches each definition below. For help, you can refer to the lessons in Chapter 15 in your textbook.

a. Soviet	**d.** command economy	**g.** censor
b. consumer goods	**e.** perestroika	**h.** glasnost
c. capital goods	**f.** reform	
	i. Commonwealth of Independent States	

_____ **1.** the name of Mikhail Gorbachev's plan for economic reform in the Soviet Union

_____ **2.** the name for people who lived in the former Soviet Union

_____ **3.** to prevent something from being published

_____ **4.** products that are used by other industries rather than by individuals

_____ **5.** the name of Mikhail Gorbachev's policy of openness

_____ **6.** a system in which the government makes most economic decisions

_____ **7.** products, such as stoves, refrigerators, and clothes, that are used by individuals

_____ **8.** an organization formed to promote cooperation among the countries that were once part of the Soviet Union

_____ **9.** to make a change for the better

Name

The People of Eastern Europe

Use the graphs to answer the questions. For help, you can refer to pages 331–334 in your textbook.

1. According to the top graph, which is the largest ethnic group in Czechoslovakia?

____

ETHNIC GROUPS IN CZECHOSLOVAKIA

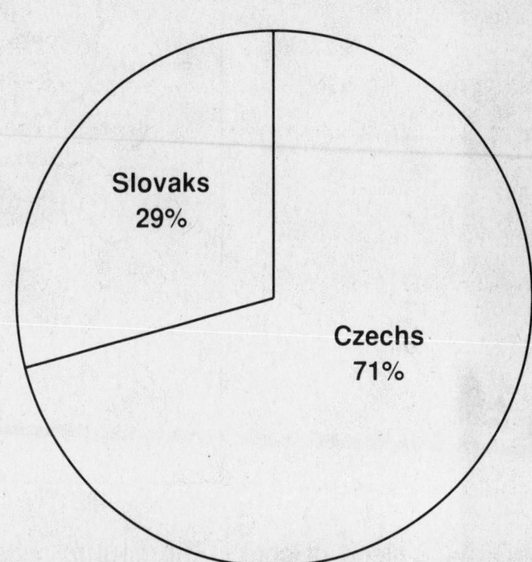

2. Name two other Eastern European countries that have large Slavic groups.

____

3. According to the bottom graph, which religion has the most followers in Czechoslovakia?

____

4. In which Eastern European country are almost all people Roman Catholic?

____

RELIGIONS IN CZECHOSLOVAKIA

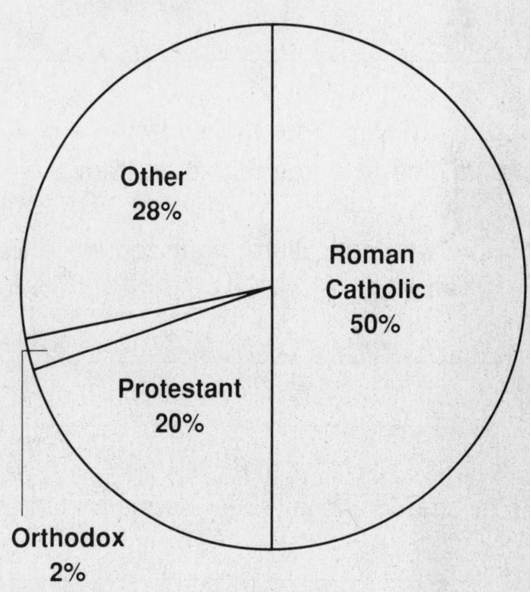

Source: 1992 Please Almanac

5. Why are there so few Jews in Eastern Europe?

____

____

6. Until the late 1980s how did the governments in Eastern European countries treat religion?

____

Name Use with pages 335–338

The Resources of Eastern Europe

Use the map to complete the activities. Then answer the questions that follow. For help, you can refer to pages 335–338 in your textbook.

1. Draw a piece of coal in the country where high-quality coal is mined.

2. Draw a spice jar in the country where paprika is a specialty.

3. Draw a rose where rose petals are a specialty.
What are the rose petals used for?

____

4. Draw a symbol for money in three countries where real progress is being made toward changing to a free market system.

5. How was agriculture organized while Eastern European countries were satellites of the Soviet Union?

____

____

6. In one sentence, state the main idea of the Lesson 2.

____

____

Name Use with pages 339–342

Interviewing a Czech Leader

Suppose you had a chance to interview Vaclav Havel, first president of Czechoslovakia. You might ask him questions similar to those below. Use the space provided to write the answers you think Mr. Havel might give. For help, you can refer to pages 339–342 in your textbook.

Interviewer: What were some of the important events in your life before you were elected president?

Mr. Havel: ______________________________

Interviewer: What was the main change that resulted from the fall of the communist government in your country?

Mr. Havel: ______________________________

Interviewer: Have democracy and freedom come to all the countries in Eastern Europe?

Mr. Havel: ______________________________

Interviewer: What was the Warsaw Pact? What happened when it ended?

Mr. Havel: ______________________________

Interviewer: Was the change to freedom and democracy in neighboring countries always peaceful?

Mr. Havel: ______________________________

Name Use with pages 343–344

The Arts and Recreation of Eastern Europe

Answer the questions below. For help, you can refer to pages 343–344 in your textbook.

1. Look at the picture. From which Eastern European country did this composer come?

2. What did this composer use as themes for much of his music?

3. Which other Eastern European composer was inspired by the music of his homeland?

The chart gives information about the Summer Olympics in 1988, the last Olympics before the many political changes that came to Eastern Europe in the late 1980s. Use the chart to answer these questions.

4. Which four Eastern European countries were among the top ten medal holders for the 1988 Summer Olympics?

5. What was the main reason for the success of the athletes of these countries?

6. How might political changes since 1988 change the outcome of later Olympics?

SUMMER OLYMPICS 1988
TOP TEN MEDAL HOLDERS

Country	Total Medals
USSR	132
East Germany	102
United States	94
West Germany	40
Bulgaria	35
South Korea	33
China	28
Romania	24
Great Britain	24
Hungary	23

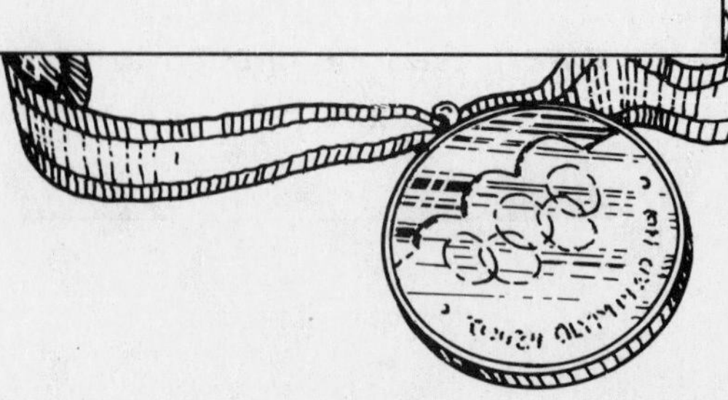

Name

Use with page 345

Reading a Newspaper Article

In June 1991 Soviet troops withdrew from Hungary. The paragraphs below might have appeared in a newspaper article describing the event. Label the headline and dateline. Then answer the questions. For help, you can refer to page 345 in your textbook.

____

SOVIET TROOPS LEAVE HUNGARY

____

Budapest, June 30—The last Soviet troops pulled out of Hungary this month, ending almost 47 years of occupation. The pullout followed months of dizzying changes in Hungary, where the first multiparty elections were held last October.

Reaction to the Soviet pullout was positive. One university student remarked, "Finally we are free to run our own lives, without interference from outside forces."

Soviet troops had been stationed in Hungary since 1956, when they were called in to crush an anti-Soviet uprising in the country.

1. The article might have appeared on page one of a newspaper. What kind of article is it?

____

2. What is the article about?

____

____

____

3. Where did the event take place?

____

4. When did the event take place?

____

5. In which kind of article might you read an editor's opinion about the pullout of Soviet troops?

____

Name Use with pages 346–347

Thinking About New Words

Use the code to figure out the words and write each word under its code in the left column. Then write the number of each word next to its meaning in the right column. For help, you can refer to the lessons in Chapter 16 in your textbook.

CODE

z = a	w = g	t = m	q = s	n = y
13 = b	10 = h	7 = n	4 = t	1 = z
y = c	v = i	s = o	p = u	
12 = d	9 = j	6 = p	3 = v	
x = e	u = k	r = q	o = w	
11 = f	8 = l	5 = r	2 = x	

1. 7 z 4 v s 7 z 8 v q t

____

2. q z 4 x 8 8 v 4 x

____

3. y n 5 v 8 8 v y

____

4. r p s 4 z

____

5. o z 5 q z o   6 z y 4

____

6. 13 p 11 11 x 5   1 s 7 x

____

_____ **a.** the alphabet used by the Russian language

_____ **b.** a region between two hostile powers

_____ **c.** a limit on the type and amount of a product that can be sold or produced

_____ **d.** a strong love of one's country or ethnic group

_____ **e.** a country that "revolved" around the Soviet Union

_____ **f.** a military alliance of the Soviet Union and its satellites that ended in 1991

Name

Use with pages 355–359

The Middle East and North Africa

Use the map on this page to complete the activities below. For help, you can refer to pages 355–359 in your textbook.

1. a. Locate and label the following peninsulas.

Sinai Peninsula   Anatolia
Arabian Peninsula

b. Which peninsula connects the continents of Africa and Asia?

____

2. a. Locate and label the Sahara Desert. Then color it brown.

b. What group has developed the special skills needed to survive in the desert?

____

3. Locate and label the following bodies of water.

Mediterranean Sea   Red Sea
Persian Gulf

4. a. Locate and label the following rivers. Then trace the rivers in blue.

Nile River   Tigris River
Euphrates River

b. Why are the areas along these rivers densely populated?

____

____

____

____

5. a. Locate and label the following cities.

Riyadh   Jerusalem

b. Which of these cities grew up around a desert oasis?

____

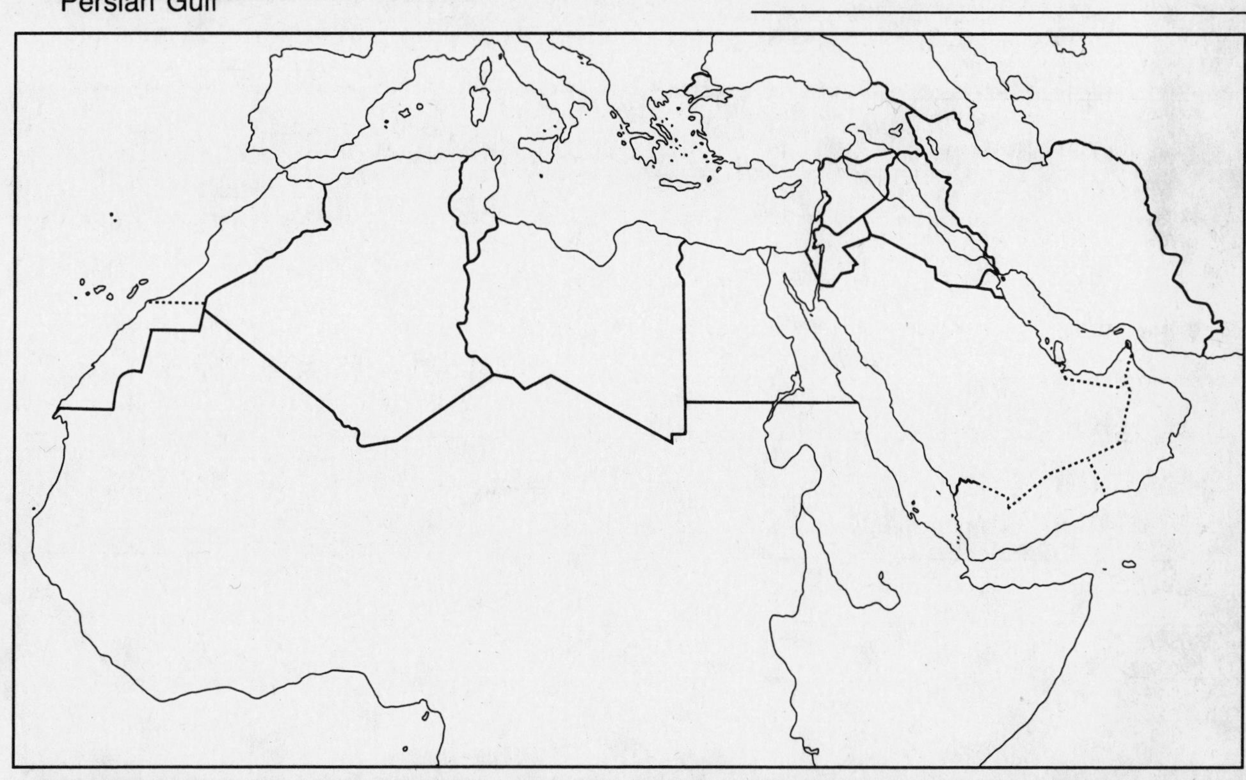

Name

Use with pages 360–361

Reading Contour Maps

Use the contour map of Cyprus below to answer the questions. For help, you can refer to pages 360–361 in your textbook.

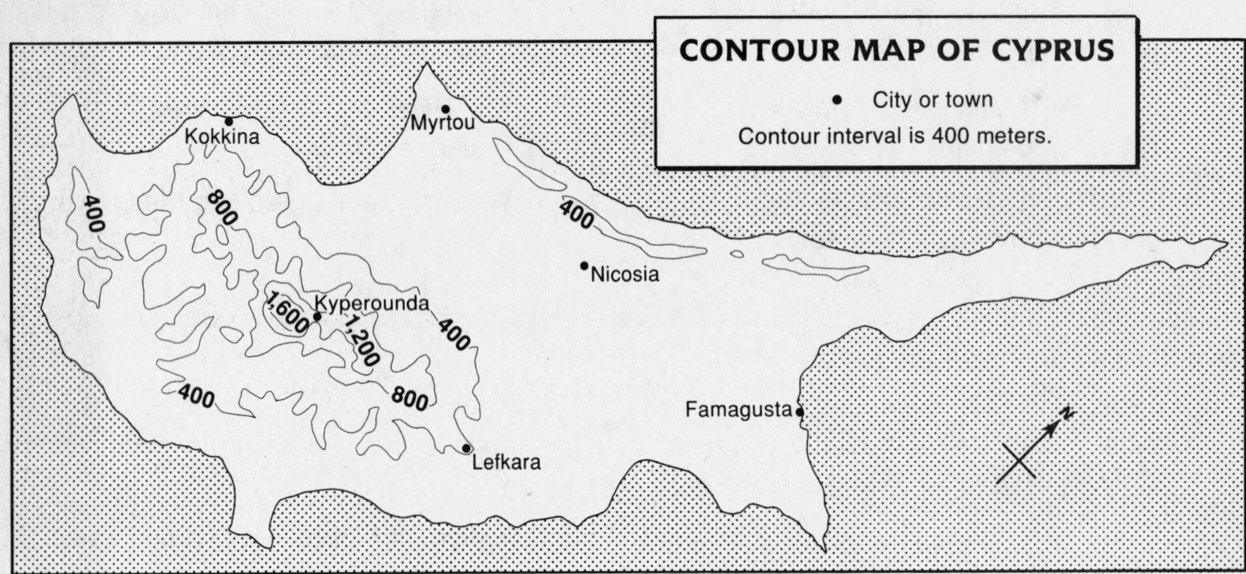

1. What is the elevation of Lefkara?

___

___

How do you know?

___

___

2. Is the land around Kyperounda steep or level?

___

How do you know?

___

___

3. List the cities on the map whose elevation is between sea level and 400 meters.

___

___

___

4. Which part of Cyprus is more level, the western part or the eastern part?

___

How do you know?

___

___

Name Use with pages 362–365

Looking at Natural Resources

The bar graph below shows the major oil-producing countries in the Middle East and North Africa. Use the graph to answer the first three questions on this page. Then answer the following questions. For help, you can refer to pages 362–365 in your textbook.

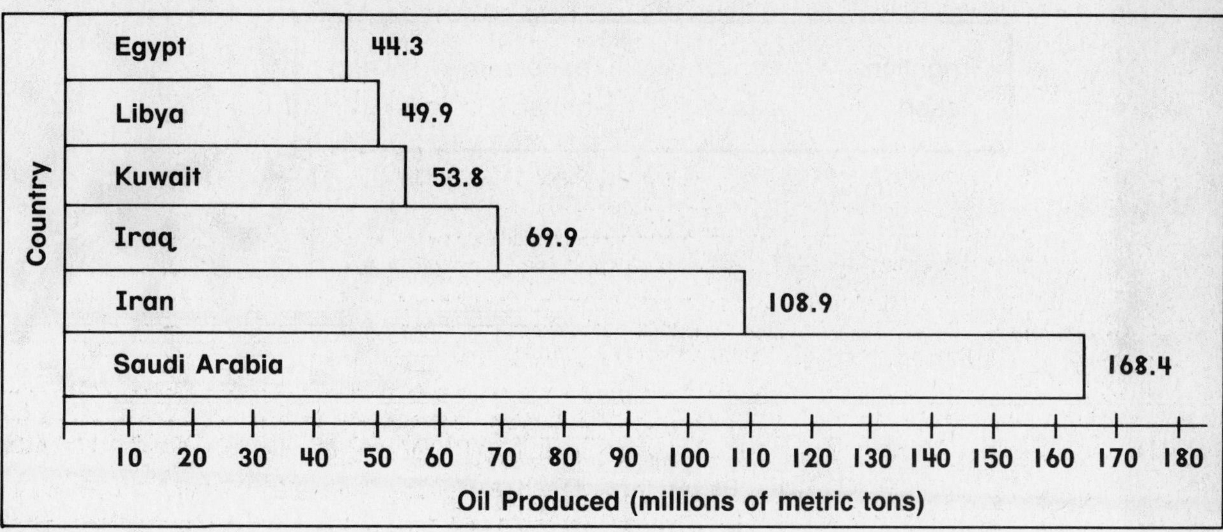

1. According to the graph, which country produces the most oil in the Middle East?

____

2. What are three other Middle Eastern countries shown on the graph? List them according to the amount of oil they produce.

_______________ _______________ _______________

3. What two North African countries are shown on the graph?

_______________ _______________

4. Where does most of the Middle East's oil lie? _______________

____

5. About which percent of the petroleum used in the world today comes from the Middle East?

____

6. Which natural resource would many people in the Middle East and North Africa consider more valuable than oil? Why? _______________

____

____

Name ______________________ Use with pages 366–367

Thinking About New Words

Each of the words listed in the box below is hidden among the letters that follow. Draw a circle around each word you find. The words may be read forward, backward, up, down, or diagonally. For help, you can refer to the lessons in Chapter 17 in your textbook.

irrigation	aquifer	petroleum	arid
desert	oasis	qanat	

L	U	T	S	S	Q	P	R	E	F	U	G	E	E	T	P	H	M	L	K	I	O	C	A
T	B	N	O	I	T	A	G	I	R	R	I	D	I	O	Z	C	Y	D	C	F	J	P	W
D	K	T	A	S	B	A	Z	R	M	R	E	F	I	U	Q	A	M	T	Q	E	T	Q	R
F	D	C	Q	A	Y	Z	E	A	T	R	N	P	R	O	B	T	Y	R	A	R	S	D	E
C	A	R	A	O	N	O	U	E	L	B	S	C	K	D	Z	T	R	E	K	N	J	L	K
I	T	O	P	Q	J	R	S	K	C	L	P	E	I	C	K	N	B	E	E	K	A	M	O
C	E	I	W	C	K	E	A	H	P	E	T	R	O	L	E	U	M	H	S	E	L	Q	Y
E	T	A	D	R	D	M	S	D	P	N	A	N	M	T	E	V	X	O	E	E	J	A	D
U	A	O	Q	S	O	E	Z	L	T	W	U	E	C	A	Z	B	K	M	E	Q	D	E	N
T	Z	A	K	S	E	D	U	D	Z	H	N	Y	F	E	U	R	D	I	W	S	L	A	O

Write each circled word in the space next to its definition.

______________________ **1.** oil

______________________ **2.** an underground layer of rock that holds or carries water

______________________ **3.** a green, fertile, well-watered spot in a desert

______________________ **4.** massive underground tunnels built in Iran to carry water

______________________ **5.** very dry

______________________ **6.** a dry, sandy region with very little plant life

______________________ **7.** the watering of dry land by means of streams, canals, or pipes

Name

The People of the Middle East

Review the picture on this page. Then answer the questions below. For help, you can refer to pages 369–372 in your textbook.

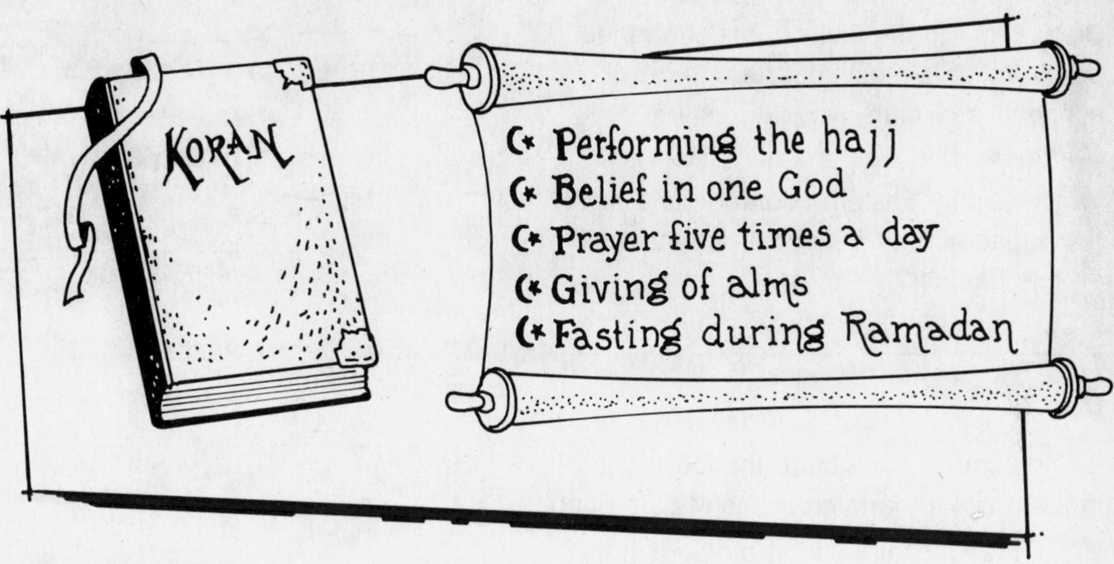

1. The religious book and the list of beliefs show above form the basis of the major religion in the Middle East. What is the name of that religion?

2. What is the list of beliefs called?

3. How was this religion spread throughout the Middle East?

4. What are two Middle Eastern countries where most of the people are Muslims, but are not Arab?

5. What are some special rules that apply to women in Saudi Arabia?

6. What are two Middle Eastern countries where many of the people are Christians?

7. In which Middle Eastern country are most of the people Jewish?

8. What role does religion play in the lives of most people in the Middle East?

Observing Contrasts in the Middle East

Use the pictures on the right to complete the activities on this page. For help, you can refer to pages 373–376 in your textbook.

1. a. Draw a line to the picture that shows the product that is most important to the economies of many Middle Eastern countries.

b. Which Middle Eastern country has a highly developed economy without dependence on this product?

____

Israeli Kibbutz

2. a. Draw a line to the picture that shows a modern way of farming in the Middle East.

b. By contrast, what kinds of methods are used on many traditional farms in the Middle East?

____

Pollution

3. a. Draw a line to the picture that shows one effect of the war in the Persian Gulf.

b. What effect did this action have on the environment and on Kuwait's oil production?

____

____

____

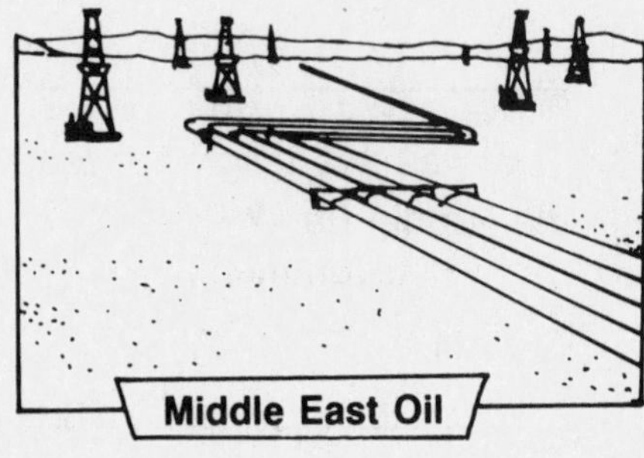

Middle East Oil

4. How is the economy of the Middle East both modern and traditional?

____

____

____

Name

Comparing Governments of the Middle East

Draw a line under the word or phrase that best completes each sentence. For help, you can refer to pages 377–379 in your textbook.

1. The man pictured above is the ______ of Oman.

a. premier

b. president

c. absolute ruler

2. Oman has no constitution and ______.

a. no elections

b. no strong leaders

c. no tradition of democracy

3. Turkey, a Muslim country, has a ______ form of government.

a. democratic

b. weak

c. religious

4. The governments of most Muslim countries are based on ______ law.

a. Jewish

b. Christian

c. Islamic

5. The woman pictured above was the ______ of Israel.

a. premier

b. president

c. absolute ruler

6. Israel has a ______ government.

a. strong, centralized

b. weak, federal

c. parliamentary

7. The government of Israel is influenced by ______ law.

a. Jewish

b. Christian

c. Muslim

8. The citizens of Israel have democratic rights and ______.

a. free elections

b. an absolute ruler

c. no religious freedom

Name **Use with pages 380–381**

Comparing Maps

Use the maps of Egypt below to answer the questions that follow. For help, you can refer to pages 380–381 in your textbook.

MAP A
Distribution of Farm Products

Alexandria
Cairo
Lake Nasser

Sugar cane
Vegetables
Wheat

Cattle
Corn
Cotton
Dates
Goats
Millet
Rice
Sheep

MAP B
Major Oases

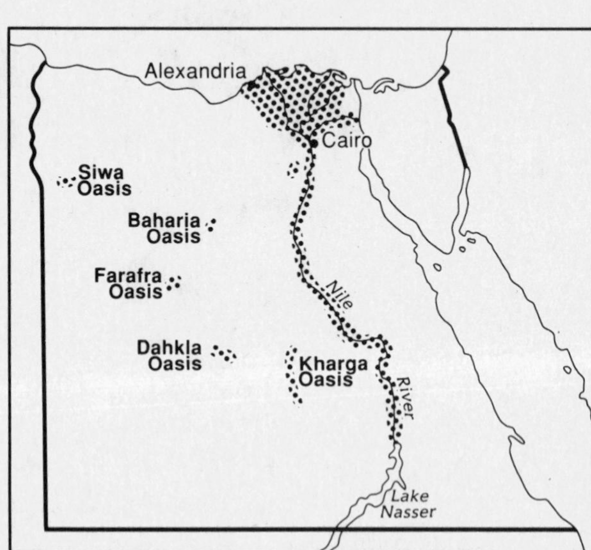

1. What do the two maps show?

   Map A: ______________________

   ____

   ____

   Map B: ______________________

   ____

   ____

2. According to Map A, what are three crops grown in the region of the Nile Delta? ______________________

   ____

   ____

3. What two kinds of farm animals are raised in this area?

   ____

4. What is the only crop grown away from the Nile River?

   ____

5. Compare Map A with Map B. What two factors seem to determine where farm products are grown in Egypt?

   ____

   ____

6. What farm product is grown around Egypt's major oases?

   ____

Name Use with pages 382–383

The Arts in the Middle East

Use the pictures below to complete the activities on this page. For help, you can refer to pages 382–383 in your textbook.

1. a. What is the form of writing in this picture called?

   ____

   b. What is one collection of Middle Eastern tales that may have been recorded in this form of writing?

   ____

   c. Where might you see writing like this today? ______________________

   ____

   ____

2. a. Along with intricate designs, what else do you see in this picture of an Islamic mosaic?

   ____

   b. Why aren't animals and people depicted in most Islamic art?

   ____

   ____

   ____

   c. Where might you see some of the finest Islamic designs today?

   ____

Name Use with pages 384–385

Thinking About New Words

Write the letter of the term in the box that matches each description below. For help, you can refer to the lessons in Chapter 18 in your textbook.

a. labor-intensive	**e.** kibbutz	**i.** moshav
b. absolute ruler	**f.** bazaar	**j.** Islam
c. calligraphy	**g.** Islamic republic	
d. hajj	**h.** sharia	

______ **1.** the Arabic word for the pilgrimage that Muslims make to the city of Mecca

______ **2.** a religion based on the teachings of Muhammad

______ **3.** a type of Arabic writing that features graceful, flowing lines

______ **4.** the term for a nation ruled by Islamic law

______ **5.** using many people rather than machinery to do work

______ **6.** an Israeli cooperative farm

______ **7.** one with complete power whose authority cannot be challenged

______ **8.** an outdoor market

______ **9.** Islamic law

______ **10.** an Israeli collective farm

Name ______________________

The People of North Africa

The graph below shows Egypt's population in the past and what the population is likely to be in the future. Review the graph and then answer the questions that follow. For help, you can refer to pages 387–390 in your textbook.

EGYPT'S POPULATION GROWTH

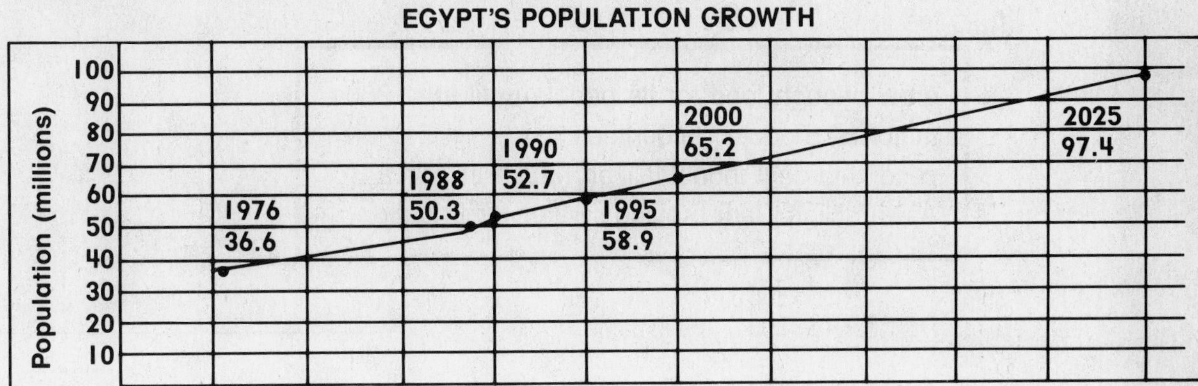

1. According to the graph, what has been happening to Egypt's population?

____

____

____

2. What does the graph show will happen to Egypt's population in the future?

____

____

____

3. What are some of the problems that the people of North Africa share because of the rapidly growing population?

____

____

____

____

____

4. How has improved health care influenced the explosive growth of North Africa's population?

____

____

____

5. In which ways does Islam affect the people of North Africa?

____

____

____

____

____

6. How do many people in North Africa feel about influences from European cultures?

____

____

____

Name Use with pages 391–393

The Economy of North Africa

Complete the map by writing the phrases from the box in the spaces provided on the map. Each space should have a separate phrase. Then answer the questions that follow. For help, you can refer to pages 391–393 in your textbook.

grew enough food for its people until the 1980s
major oil producing countries
second-largest industrialized nation in Africa
Aswan High Dam provides water for irrigation

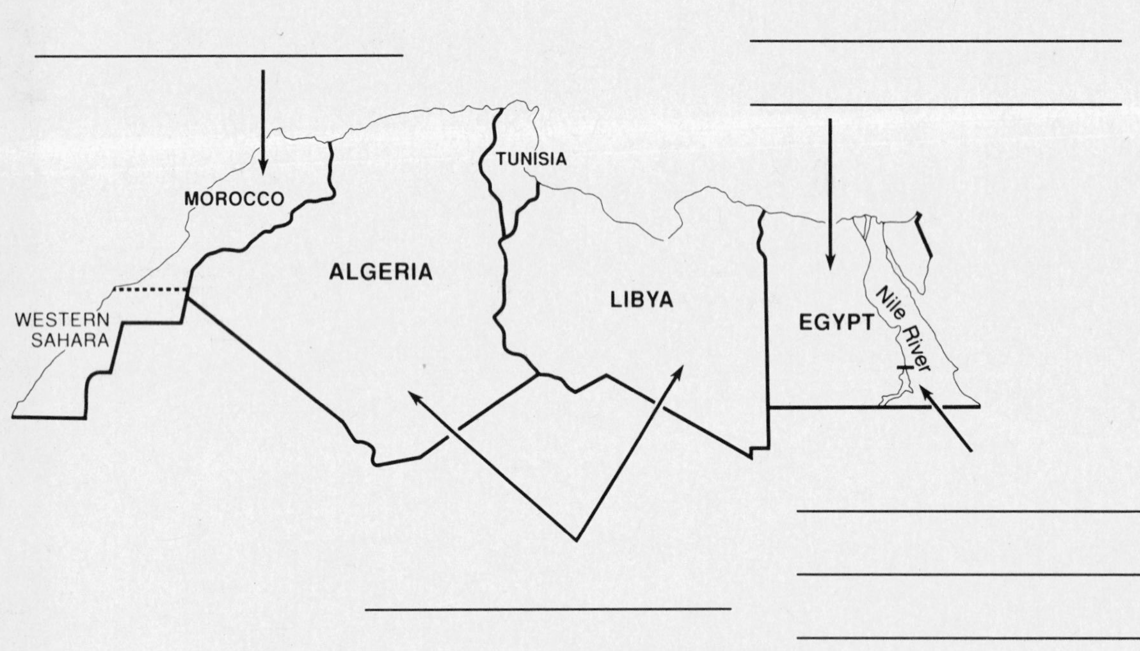

1. Why must most of the countries of North Africa import food? ______

2. On what does the economic future of North Africa depend? ______

Name Use with pages 398–399

The Assassination of Anwar Sadat

The headlines and articles below are from the October 7, 1981, issue of *The New York Times.* Read the headlines and articles and then answer the questions that follow. For help, you can refer to pages 398–399 in your textbook.

SADAT ASSASSINATED AT ARMY PARADE AS MEN AMID RANKS FIRE INTO STANDS; VICE PRESIDENT AFFIRMS 'ALL TREATIES'

Israel Stunned and Anxious; Few Arab Nations Mourning

WORRY IN JERUSALEM

JERUSALEM, Oct. 6—Israel, which had such a high stake in the survival of President Anwar el-Sadat, reacted with stunned anxiety today to the assassination in Cairo.

A fear for the peace treaty between Egypt and Israel dominated all emotions.

JUBILATION IN BEIRUT

BEIRUT, Lebanon, Oct. 6—There was no mourning in most of the Arab world today for President Anwar el-Sadat of Egypt, whose separate peace with Israel had led to his isolation.

Public jubilation was reported in the streets of Syria, Iraq, and Libya. . . .

1. According to the articles, who was Sadat and what happened to him?

____

____

2. According to the articles, how did many of the Arab countries feel about what happened to Sadat? ____

____

3. According to the articles, what had isolated Sadat from the other Arab countries?

____

4. According to the articles, why was Israel worried about the assassination?

____

____

Name Use with pages 400–401

Asking the Right Questions

Use the picture and caption below to complete the activity that follows. For help, you can refer to pages 400–401 in your textbook.

Berbers in a Marrakesh market.

Suppose a friend of yours had recently returned from a trip to Morocco. As you looked through his photographs of the trip, you came across the one shown above. You knew nothing about the Berbers except what was written under the picture. Yet you became interested in them as a topic of study. Place an X next to each question that would help you to learn more about the topic.

______ **a.** Who are the Berbers?

______ **b.** Where did the Berbers come from?

______ **c.** What kinds of things can you buy in a Marrakesh market?

______ **d.** Why were Berbers in a Marrakesh market?

______ **e.** In which part of Africa is Morocco?

______ **f.** How and where do most Berbers live?

______ **g.** What is the population of Morocco?

______ **h.** How long have there been Berbers in Morocco, and are there Berbers in other parts of the world?

______ **i.** Why is the woman in the picture wearing a veil?

______ **j.** What are some Berber customs and religious practices?

______ **k.** What is the major religion of the people of North Africa?

______ **l.** Who are the people that operate the markets in Marrakesh?

Name ______________________ Use with pages 402–403

Islamic Influence on the Arts and Recreation

Briefly explain how Islam influences each of the activities shown below. For help, you can refer to pages 402–403 in your textbook.

ARTISTIC AND RECREATIONAL ACTIVITIES	ISLAMIC INFLUENCE
Painting	______________________
Literature	______________________
Holidays	______________________
Television	______________________

Name Use with pages 404–405

Using New Words

Use the code in the box to figure out each word. For help, you can refer to the lessons in Chapter 19 in your textbook.

CODE

a = ○	g = ▽	l = ◡	q = ●	v = ⌒
b = □	h = ✳	m = ■	r = !	w = ⧅
c = △	i = ¿	n = ฤ	s = ☽	x = ∴
d = ➔	j = ◡̇	o = ⌒̇	t = ◩	y = ⊠
e = ❩	k = ?	p = ▼	u = ¡	z = ☾
f = ▲				

______ 1. __________________________________

▲ ❩ ◡ ◡ ○ ✳ ¿ ฤ

______ 2. __________________________________

! ○ ■ ! ➔ ○ ฤ

______ 3. __________________________________

△ ⌒̇ ◡ ⌒̇ ฤ ¿ ○ ◡ ¿ ☽ ■

______ 4. __________________________________

■ ¡ ❩ ☾ ☾ ¿ ฤ

In the space before each decoded word above, write the letter of each definition it matches.

a. a crier who announces each of the five times every day when Muslims are supposed to pray

b. an Egyptian farmer

c. the control of a country as a colony by another country

d. the most holy month of the Muslim year

Name　　　　　　　　　　　　　　　　　　　　　　**Use with pages 415–418**

A Look at Sub-Saharan Africa

Read the directions and complete the map activities below. For help, you can refer to pages 415–418 in your textbook.

1. Locate and label the following regions of Sub-Saharan Africa. Then color each region as indicated.
   - **a.** West Africa—brown
   - **b.** East and Equatorial Africa—green
   - **c.** Southern Africa—orange
2. Locate and label the following landforms.

   Mount Kilimanjaro　　Mount Kenya

   Zaire Basin　　Ethiopian Highlands
3. Locate and label Madagascar.
4. Locate and label the Great Rift Valley. Then color it red.
5. Locate and label the following bodies of water. Color the lake and trace the rivers in blue.

   Lake Victoria　　Niger River

   Zaire River　　Nile River

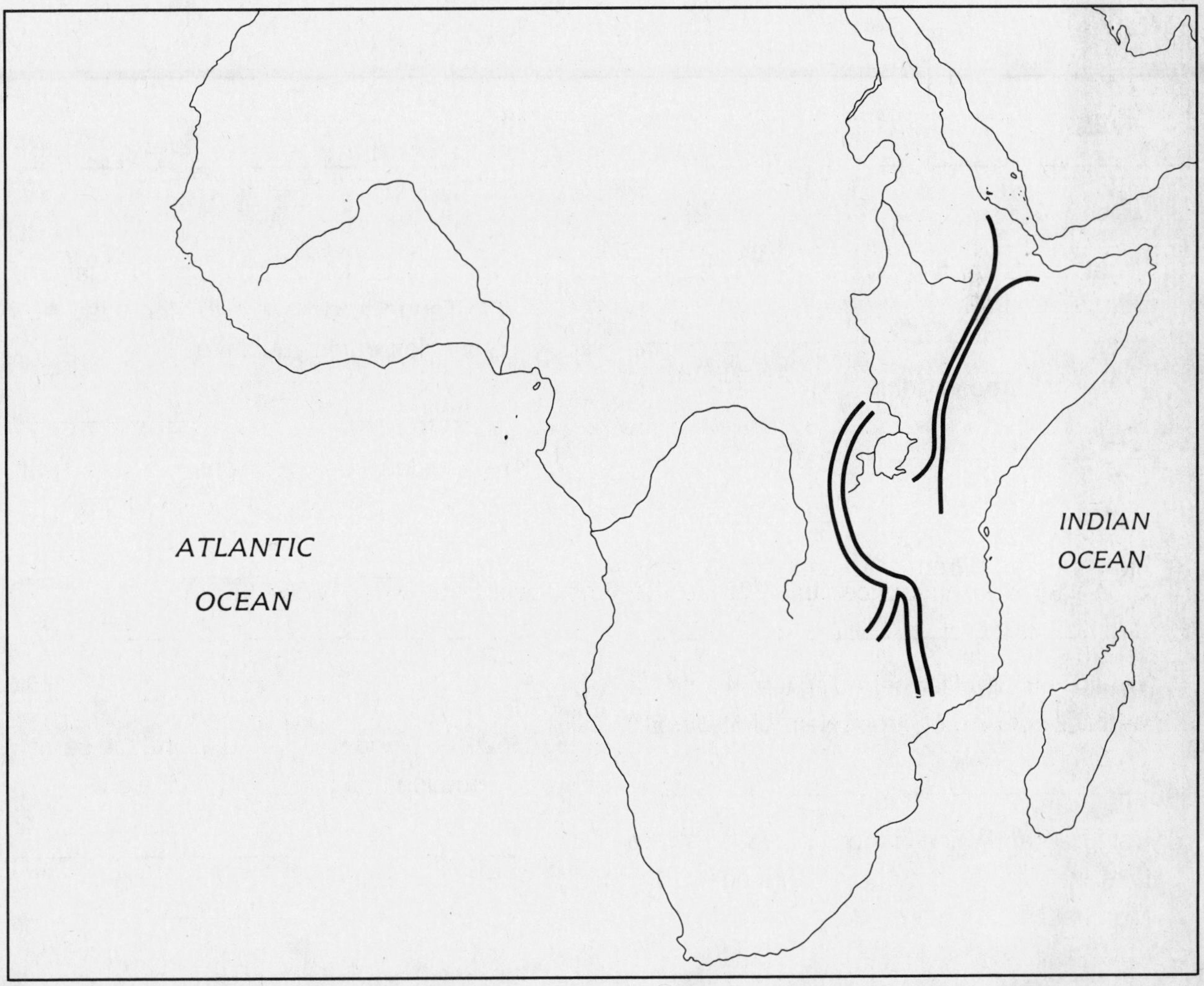

ATLANTIC OCEAN

INDIAN OCEAN

Name Use with page 419

Figuring Distances

Study the chart below. Then answer the questions that follow. For help, you can refer to page 419 in your textbook.

Road Distances in Miles	Jinga	Kampala	Mombasa	Nairobi	Tanga
Jinga		50	668	364	764
Kampala	50		718	414	814
Mombasa	668	718		304	96
Nairobi	364	414	304		401
Tanga	764	814	96	401	

1. What is the chart above called?

____

2. For what purpose is this kind of chart used?

____

____

3. How far is it from Kampala to Nairobi?

____

4. Would you travel farther going from Kampala to Nairobi or going from Nairobi to Jinga?

____

5. Using a car, which trip could you most likely take in a day—from Nairobi to Jinga or from Mombasa to Tanga?

____

6. If you traveled by car from Jinga to Nairobi, on to Tanga, and then on to Mombasa, how many miles would you drive?

____

7. Are the distances you found on the chart by land or by air? How do you know?

____

____

____

8. How could you use a map to find the same information that you found on the chart?

____

____

____

Name

The Resources of Sub-Saharan Africa

Read the following statements carefully. If a statement is true, write **True** in the space provided. If a statement is false, write **False** after it. Then write the reason for your answer. For help, you can refer to pages 420–423 in your textbook.

1. The picture above shows a herd of migrating animals at a drinking hole on the African savanna. Migrating wildlife is an important resource in Sub-Saharan Africa.

____

____

2. The entire African savanna is densely populated. ______________________

____

____

3. In some areas of the savanna, people can raise grain crops. ______________

____

____

4. The rain forest of Sub-Saharan Africa provides many products and natural resources.

____

____

____

5. Sub-Saharan Africa has very few mineral resources. ____________________

____

____

____

Name Use with pages 424–425

Thinking About New Words

Answer each question in the space provided. For help, you can refer to the lessons in Chapter 20 in your textbook.

1. What is a **rift valley**? ______

   ______

   What is the name of the large area of rift valleys in Sub-Saharan Africa?

   ______

2. What is an **escarpment**? ______

   ______

   What happens when a river flows over an escarpment? ______

   ______

3. Why did sailors refer to the winds of Sub-Saharan Africa as **trade winds**?

   ______

4. What is the **harmattan** and how does it affect the climate in Sub-Saharan Africa?

   ______

   ______

5. What is a **savanna** and how much of the African continent is covered by it?

   ______

   ______

6. What is a **basin**? ______

   Why is the huge Zaire Basin sometimes called "The Heart of Africa"?

   ______

   ______

7. What is a **drought**, and how have droughts affected many of the people of Africa?

   ______

   ______

   ______

Name

Use with pages 427–431

Influences on West African Cultures

Study the picture and answer the questions below. For help, you can refer to pages 427–431 in your textbook.

1. The picture above shows what a mosque might have looked like in West Africa hundreds of years ago. How and when did Islam reach this part of Africa?

2. How has the religion of Islam influenced the cultures of West Africa today?

3. a. What happened in the 1500s that had a major influence on West African cultures?

   b. What was the result of this event?

   c. How has this influenced the cultures of West Africa today?

4. How did the tradition of cooperation develop in West African cultures? How important is this tradition?

Name

Use with pages 432–434

Some Methods of Farming in West Africa

Follow the directions to answer the questions below. For help, you can refer to pages 432–434 in your textbook.

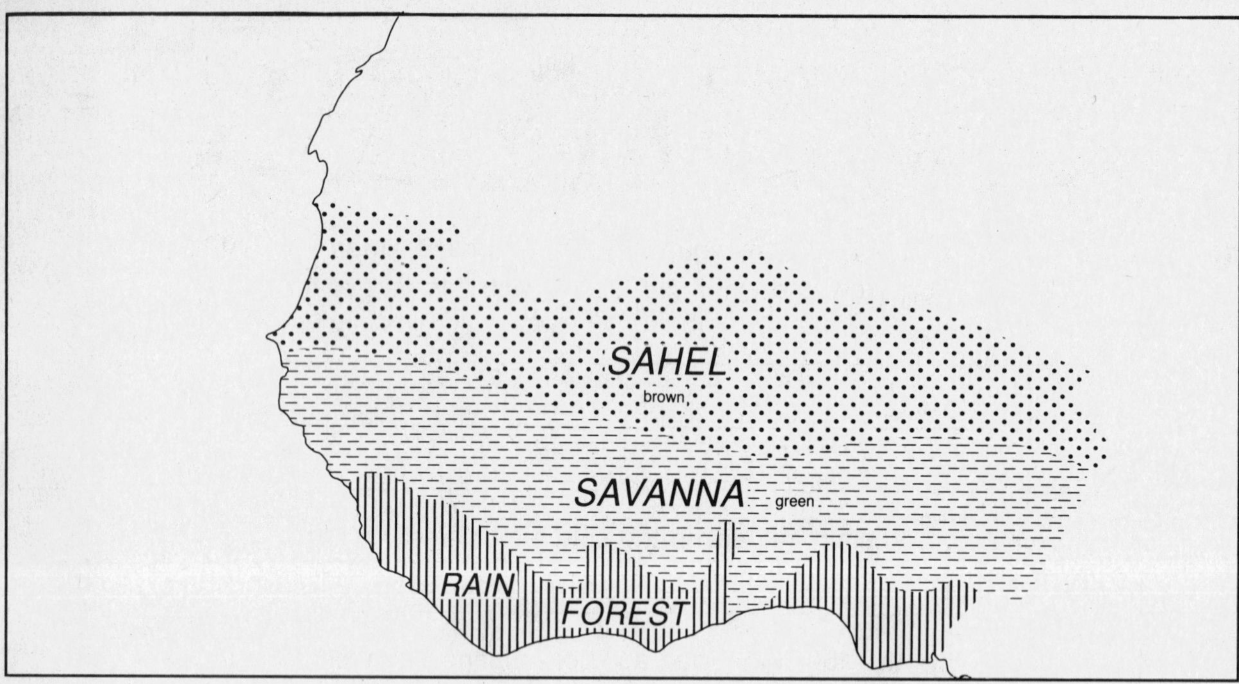

1. a. On the map above locate the region where desertification is occurring. Then color it brown.

   b. Why is desertification increasing?

   ____

   ____

   ____

   ____

   ____

   c. What may happen to this region if desertification continues?

   ____

   ____

2. a. On the map above locate the region where people practice shifting cultivation. Then color it green.

   b. What are two ways in which shifting cultivation is practiced?

   ____

   ____

   c. What is required for shifting cultivation to be successful?

   ____

   ____

3. What are four crops produced by shifting cultivation in West Africa?

______________ ______________ ______________ ______________

Name Use with pages 435–438

A Look at a West African Government

Study the table and answer the questions below. For help, you can refer to pages 435–438 in your textbook.

FACTS ABOUT GAMBIA

Population: 773,000 (est. 1988)
Official Language: English
Major Religions: 90% Islam, 10% Christian and traditional
Ethnic Groups: Mandingo (41%), Fulani (14%), Wolof (13%), Serahuli (10%), Jola (8%), Other (14%)
Independence Day: February 18, 1965
Type of Government: Republic
Head of State: President elected to a five-year term
Major Political Parties: People's Progressive party
United party
National Convention party

1. a. According to the table, what kind of government does Gambia have?

____

b. What kinds of governments do most other West African countries have?

____

____

2. What is the Head of State of Gambia called?

____

3. How does a person become Head of State in Gambia?

____

4. a. According to the table, how many major ethnic groups are in Gambia?

____

b. What challenge do so many ethnic groups present to the governments of West Africa?

____

5. How many major political parties does Gambia have?

____

6. In your opinion, is Gambia more or less democratic than most other West African countries? Give a reason for your answer.

____

____

____

Name Use with page 439

Distinguishing Fact from Opinion

Read the selection below. Then follow the directions and answer the questions. For help, you can refer to page 439 in your textbook.

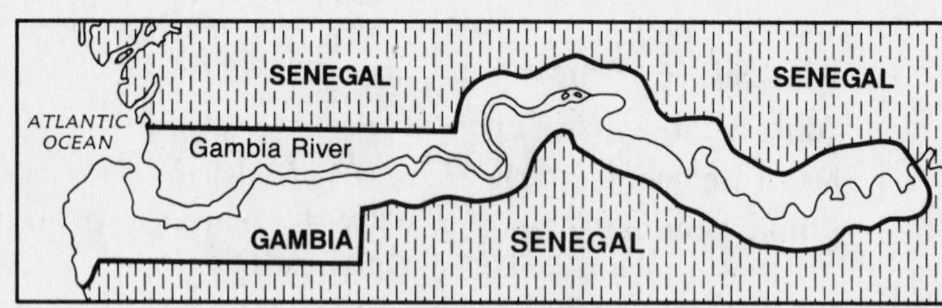

Gambia is the smallest independent country in Africa. I've always thought that the shape of Gambia is unusual. It is about 200 miles long but only from 10 to 40 miles wide. As it winds its way into the continent of Africa, it is surrounded by the country of Senegal. The entire length of Gambia follows the Gambia River, which is the major means of transportation through its interior. Gambia is planning to build a bridge and dam complex so that the river can be used for irrigation. I feel the dam will greatly benefit the Gambian people. It should allow them to grow more crops along the river's banks. In 1982 Gambia and Senegal established an organization for mutual cooperation. I believe this is one of the best things the two countries could have done.

1. Underline the sentences in the selection that state facts.
2. List two reasoned opinions stated in the selection. Then list the evidence the author gives to support each opinion.

reasoned opinion: ______________________________

____

supporting evidence: ______________________________

____

reasoned opinion: ______________________________

____

supporting evidence: ______________________________

____

3. Which reasoned opinion is supported by the map of Gambia?

____

____

Name

Arts and Recreation in West Africa

Use the pictures on the right to complete the exercises below. For help, you can refer to pages 440–441 in your textbook.

1. a. Draw a line to the picture that shows West Africa's oral tradition.
   b. Who are the most famous West African storytellers?

   ____

   c. What role do they play in many groups?

   ____

   ____

   ____

2. a. Draw a line to the picture that shows how many West Africans mark the main events in human life.
   b. What is the main musical instrument used for these events?

   ____

3. a. Draw a line to the picture that shows how West Africans traditionally called the gods and spirits to talk to humans.
   b. What materials may be used in the making of West African masks?

   ____

   ____

   ____

Name

Thinking About New Words

Choose a term from the box to answer each question. For help, you can refer to the lessons in Chapter 21 in your textbook.

slash-and-burn farming	lineage	desertification
shifting cultivation	clan	oral tradition
griot	oba	talking drums

1. Which term refers to a West African storyteller? ______________________
2. Which term refers to a West African ruler? ______________________
3. Which term describes a way of farming that involves clearing the land by burning? ______________________
4. Which term describes literature and history that are passed down from person to person by the spoken word? ______________________
5. Which term would you use to refer to drums that imitate the sound of human speech? ______________________
6. Which term describes a group of families that are descended from the same ancestor? ______________________
7. Which term would you use to refer to a kind of farming that allows some fields to rest while others are planted? ______________________
8. Which term best describes what is happening to the Sahel of West Africa? ______________________
9. Which term would you use to refer to a line of direct descent from an ancestor? ______________________

Name Use with pages 449–452

Migration into East and Equatorial Africa

The chart below lists some of the major groups of people that migrated throughout East and Equatorial Africa. Read the list of groups. Then complete the chart by filling in the columns. For help, you can refer to pages 449–452 in your textbook.

MIGRATION INTO EAST AND EQUATORIAL AFRICA

Migrating Group	Area of Migration	Influence and Skills
Bantus		
Arab Muslims		
Kushites		
Nilotes		
Europeans		

Name _______________ Use with pages 453–455

The Economy of East and Equatorial Africa

Read the following statements carefully. If a statement is true, write **True** after it. If a statement is false, write **False** after it. Then, in the space provided, write the reasons for your answer. For help, you can refer to pages 453–455 in your textbook.

1. The picture above shows the tradition of cattle herding among the people of East and Equatorial Africa. To these people, cattle are much more than just a source of food.

____

____

2. Many of the people in East and Equatorial Africa are nomadic herders of cattle, moving their herds from one area to another. _______________________

____

____

3. The area of cattle herding has plenty of rainfall and an abundance of vegetation for grazing. _______________________

____

____

4. In the southern areas, the people farm land that is usually owned by wealthy individuals. _______________________

____

____

5. To become more developed economically, the countries of East and Equatorial Africa need to take several costly steps all at once. _______________________

____

____

Name

Use with pages 458–460

Governments in East and Equatorial Africa

Use the lines below the box to answer the questions in the box. Write your answers as complete sentences and arrange them in paragraphs. When you finish, you should have a brief summary of the typical government in the area, as well as a requirement for change. For help, you can refer to pages 458–460 in your textbook.

- How do most East and Equatorial African leaders feel about democratic rights for their people?
- What kinds of governments have the countries of this region had?
- How many candidates are on the ballot in most elections?
- How has power usually changed hands in these countries?
- What changes are coming to this region?
- What do many people think must happen before the governments of East and Equatorial Africa will change?
- Why do these people think future governments will be better?

Name Use with pages 461–462

Looking at an Oral Tradition

The song, saying, and proverb below are from the oral tradition of the people of East and Equatorial Africa. On the lines provided, briefly explain what each means to you. For help, you can refer to pages 461–462 in your textbook.

In the time when Dendid created all things,
He created the sun,
And the sun is born, and dies, and comes again.
He created the moon,
And the moon is born, and dies, and comes again;
He created the stars,
And the stars are born, and die, and come again;
He created man,
And man is born, and dies, and does not come again.

–Old Dinka Chant

____

____

____

Somewhere the Sky touches the Earth,
and the name of that place is the End.

–A Kamba Saying

To stumble is not to fall down but
to go forward.

–A Swahili Proverb

_______________________ _______________________

_______________________ _______________________

_______________________ _______________________

_______________________ _______________________

Name Use with page 463

Making a Graph from a Chart

Make a line graph from the information in the chart. Use a different color for each point on your graph. Then use your graph to answer the questions that follow. For help, you can refer to page 463 in your textbook.

POPULATIONS OF TWO AFRICAN CITIES

Country	Population in Millions						
	1960	1965	1970	1975	1980	1985	1990
Lagos, Nigeria	0.7	1.0	1.4	2.1	2.8	3.7	3.9
Casablanca, Morocco	1.1	1.3	1.5	1.9	2.2	2.7	3.2

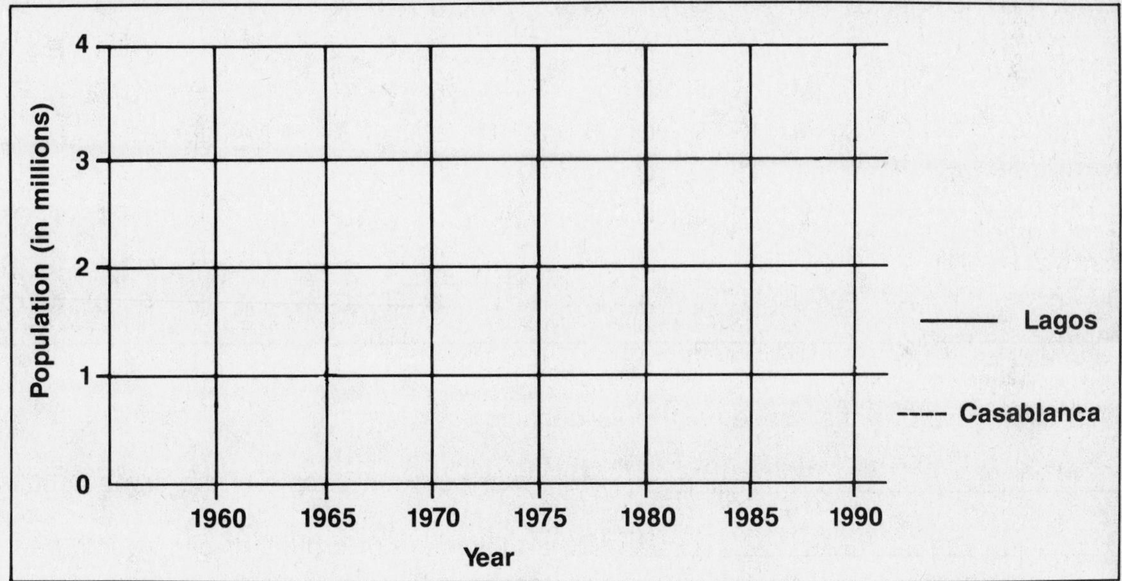

1. Has the population of each city decreased or increased since 1960? **decreased** **increased**
2. Which city had the larger population in 1960? **Casablanca** **Lagos**
3. Which city had the larger population in 1990? **Casablanca** **Lagos**
4. Which city's population grew faster between 1960 and 1990? **Casablanca** **Lagos**

   How can you tell? ______________________________

5. Is it easier to compare the population growth of the two cities in the graph or in the chart? Give a reason for your answer. ______________________________

____

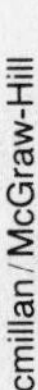

Name Use with pages 464–465

Thinking About New Words

Each of the terms listed in the box below is hidden among the letters that follow. Draw a circle around each term you find. The words may be read forward, backward, up, down, or diagonally. For help, you can refer to the lessons in Chapter 22 in your textbook.

migration	Swahili	famine	malnutrition
civil war	proverb	barter	

P O K U E L A S P A E O R R L I L A R O P M B E
R L R N K E M E M F C I V I L W A R Z I R A U W
E L X R O I G F S O T A C X D U A E K P O O V R
C N T Z Y O O S N O A T D I O O Q T E C V A E V
I D I A L I E M I G R A T I O N O C L P E T N X
E W S M T E O R K B O N S D L A K R A E R E N T
I L I H A W S E D A O E P A N B O J S A B U E I
R E S R L F A E D U O T R Q A D I O B K N T I Y
A S E Q H D S O L R M V I L U D P Z S R Z K C P
N O I T I R T U N L A M R O S I O Z S E T C A C

Write each circled word in the space next to its definition.

____________________ 1. a war between people of the same country

____________________ 2. a movement of groups of people into new lands

____________________ 3. a short, popular saying that illustrates a truth

____________________ 4. a condition that occurs when people have too little food

____________________ 5. the widespread and extreme shortage of food

____________________ 6. one of the most common languages in East and Equatorial Africa

____________________ 7. to swap one thing for another

Name Use with pages 467–470

The People of Southern Africa

Follow the directions and answer the questions that follow. For help, you can refer to pages 467–470 in your textbook.

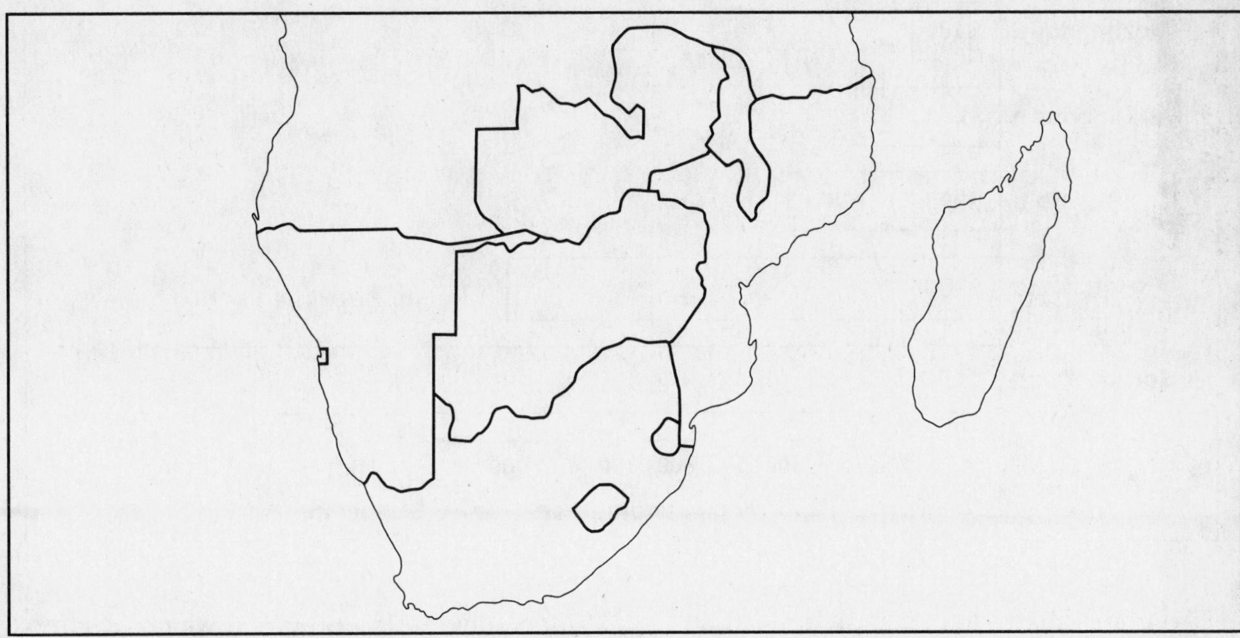

1. On the map above, locate and label the countries of Southern Africa.

Botswana	Lesotho
Madagascar	Malawi
Mozambique	Namibia
Swaziland	Zimbabwe
South Africa	Zambia

2. On the map above, locate and label the area where most Bushmen lived until recently. Then color the area orange.

3. a. From what group are the majority of people in Southern Africa descended?

____

b. When did this group migrate into the lands of the Bushmen?

____

4. a. Locate the only country in Southern Africa that is ruled by a white minority. Then color the country red.

b. How are different racial groups treated in this country?

____

____

5. a. Locate a country that is ruled by its black majority. Then color it green.

b. What is one way this country tries to promote understanding between its different ethnic groups?

____

____

____

Name Use with pages 471–473

The Economies of Southern Africa

Answer the questions below. For help, you can refer to pages 471–473 in your textbook.

AVERAGE YEARLY INCOMES IN SOME SOUTH AFRICAN COUNTRIES

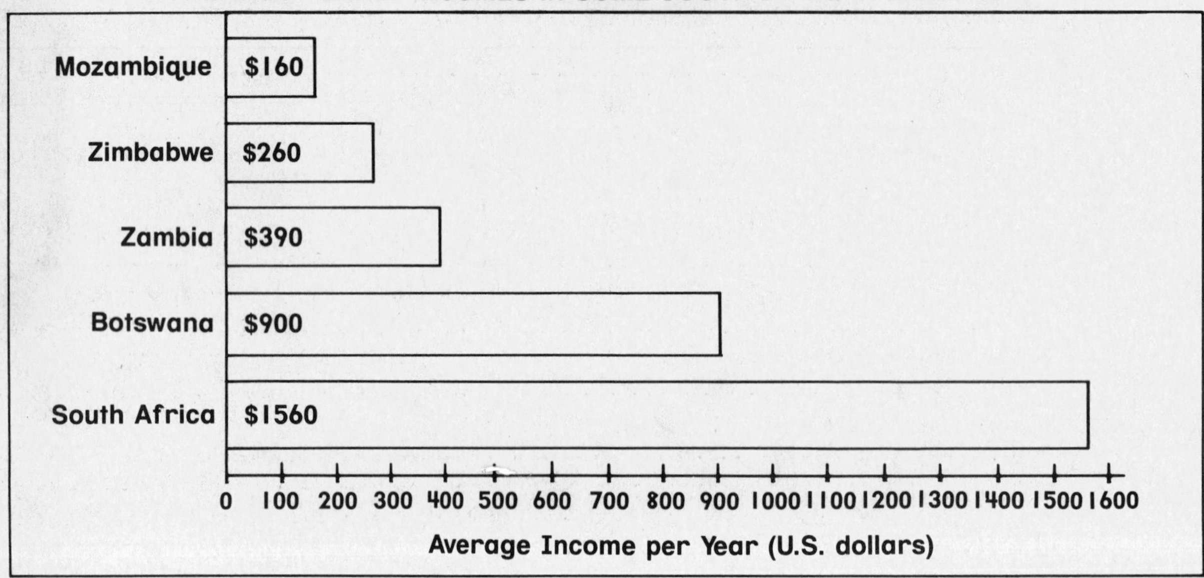

1. The graph shows the average amount of money that people in the countries of Southern Africa earn in a year. In which of these countries do people earn the least amount of money?

   ____

2. What two factors have contributed to this low per capita income?

   ____

   ____

3. In which country shown on the graph do whites and blacks work equally and peacefully together?

   ____

4. How do most people make a living in this country?

   ____

5. According to the graph, in which country do people have the highest income?

   ____

6. What two mineral resources does this country have in vast abundance?

   ____

7. How do the incomes of white miners and black miners differ in South Africa?

   ____

   ____

8. Which country shown on the graph has one fourth of the world's copper?

   ____

   ____

   ____

Name Use with pages 474–477

A Look at Apartheid

The graph below shows the categories of races in South Africa. After studying the graph, complete the activities that follow. For help, you can refer to pages 474–477 in your textbook.

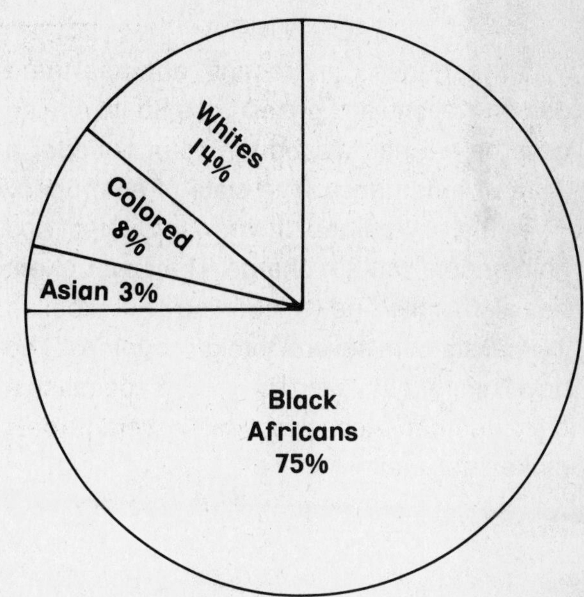

1. How many racial categories had been created by the South African system of apartheid?

____

2. Which category is the largest?

____

3. Which racial category is firmly in control of the South African government?

____

About what percentage of the population does this category make up?

____

4. What did many countries and international organizations do to protest the apartheid system? Give an example. _______________

____

____

____

5. What changes began to take place in South Africa by 1990?

____

____

____

____

____

____

Name Use with page 478

Recognizing Bias

Read the accounts below of the "state of emergency" declared by the South African government in 1986. Then complete the activities that follow. For help, you can refer to page 478 in your textbook.

ACCOUNT A

In response to recent anti-apartheid demonstrations and protests, the South African government has placed the country under a state of emergency. The state of emergency gives the government the power to arrest and hold people without charge. The government has also limited news reporting and expelled journalists from several foreign countries. The government has taken these steps because it believes that excessive news coverage only makes the matter worse.

ACCOUNT B

In response to recent anti-apartheid demonstrations, the repressive white government of South Africa has assumed dictatorial power by placing the country under a state of emergency. Under the state of emergency the government has jailed tens of thousands of peaceful demonstrators and terrorized their leaders. It has also suppressed reporting of the protests and expelled any foreign journalists daring to report what is really happening.

1. Which account do you think shows bias? ______________________

2. What are some clues that alerted you to the bias? ______________________

____

____

____

____

____

3. Describe the bias in your own words. ______________________

____

____

____

____

____

____

Name ____________ Use with pages 479–481

Arts and Recreation in Southern Africa

You might see the announcements on this page in almost any Southern African country. Read each one. Then answer the questions. For help, you can refer to pages 479–481 in your textbook.

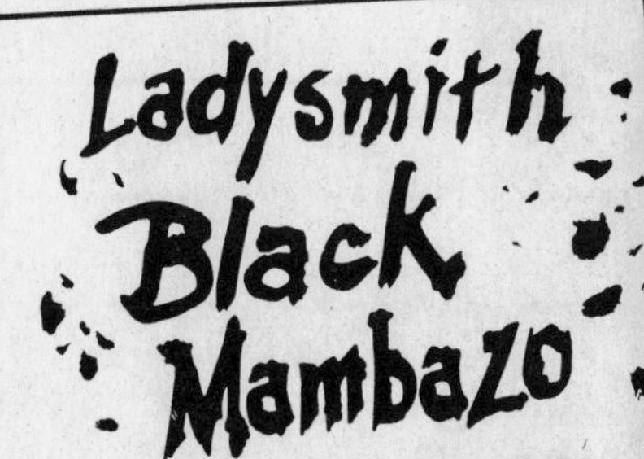

1. a. What is the music called that is performed by the group in the top announcement?

____

b. How was this music created?

____

____

____

AMAMPONDO

The traditional instruments of Southern Africa as you've never heard them before.

2. a. What kinds of instruments does the group in the middle announcement use?

____

____

b. What is the main instrument used by this group called?

____

SOCCER OUTLIVES APARTHEID

South Africa Reenters World Competition.

3. a. Who introduced the popular sport in this bottom announcement to Africa?

____

b. What group ended its 21-year ban against competition by South African athletes in 1991?

____

____

Name ______________________ Use with pages 482–483

Learning New Words

Look at the box containing the Morse Code. The Morse Code uses dots and dashes to stand for the letters of the alphabet. Use the code to figure out the words and write each word on the lines provided. For help, you can refer to the lesson in Chapter 23 in your textbook.

A	B	C	D	E	F	G	H	I
•—	—•••	—•—•	—••	•	••—•	——•	••••	••
J	**K**	**L**	**M**	**N**	**O**	**P**	**Q**	**R**
•———	—•—	•—••	——	—•	———	•——•	——•—	•—•
S	**T**	**U**	**V**	**W**	**X**	**Y**	**Z**	
•••	—	••—	•••—	•——	—••—	—•——	——••	

_____ 1. ______________________________
••• •— —• —•—• — •• ——— —• •••

_____ 2. ______________________________
•••— • •—•• —••

_____ 3. ______________________________
— ——— •—— —• ••• •••• •• •——•

_____ 4. ______________________________
—— —••• •• •—• •—

_____ 5. ______________________________
•— •——• •— •—• — •••• • •• —••

Match the definitions below with the words above. Write the letter of each definition in the space before the appropriate word.

a. a racially segregated urban area in South Africa

b. the system used in South Africa for keeping racial groups separated

c. actions taken against a country by other nations to try to get the country to change

d. the vast, dry, treeless plateau that covers much of South Africa

e. an African finger piano made of metal or bamboo strips tied to a wood bowl

Name   Use with pages 491–495

Southern and Eastern Asia

Use the map and follow the directions to complete the activities below. For help, you can refer to pages 491–495 in your textbook.

1. Locate and label the subcontinent of India.
2. Color the area of the Gobi and Takla Makan deserts brown.
3. Draw a red circle around the Indonesian archipelago.
4. Draw a green circle around the Philippine archipelago.
5. Locate and label the following rivers.

   Huang River   Chang River

   Ganges River   Mekong River

   Indus River
6. Locate and label the Pamir Knot.
7. Color the area of the North China Plain and the Tibetan Plateau orange.

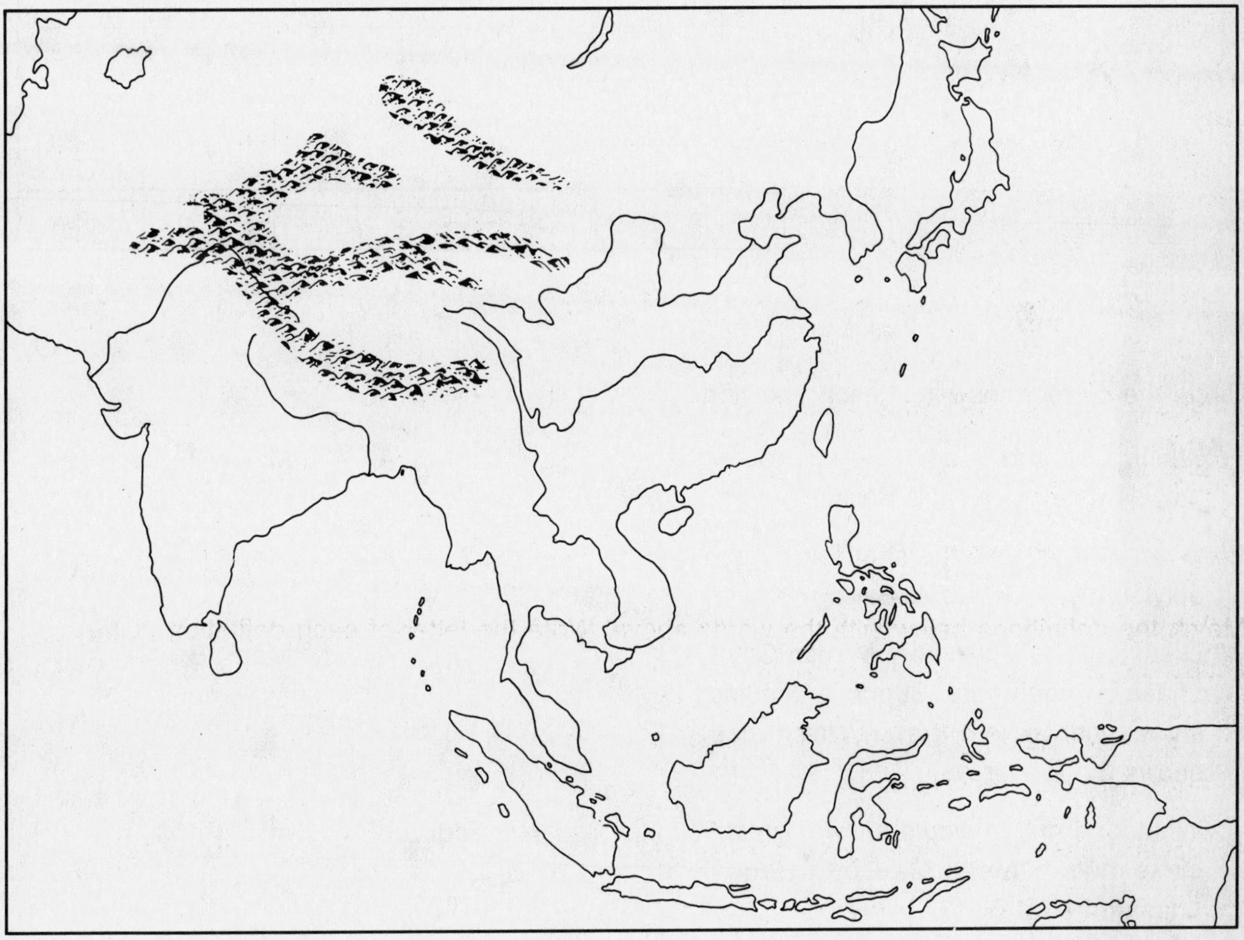

Name Use with pages 496–497

Thinking About Great-Circle Routes

Use the maps to answer the questions and complete the activities that follow. For help, you can refer to pages 496–497 in your textbook.

MAP A **MAP B**

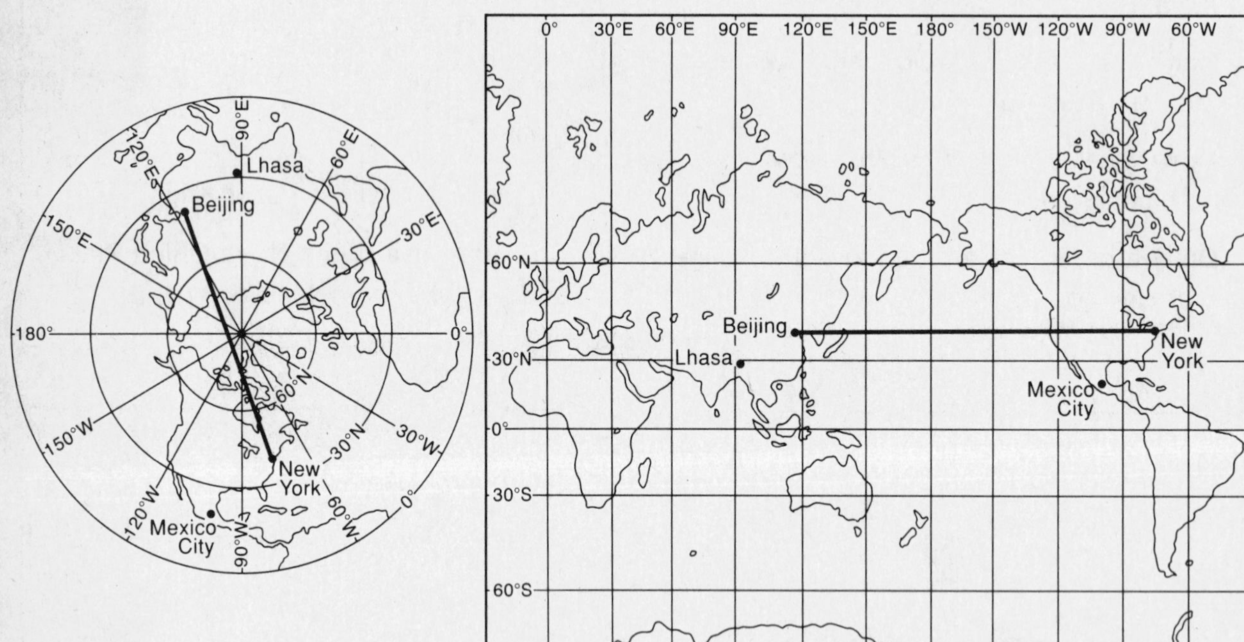

Circle the correct answer to each question.

1. Which map shows a great-circle route between New York and Beijing? Map A Map B

2. Which map shows the shortest route between New York and Beijing? Map A Map B

3. Draw a straight line from Mexico City to Lhasa on each map. Suppose this line shows your route of travel. Which map shows the longer route? Map A Map B

4. What kind of line would show a great-circle route between Mexico City and Lhasa on Map B? curved straight

Name ______________________ Use with pages 498–501

Climate in Southern and Eastern Asia

Study the maps and answer the questions. For help, you can refer to pages 498–501 in your textbook.

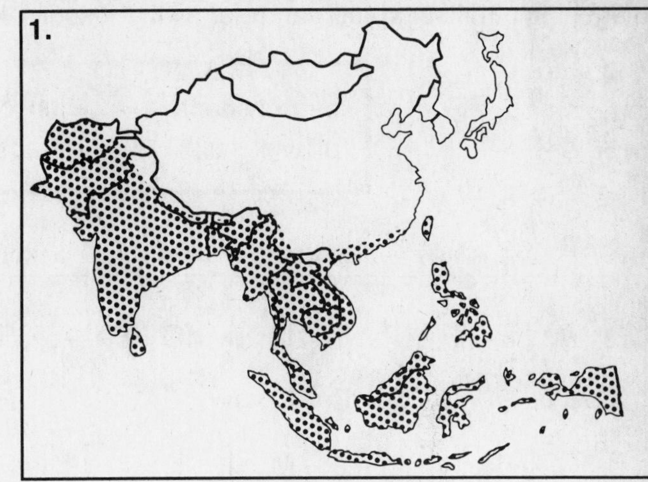

1. a. What kind of climate does most of this part of Asia have?

   ____

   b. What is the major seasonal feature of this region?

   ____

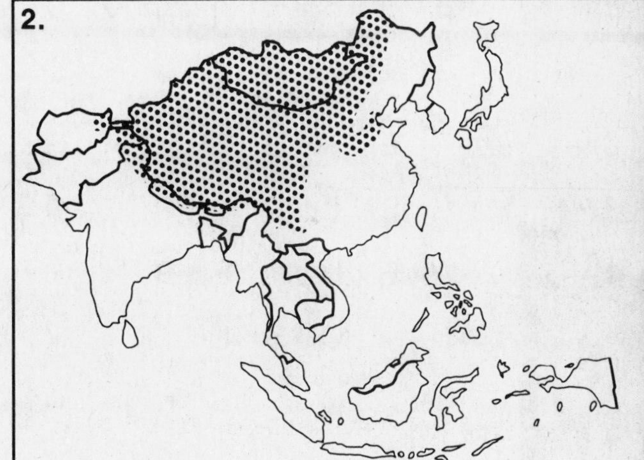

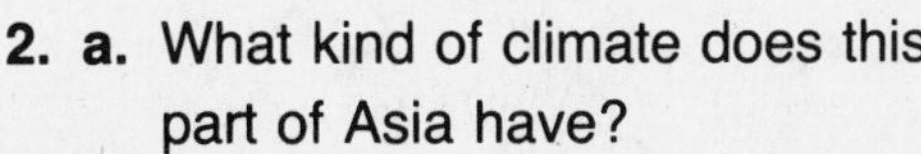

2. a. What kind of climate does this part of Asia have?

   ____

   b. Why is this region cold and dry?

   ____

   ____

   ____

   ____

   ____

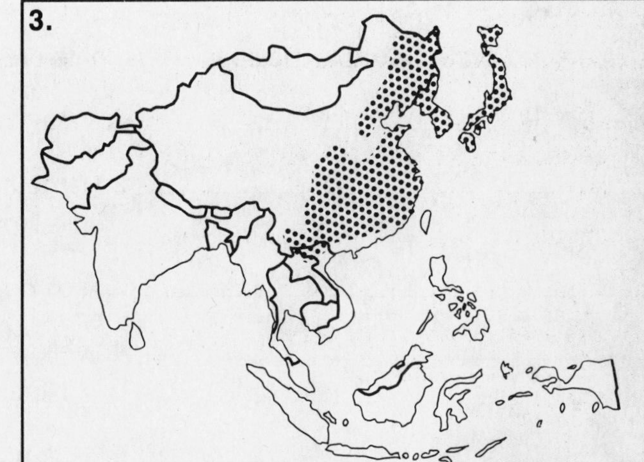

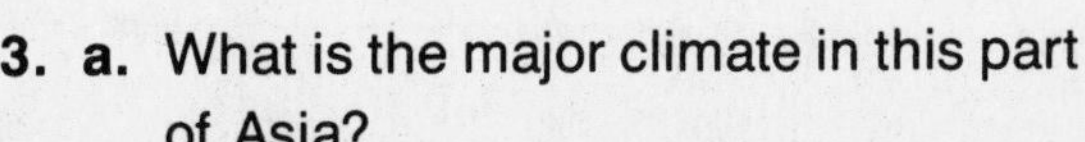

3. a. What is the major climate in this part of Asia?

   ____

   b. How is this climate like the climate in the eastern part of United States?

   ____

   ____

   ____

Name Use with pages 502–503

Using New Words

Each of the terms listed in the box below is hidden among the letters that follow. Draw a circle around each term you find. The words may be read forward, backward, up, down, or diagonally. For help, you can refer to the lessons in Chapter 24 in your textbook.

subcontinent	monsoons	loess
alluvial soil	terraces	

Q	W	E	R	T	Y	U	I	O	P	A	S	D	F	G	H	J	K	L	Z
X	C	S	U	B	C	O	N	T	I	N	E	N	T	C	R	F	V	T	G
B	Y	H	N	U	J	M	I	K	O	L	P	E	A	Q	X	S	W	S	D
E	V	F	R	B	G	T	N	H	Y	M	R	U	K	I	L	O	P	N	I
U	Y	T	R	E	W	Q	L	K	J	R	G	F	S	S	A	M	N	O	V
C	X	Z	Q	E	T	U	O	L	A	G	D	A	X	S	S	L	M	O	C
Z	K	H	F	S	L	K	J	C	S	D	F	M	N	Z	E	E	V	S	P
I	U	Q	W	E	R	I	E	B	W	E	F	B	K	J	B	O	O	N	H
T	P	I	L	I	O	S	L	A	I	V	U	L	L	A	E	K	L	O	A
S	K	F	J	H	Q	F	H	K	K	D	D	W	E	T	Y	B	P	M	C

Write each circled word in the space next to its definition.

_______________ **1.** heavy rains brought on by seasonal winds

_______________ **2.** large steps that have been carved into hillsides for the raising of crops

_______________ **3.** soil deposited by a river as it flows

_______________ **4.** yellowish, fertile soil that has been deposited by the wind

_______________ **5.** a large landmass that is smaller than a continent

Name Use with pages 505–513

The People of South Asia

Study the table. Then answer the questions that follow. For help, you can refer to pages 505–513 in your textbook.

THE PEOPLE AND RELIGIONS OF SOUTH ASIA

Country	Major Religion	Population Density	Major Occupation Percentage of Workers
Afghanistan	Islam	65/per sq. mi.	68% farming/10% industry
Bangladesh	Islam	2,028/per sq. mi.	74% farming/11% industry
Bhutan	Buddhism	84/per sq. mi.	95% farming
India	Hinduism	658/per sq. mi.	70% farming/19% industry
Maldives	Islam	1,756/per sq. mi.	80% fishing and farming
Nepal	Hinduism	334/per sq. mi.	91% farming
Pakistan	Islam	335/per sq. mi.	53% farming/10% industry
Sri Lanka	Buddhism	692/per sq. mi.	46% farming/27% industry

source: *World Almanac, 1989*

1. According to the table, what are the three major religicns in South Asia?

____

____

____

2. How did religious differences contribute to the formation of Pakistan?

____

____

____

____

3. According to the table, what is the major occupation of South Asians?

____

4. According to the table, which South Asian country has the highest population density?

____

5. How has a high population density contributed to a low standard of living for many South Asians?

____

____

____

6. What is being done to ease the problems of famine and malnutrition in South Asia?

____

____

____

Name Use with pages 514–517

The Governments of South Asia

Complete the map by writing phrases from the box in the spaces provided on the map. Each space should have a separate phrase. For help, you can refer to pages 514–517 in your textbook.

a socialist government	among the world's last monarchies
an Islamic country	gained independence with India's help
a threatened island democracy	the world's largest democracy

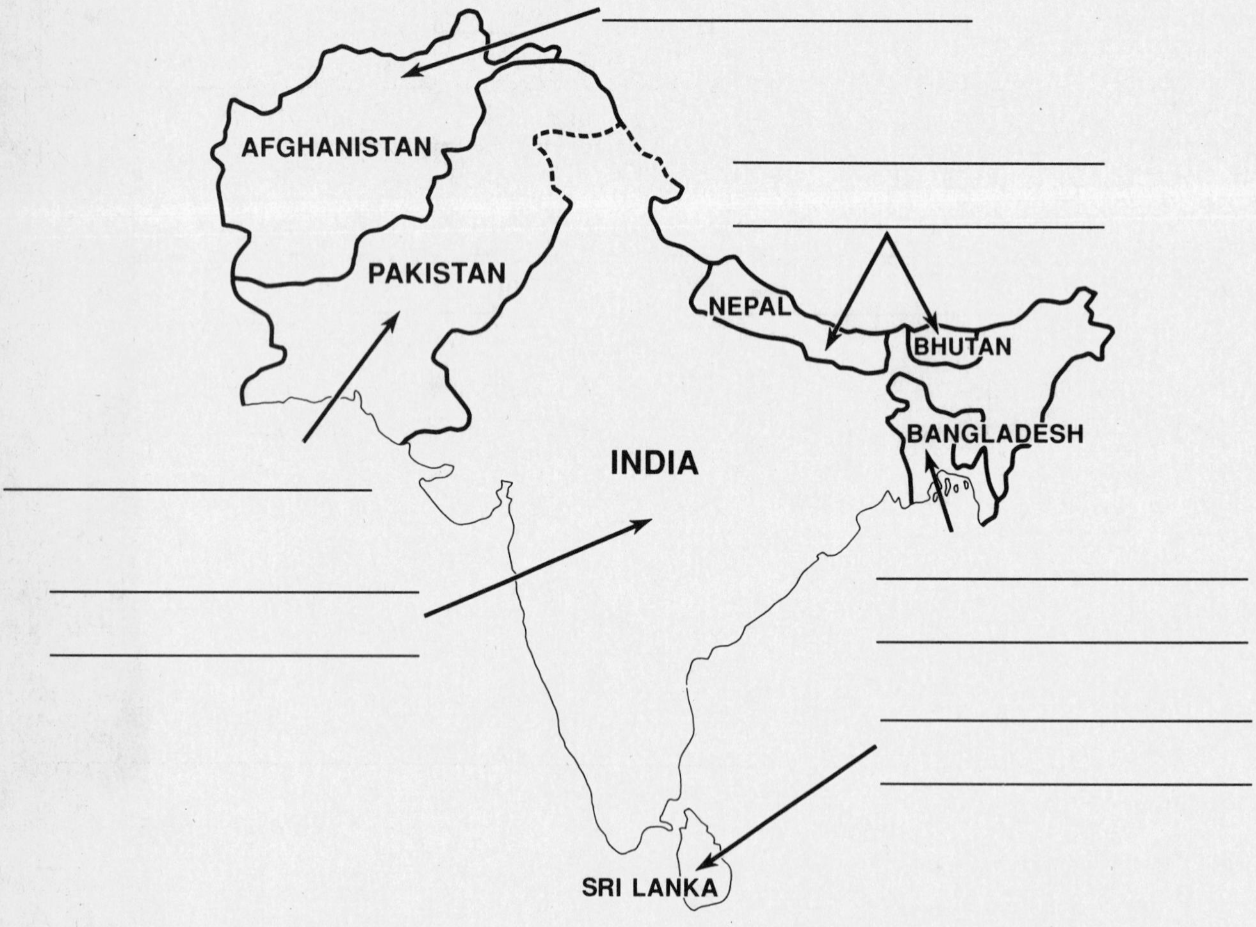

What have the nations of South Asia done to preserve their independence?

Macmillan/McGraw-Hill

Name Use with page 518

Determining Point of View

Read the selection to complete the activities that follow. For help, you can refer to page 518 in your textbook.

Anyone visiting India should put the city of Agra at the top of his or her list of things to do and places to see. Agra is one of India's oldest cities and is famous for the Taj Mahal. The Taj Mahal may be the most beautiful building in the world. It was built in the 1600s by Emperor Shah Jahan as a memorial to his wife. The city of Agra is also famous for its gold lace and inlaid mosaics that are made mostly by hand. A visit to Agra is the best way to introduce yourself to the history, life, and customs of India.

1. List three sentences from the selection that are statements of fact.

   a. ______________________________

   b. ______________________________

   c. ______________________________

2. List three sentences that are statements of opinion.

   a. ______________________________

   b. ______________________________

   c. ______________________________

3. What is the writer's point of view? ______________________________

Name Use with pages 519–521

Arts and Recreation in South Asia

Study the pictures. Then follow the directions to answer the questions that follow. For help, you can refer to pages 519–521 in your textbook.

1. Circle the pictures that represent things from Indian culture that have spread to other parts of the world.

____

2. Shade the picture that represents Islamic influence in art and architecture.

____

3. Draw a triangle around the picture that represents Buddhist influence in art and architecture.

____

4. Put an **X** on the picture that represents a popular recreational activity imported from Britain.

____

5. Draw a box around the picture that represents the telling of Hindu tales.

____

6. What plays a major role in the arts and recreation of South Asia?

____

7. What is meant by a cultural exchange between South Asia and other parts of the world?

____

____

____

____

____

Name

Using New Words

Use the words in the box to complete the puzzle below. For help, you can refer to the lessons in Chapter 25 in your textbook.

nonaligned nations	Hinduism	Vedas
Green Revolution	Brahmans	yoga
cottage industry	Sikhism	
partition	caste	

Across

2. division

6. countries that do not want to take sides in the struggles between the world's superpowers

9. the religion that grew out of the legends and customs of the Aryans

10. a social group that identifies people according to the occupation of their ancestors

Down

1. changes in South Asian farming techniques that have resulted in larger harvests

3. a way of training body and mind through exercise and meditation

4. a collection of Hindu writings

5. manufacturing that takes place inside people's homes

7. a religion combining some elements of Hinduism and Islam

8. the priestly caste of ancient India

Name Use with pages 525–528

People and Tradition in East Asia

Follow the directions to complete the activities below. For help, you can refer to pages 525–528 in your textbook.

1. a. Draw a line to the picture of the person who helped to establish the tradition of family loyalty in China.
   b. After the communists took power, with what did they try to replace family loyalty?

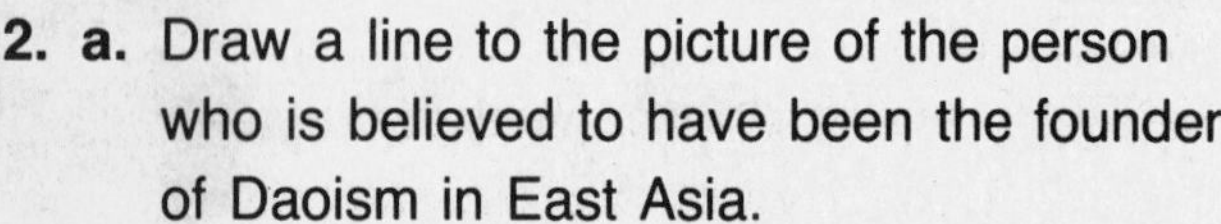

2. a. Draw a line to the picture of the person who is believed to have been the founder of Daoism in East Asia.
   b. What does Daoism teach?

3. a. Draw a line to the picture of the person who began Buddhism.
   b. What did this person come to be called?

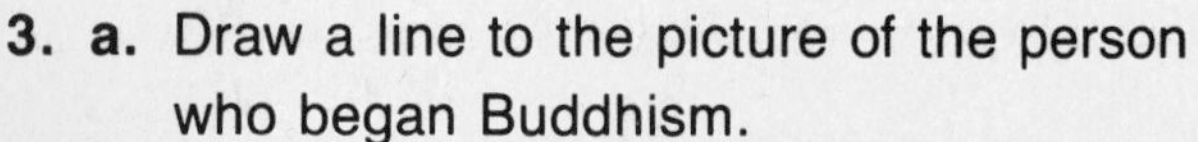

   c. What does Buddhism teach?

4. a. Draw a line to the picture that shows the person who wanted China to break with the past.
   b. What system of government did he establish in China?

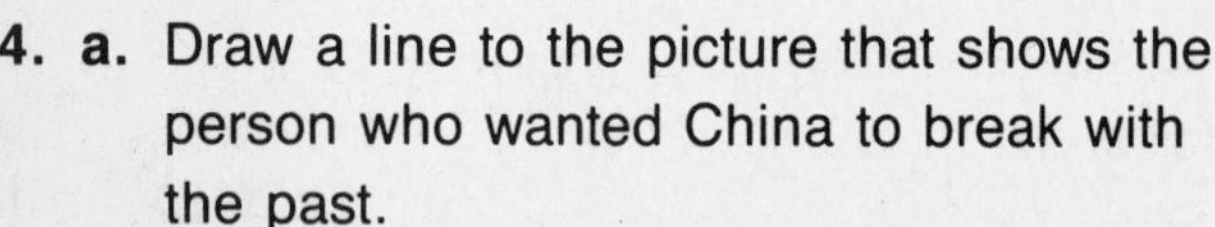

Name _______________ Use with pages 529–531

The Economies of East Asia

The headlines below might have been written about the economies of East Asia. Answer the questions about each headline. For help, you can refer to pages 529–531 in your textbook.

CHINA LOOSENS GRIP ON PRIVATE ENTERPRISE

a. During which years would this headline have been written? _______________

b. Why did China's leaders decide to allow limited private enterprise?

____

____

c. Was China's new economic program successful? Explain your answer.

____

____

CHINA SLOWS CHANGE TO PRIVATE ENTERPRISE

a. During which years would this headline have been written? _______________

b. List two problems that caused the government of China to tighten its control over private enterprise.

____

____

____

EAST ASIA WORKS ECONOMIC MIRACLES

a. Which countries and colony of East Asia would this headline describe?

____

b. Why did these countries and colony produce goods more cheaply than other countries?

____

c. How did the people in these countries make their economies successful?

____

____

Name Use with pages 532–534

The Governments of East Asia

Look at the map and follow the directions to answer the questions below. For help, you can refer to pages 532–534 in your textbook.

1. Put an **X** on the countries that have communist governments.

2. Shade the countries that have republican forms of governments.

3. Circle the area that is a colony. What will happen to this colony in 1997?

____

____

4. What led to the present systems of government in China and Taiwan?

____

5. What led to the present systems of government in North Korea and South Korea?

____

____

____

____

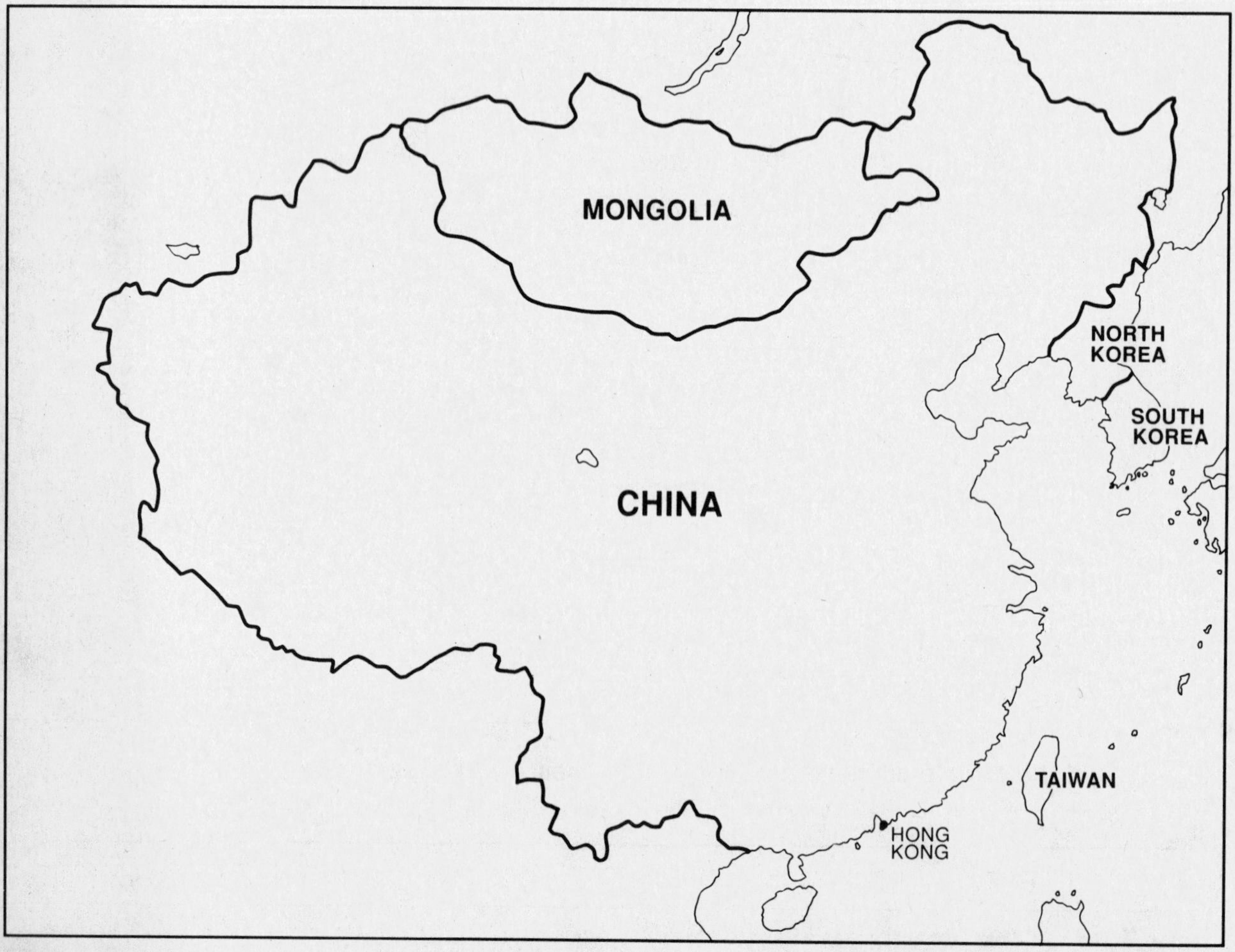

MONGOLIA

NORTH KOREA

SOUTH KOREA

CHINA

TAIWAN

HONG KONG

Reading Political Cartoons

The political cartoon below might have appeared in a newspaper during the time of the Korean War. Study the cartoon. Then answer the questions that follow. For help, you can refer to page 535 in your textbook.

1. What is the political cartoon about? ______________________________

2. What are four symbols in the cartoon? What do they stand for?

   a. ______________________________

   ____

   b. ______________________________

   ____

   c. ______________________________

   ____

   d. ______________________________

3. What point do you think the cartoonist was trying to make in the cartoon?

____

____

____

Name Use with pages 536–537

Arts and Recreation in East Asia

Study the pictures and answer the questions that follow. For help, you can refer to pages 536–537 in your textbook.

1. What is the form of art called that is represented by the Chinese painting above?

2. What is the purpose of this form of art?

3. In painting, what did this form of art replace?

4. In which parts of East Asia do traditional arts and crafts continue to thrive?

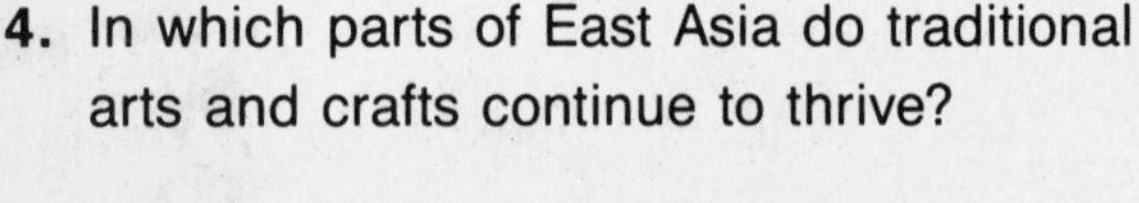

5. What is the popular form of Chinese exercise called that is shown in the picture above?

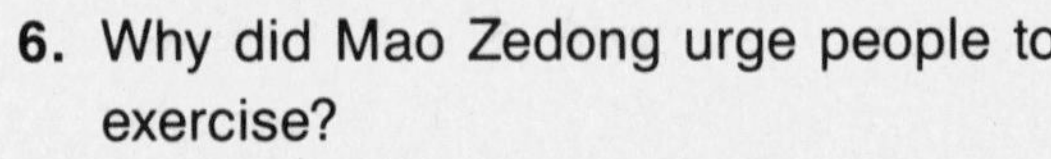

6. Why did Mao Zedong urge people to exercise?

7. What are three forms of the martial arts that are popular throughout East Asia?

8. What are two crafts that are still practiced throughout East Asia?

Using New Words

Write the letter of the term that matches each description below. For help, you can refer to the lessons in Chapter 26 in your textbook.

a. autonomous region	**e.** Confucianism	**i.** Daoism
b. socialist realism	**f.** aquaculture	**j.** pinyin
c. iron rice bowl	**g.** Pacific Rim	
d. martial arts	**h.** Buddhism	

_____ **1.** the teachings of Confucius

_____ **2.** a new way of spelling Chinese words

_____ **3.** a self-governing area in China that is supervised by the central government in Beijing

_____ **4.** fish farming

_____ **5.** part of an economic policy in China where people are paid whether or not they work

_____ **6.** all the countries that border the Pacific Ocean

_____ **7.** a system of belief that teaches that suffering is caused by selfishness

_____ **8.** a form of art that depicts true-to-life views of working people or heroes performing great deeds for the nation

_____ **9.** ancient forms of hand-to-hand combat

_____ **10.** a system of belief that teaches that people should accept their fate calmly

Name Use with pages 541–543

The People of Japan

Study the illustration, and then answer the questions that follow. For help, you can refer to pages 541–543 in your textbook.

1. The picture at the right shows a samurai who may have lived in Japan one thousand years ago. Who were the samurai?

2. What Japanese traditions were passed down by the Samurai?

3. In today's Japan what happens if a person doesn't fulfill his or her duties to the family?

4. Why are politeness and good manners important aspects of Japanese culture?

5. How does the Japanese view of society and the individual differ from the Western view?

6. Why do you think the Japanese developed such a distinctive culture?

Name Use with page 544

Writing a Summary

Read the selection below. Then complete the activities that follow. For help, you can refer to page 544 in your textbook.

Samurai warriors were part of a privileged military class that ruled Japan from the twelfth to the nineteenth centuries. They pledged total loyalty to their feudal lords and defended their masters' territories. At the top of the samurai class was the shogun. He was the greatest of all feudal lords. Though shoguns were appointed by the emperor, it was the shoguns themselves who were the real rulers of Japan.

The samurai warrior was an awesome fighting machine. He was highly skilled in the use of the bow and sword. To protect himself he wore an elegant but very effective suit of armor. It was designed to provide freedom of movement while offering maximum protection. Because it was lightweight and flexible, it was unmatched by any other armor in the world.

The sword symbolized all that was important to a samurai warrior. In his hands it was a fearful weapon that had required strict training to master. The sword also stood for the samurai code of honor, bravery, and respect. All disagreements and problems were resolved by the sword, and the warrior lived and died by its laws. Strict rules were observed. For example, it was an offense to touch or step over another man's weapon. To lay your own sword on the floor and kick it in someone's direction was a challenge to the death.

1. Underline the topic sentence in each of the paragraphs.

2. Write a summary of the selection in three or four sentences.

____

____

____

____

____

____

____

Name Use with pages 545–547

Interviewing Akio Morita

Suppose you could interview Akio Morita. You might ask him questions similar to the ones below. Use the space to write the answers you think he might give. For help, you can refer to pages 545–547 in your textbook.

Interviewer: Japan has experienced remarkable growth since World War II. Yet, your country has very few natural resources. What made this growth possible?

Morita: ____

____

____

____

____

____

Interviewer: What are some of the products made by Japanese companies?

Morita: ____

____

____

Interviewer: What is it like to work in a Japanese company?

Morita: ____

____

____

____

____

Interviewer: Suppose you could give advice to the children of Japan. What would you tell them?

Morita: ____

____

____

____

Name Use with pages 550–551

The Japanese Government

The diagram below shows the organization of the Japanese government. Study the diagram and then answer the questions on this page. For help, you can refer to pages 550–551 in your textbook.

Emperor

Although the Emperor is nominally the head of state, the power of day-to-day government of the country lies with the Prime Minister and his Cabinet. The Diet (parliament) consists of two houses, with a total of 763 elected members.

Prime Minister

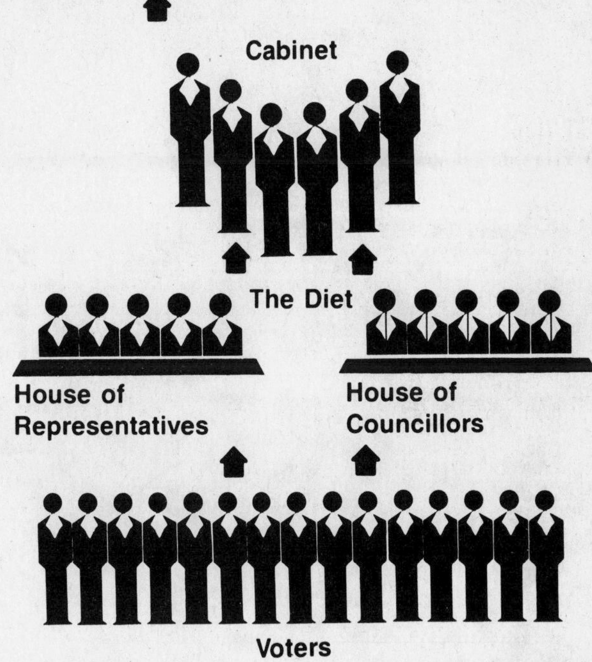

1. How did Japan's current form of government come about?

____

____

____

____

____

____

____

2. According to the diagram, who is Japan's head of state?

____

3. Which person shown on the diagram is the head of the government?

____

4. According to the diagram, from where are members of the cabinet selected?

____

Who selects them?

____

5. According to the diagram, what two Houses make up the Diet?

____

____

6. How are members of the Diet selected?

____

____

7. What other country's government that you have studied is like that of Japan?

____

____

Name Use with pages 552–553

Arts and Recreation in Japan

Use the terms in the box to label each picture according to the artistic or recreational activity it represents. Then answer the question that follows. For help, you can refer to pages 552–553 in your textbook.

haiku	calligraphy	sumo wrestling
judo	flower arranging	

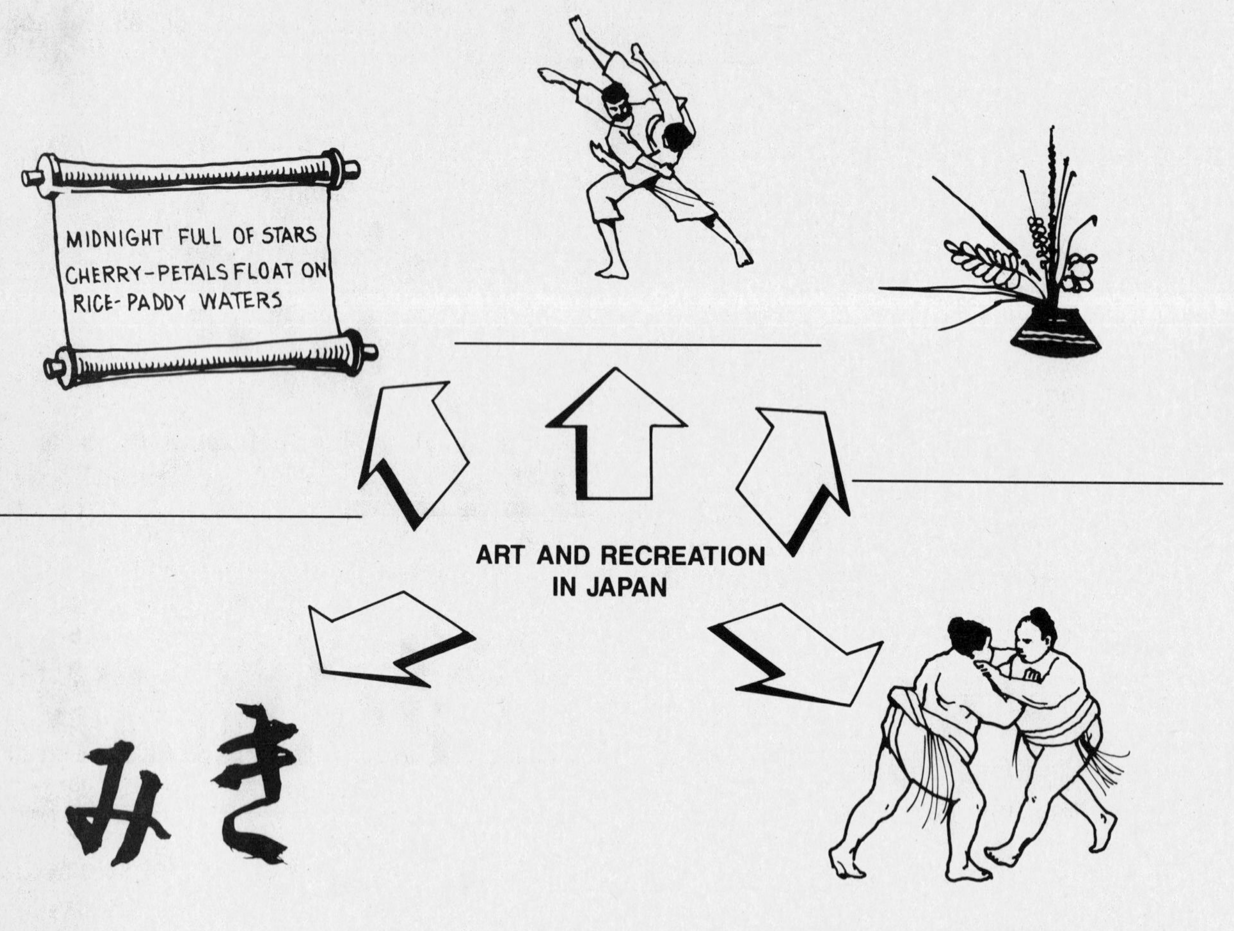

Why are flower arranging, gardening, and calligraphy among admired art forms in Japan?

Name Use with pages 558–559

Using New Words

Follow the directions to find each hidden term. Then, write the definition on the line below the letters. For help, you can refer to the lessons in Chapter 27 in your textbook.

1. Cross out the letters d, t, m, z, s

c d a t l l m i z g s r d a t p m h y

2. Cross out the letters a, g, m, r, y

a g s r h y g i n a g t r o m

3. Cross out the letters a, c, j, k, y, x

c a s k u j a m o y w a c r e k s t c a l i x n g

4. Cross out the letters c, g, o, r, u, w

w o d g r i c e u r g t

5. Cross out the letters b, d, e, h, t

s e b a t e m h u r d a i t

6. Cross out the letters d, i, p, r, w

h i p o m r o w i g e n r e i o d u r s

Name

Use with pages 561–564

The Countries and People of Southeast Asia

Use the map and follow the directions to complete the activities below. For help, you can refer to pages 561–564 in your textbook.

1. Locate and label the countries that make up Southeast Asia. List them below.

   ____

   ____

   ____

   ____

   ____

2. Locate the country that was settled by people from southwest China about 2,500 years ago. Then color it brown.

   ____

3. Shade the other countries that were settled by people from southern China.

   ____

   ____

4. Draw a circle around the country in which the Dutch built canals.

   ____

5. Draw a rectangle around the country into which the Spanish introduced the Roman Catholic religion.

   ____

6. From which two Asian countries have people immigrated to Southeast Asia during the last 100 years?

   __________ __________

7. What are the two major religions in Southeast Asia today? List them below.

   ____

   ____

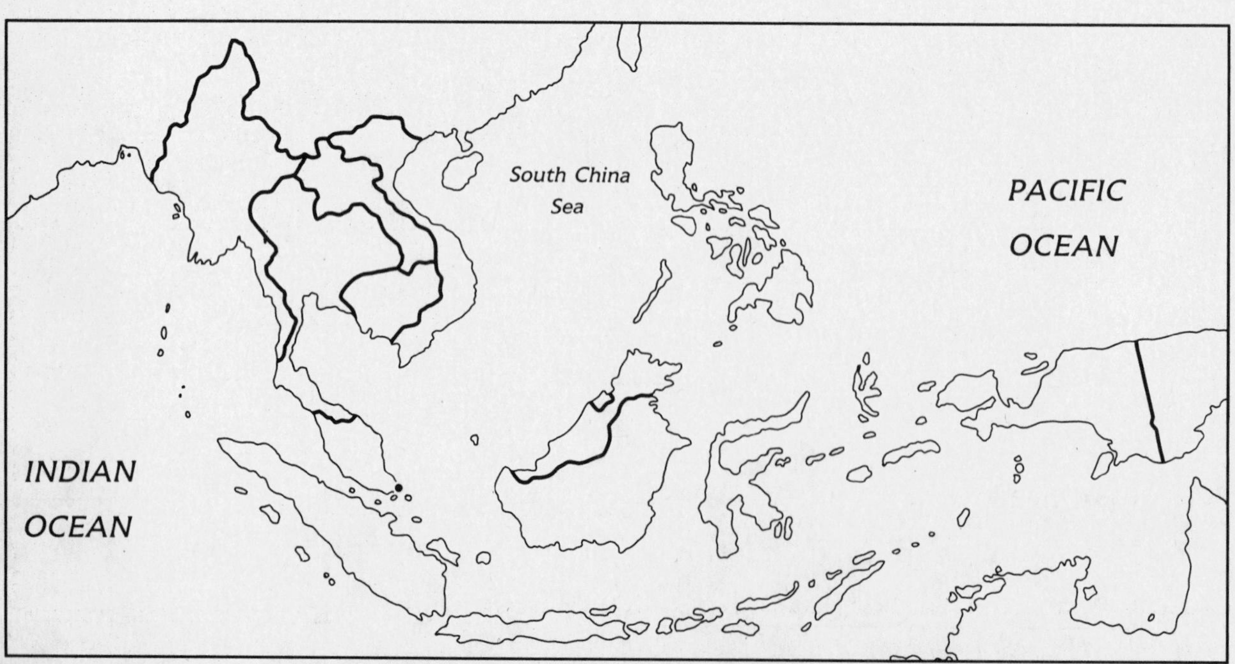

Southeast Asia: Government and Economy

Use the terms and phrases in the box to complete the chart below. You will need to use some terms and phrases more than once. For help, you can refer to pages 565–570 in your textbook.

- constitutional monarchy
- republic ruled by military leaders
- republic headed by a president
- communist
- absolute monarchy
- parliamentary system
- richest country in the region
- financial and industrial center
- making economic gains with the help of foreign companies
- poor economy due to war
- third-richest country in the region
- poor economy due to poor planning, debt, and civil unrest

THE GOVERNMENTS AND ECONOMIES OF SOUTHEAST ASIA

Country	Type of Government	Condition of Economy
Philippines		
Singapore		
Brunei		
Malaysia		
Indonesia		
Laos		
Myanmar		
Cambodia		
Thailand		
Vietnam		

Drawing Conclusions

Read the article below. Then put an **X** next to each conclusion you can draw from the article. For help, you can refer to page 571 in your textbook.

During the Philippine elections of 1986, the Marcos government sent troops into most communities to destroy ballot boxes and votes that had been cast for Corazon Aquino. But the people of the Philippines formed human chains around the ballot boxes to protect them. Large crowds filled the streets, blocking the movement of military tanks. Soldiers put down their guns and joined the masses. Faced with such massive protests, Marcos and his followers were forced to flee the country, and Corazon Aquino became the president.

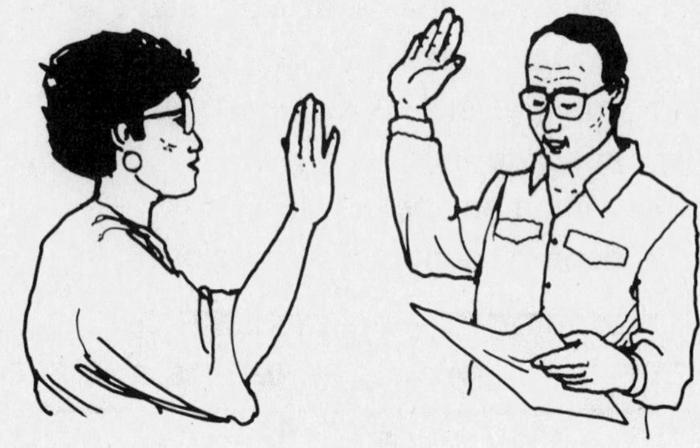

_____ **1.** Ferdinand Marcos and Corazon Aquino were political opponents.

_____ **2.** Corazon Aquino disliked Marcos and his family.

_____ **3.** Corazon Aquino had the support of the majority of the Philippine people.

_____ **4.** The Philippine people were tired of the government of Ferdinand Marcos.

_____ **5.** No one supported the Marcos government.

_____ **6.** Marcos's high-level military generals gave their support to Aquino.

_____ **7.** Marcos feared losing the 1986 presidential election.

_____ **8.** Marcos did almost everything he could to keep Aquino from winning the election.

_____ **9.** Corazon Aquino had run for president in the previous election.

_____ **10.** The Philippine people based their decisions on debates between Marcos and Aquino.

Name Use with pages 572–573

Arts and Recreation in Southeast Asia

Follow the directions to complete the activities below. For help, you can refer to pages 572–573 in your textbook.

1. a. Draw a line to the picture that shows a popular sport in Southeast Asia.
   b. In which country did this sport originate?

   ____

   c. How is this sport different in Asia than it is in the United States?

   ____

   ____

   ____

Gamelan

2. a. Draw a line to the picture that shows a form of entertainment that is also part of the education of most Indonesian children.
   b. What kinds of stories are depicted this way?

   ____

   ____

   ____

Thai Boxing

3. a. Draw a line to the picture that shows one kind of traditional music being performed in Indonesia.
   b. Why does almost every village in Indonesia have this kind of orchestra?

   ____

   ____

   ____

Shadow Plays

Name **Use with pages 574–575**

Learning New Words

Each of the words listed in the box below are hidden among the letters that follow. Draw a circle around each word you find. The words may be read forward, backward, up, down, or diagonally. For help, you can refer to the lessons in Chapter 28 in your textbook.

meditate	Vietnam War shadow play gross national product	paddy gamelan

A	G	Y	E	D	I	M	T	R	A	B	C	K	H	I	K	L	M	H	P	C	K	C	Q
H	I	A	B	R	O	E	D	V	T	Z	N	C	A	Z	P	O	M	A	Y	A	L	A	M
S	I	L	M	K	U	D	L	A	L	B	X	E	A	T	R	O	K	M	D	A	Y	O	S
U	I	P	M	E	E	I	S	L	K	E	F	V	R	S	L	E	O	M	D	K	G	E	D
K	W	W	M	S	L	T	I	W	S	O	L	A	E	A	E	D	N	O	A	S	N	O	M
G	O	O	P	S	O	A	M	E	N	U	I	E	Q	L	K	A	N	Z	P	E	N	S	A
A	D	D	V	I	E	T	N	A	M	W	A	R	E	O	W	E	Q	R	K	O	A	K	Q
D	A	A	K	D	A	E	T	J	R	X	Q	O	A	K	L	E	U	I	S	Y	E	D	S
S	H	H	E	E	K	O	T	E	S	R	X	A	S	L	O	B	A	E	A	C	T	S	O
T	S	S	E	T	C	U	D	O	R	P	L	A	N	O	I	T	A	N	S	S	O	R	G

Write each circled word in the space next to its definition.

_______________ **1.** The longest and most damaging war in Southeast Asia

_______________ **2.** An Indonesian orchestra

_______________ **3.** Think deeply

_______________ **4.** The total amount of goods and services produced in a country during a year
____

_______________ **5.** A form of entertainment in which puppets are used to act out well-known stories by casting shadows

_______________ **6.** Flooded field where rice is grown

Name _______________ Use with pages 583–587

Looking at the Geography of the Pacific

The map below shows how the Pacific Islands are divided into three main groups. Study the map. Then complete the activities on this page. For help, you can refer to pages 583–587 in your textbook.

1. Collectively, what are the Pacific Islands called that are shown on the map?

____

2. Locate and label the area known as Polynesia. Then color the area green.

3. Locate and label the area known as Micronesia. Then color the area red.

4. Locate and label the area known as Melanesia. Then color the area brown.

5. Locate and label the island country known as New Zealand. Color North Island yellow. Color South Island orange.

6. Locate and label the world's smallest and oldest continent.

7. Which three main inland regions make up this continent?

____

____

____

8. What large underwater area can be found off the northeast coast of this continent?

____

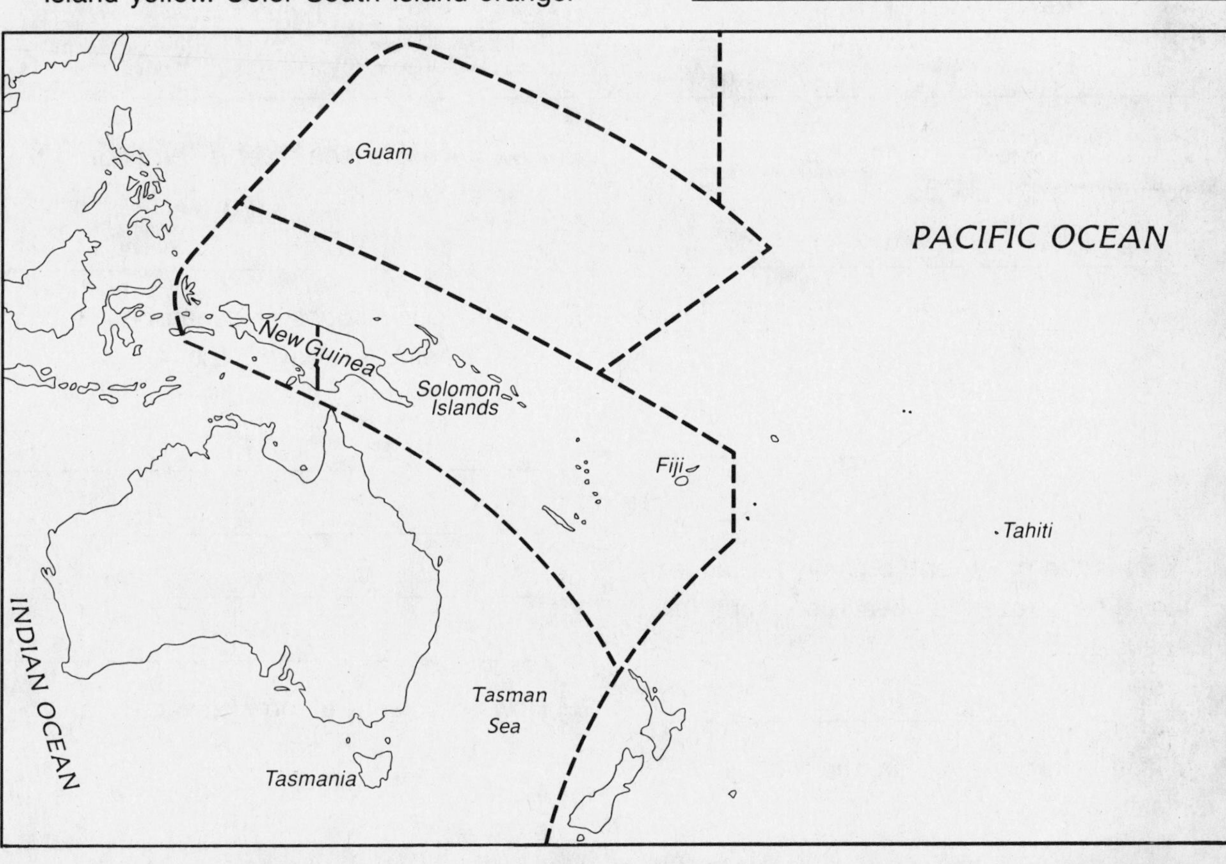

Using Maps of the Ocean Floor

The map below shows the floor of the South Pacific Ocean around the continent of Australia. Use the map to answer the questions. For help, you can refer to pages 588–589 in your textbook.

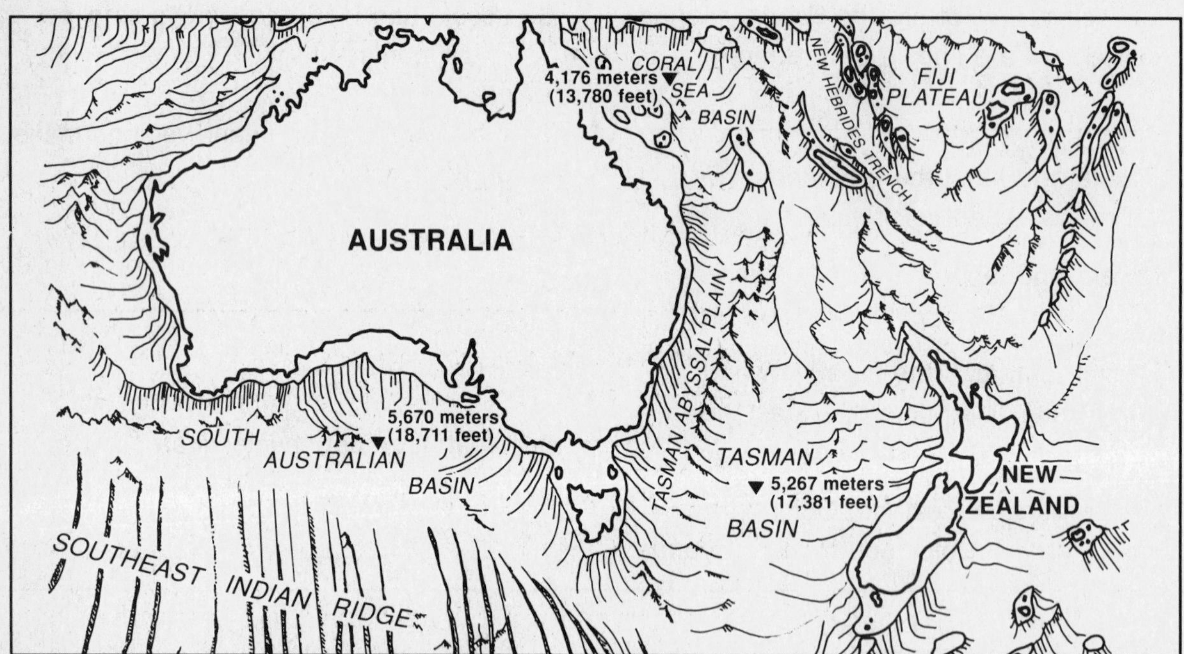

1. Is the map above a relief map or a contour map? How do you know?

2. What is the name of the mountain range that runs across the ocean floor south of Australia?

3. Which feature curves around the Fiji Plateau?

4. How far below sea level is the floor of the Tasman Basin?

5. Would ocean ridges or ocean basins be further below sea level? Explain your answer.

6. How do scientists show elevations and features of the ocean floor more accurately than they are shown on the map above?

Name _______________ Use with pages 590–593

Products of Australia and the Pacific Islands

Circle the pictures that represent products from Australia. Draw a box around the pictures that represent products from New Zealand. Draw a triangle around the picture that represents an important natural resource found on many of Oceania's tropical islands. Then answer the questions that follow. For help, you can refer to pages 590–593 in your textbook.

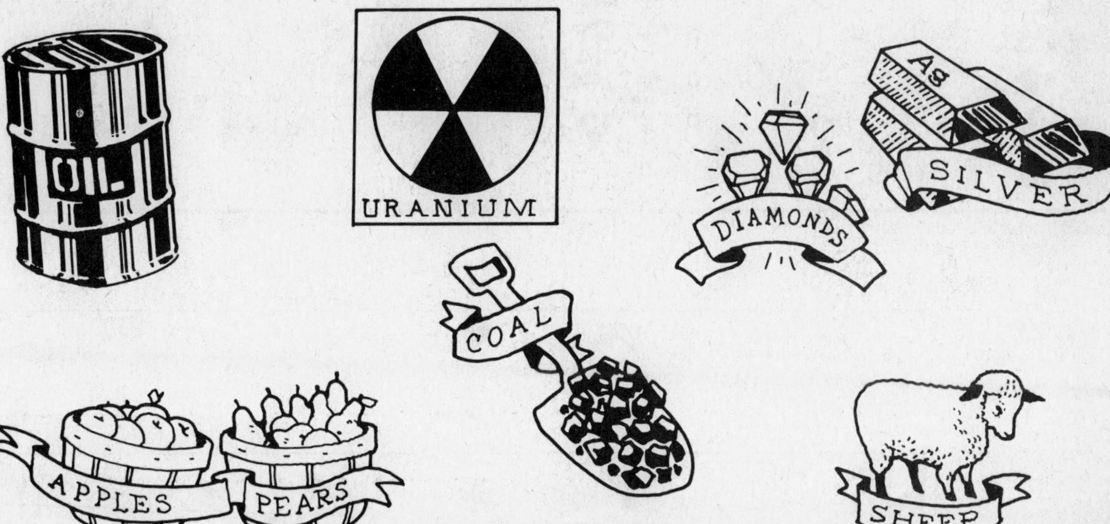

1. Why is Australia called the "Lucky Country"?

____

____

2. What are two minerals mined in Australia that are not shown in the picture?

____

____

3. Why do the ranches in Australia have to be so large?

____

____

____

4. What are two major natural resources that New Zealand has that are not shown in the picture?

____

____

5. Why can a variety of fruits be grown by New Zealand farmers?

____

____

6. Why do the people of Oceania's tropical islands call the coconut palm the "Tree of Life"?

____

____

Name ______ Use with pages 594–595

Using New Words

Use the code in the box to figure out each word. Then write the word on the line above its code. For help, you can refer to the lessons in Chapter 29 in your textbook.

CODE

a = ○	g = ▽	l = ◡	q = ●	v = ⌒
b = □	h = ✳	m = ■	r = !	w = ⧄
c = △	i = ¿	n = ɿl	s = ❩	x = ∴
d = ➡	j = ¿◡	o = ⌒̂	t = ◩	y = ⊠
e = ❩	k = ?	p = ▼	u = ¡	z = (
f = ▲				

______ **1.** ____________________

△ ⌒ ▼ ! ○

______ **2.** ____________________

◩ ⊠ ▼ ✳ ⌒ ⌒ ɿl

______ **3.** ____________________

¿ △ ❩ □ ❩ ! ▽

______ **4.** ____________________

○ ◩ ⌒ ◡ ◡

______ **5.** ____________________

⌒ ¡ ◩ □ ○ △ ?

Write the letter of each of the following definitions in the space before the above word that it matches.

a. a doughnut-shaped coral reef looped around an area of still, warm water
b. a whirling tropical hurricane of the Pacific
c. a huge, arid area of Australia
d. the dried meat of a coconut
e. a large body of ice that has broken away from a glacier

Name ______________________ Use with pages 597–599

The People of Australia and the Pacific Islands

The words below were written by Louis-Antoine de Bougainville. Read what he wrote. Then answer the questions. For help, you can refer to pages 597–599 in your textbook.

1. What island was de Bougainville writing about?

____

2. Who were the people he mentions?

____

____

3. Why have these people been called the "Vikings of the Sunrise"?

____

____

4. Which group of these people sailed south to settle New Zealand?

____

5. Which group of people were the first to settle in Australia?

____

6. How were these people treated by the early European explorers?

____

____

7. Why did many European immigrants come to New Zealand and Australia?

____

____

____

____

Name _______________

ECONOMIES: Australia and Pacific Islands

Study the graphs. Then answer the questions. For help, you can refer to pages 600–601 in your textbook.

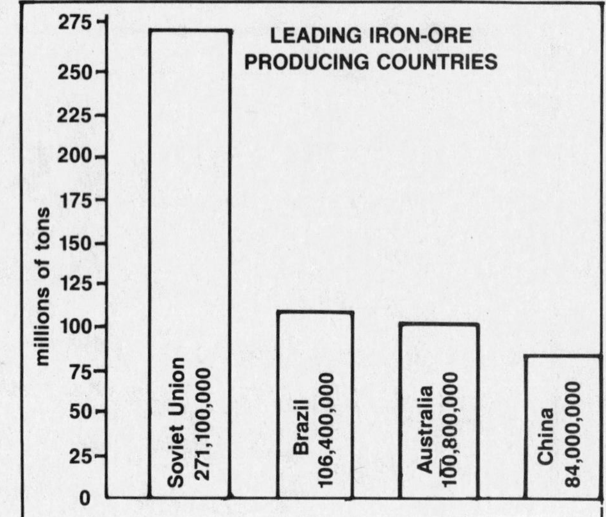

1. a. According to the bar graph on the right, which South Pacific country is one of the leading iron-ore producers in the world?

   ____

   b. This country is a top producer of what other three mineral resources?

   ____

   ____

   ____

   c. This country's developed economy includes a mixture of what economic activities?

   ____

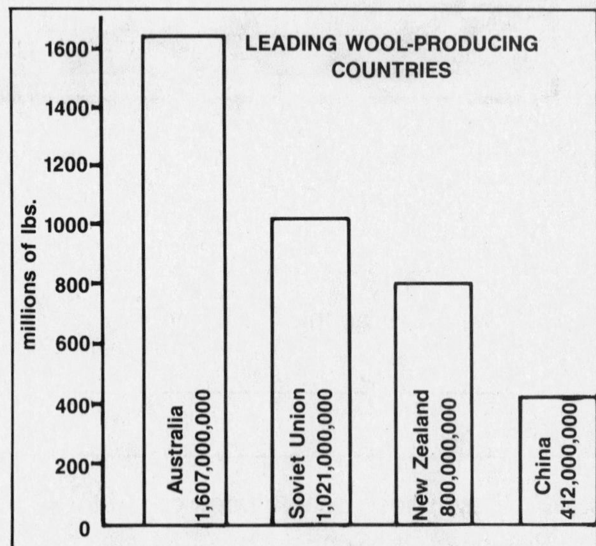

2. a. According to the graph on the right, which two Pacific countries are leading producers of wool?

   ____

   ____

   b. Which of these countries is the largest exporter of wool?

   ____

   c. What is the most important part of this country's economy?

   ____

3. a. What is the main source of income for the many Pacific Islands not shown in the graphs? ______________________________

   b. How do the economies of these islands differ from the economies of New Zealand and Australia? ______________________________

   ____

Name ______ Use with page 602

Making Decisions

Sonia's teacher has given the class three choices for a field trip. Tomorrow they will vote on where the class will go. Read how Sonia decided which trip to vote for. Then answer the questions. For help, you can refer to page 602 in your textbook.

I know that I want to go to the place where I can learn the most. The first choice is going to the botanical gardens. I could learn about many different kinds of plants and it's nearby. But I've already been there several times.

Our second choice is going to the Metropolitan Museum. They have many different kinds of exhibits including some on Pacific cultures. We are learning about the people of the Pacific Islands in our social studies class. The only problem is that it takes about two hours to get to the museum. We would have to leave early in the morning.

Our third choice is taking a tour of the historic district of our town. That sounds like fun, but it's fall and it may be cold. Besides, I have been to the district several times with my family, and I already know quite a lot about the history of our area.

The more I think about it, the better the museum sounds. I can learn about something I am studying in class, and there are lots of other things to see and do, too.

1. What decision did Sonia have to make? ______________________

____

2. What was her goal? ______________________

____

3. Which trip did Sonia finally decide to vote for? ______________________

4. Which two things didn't Sonia consider as she thought about her decision? Put an **X** next to each one.

______ **a.** Each trip would cost a different amount of money.

______ **b.** Her social studies class is studying the people of the Pacific Islands.

______ **c.** She has been to the historical district of her town several times with her family.

______ **d.** A long trip might not leave much time at the museum.

Name Use with pages 603–605

GOVERNMENTS: Australia and Pacific Islands

Complete the map by writing phrases from the box in the spaces provided on the map. Each space should have only one phrase, but you may use a phrase more than once. Then answer the question that follows. For help, you can refer to pages 603–605 in your textbook.

- parliamentary system of government
- trust territory of the United States
- elected legislature and a council of chiefs
- ruled by a monarch and a council
- only matai can vote for government officials

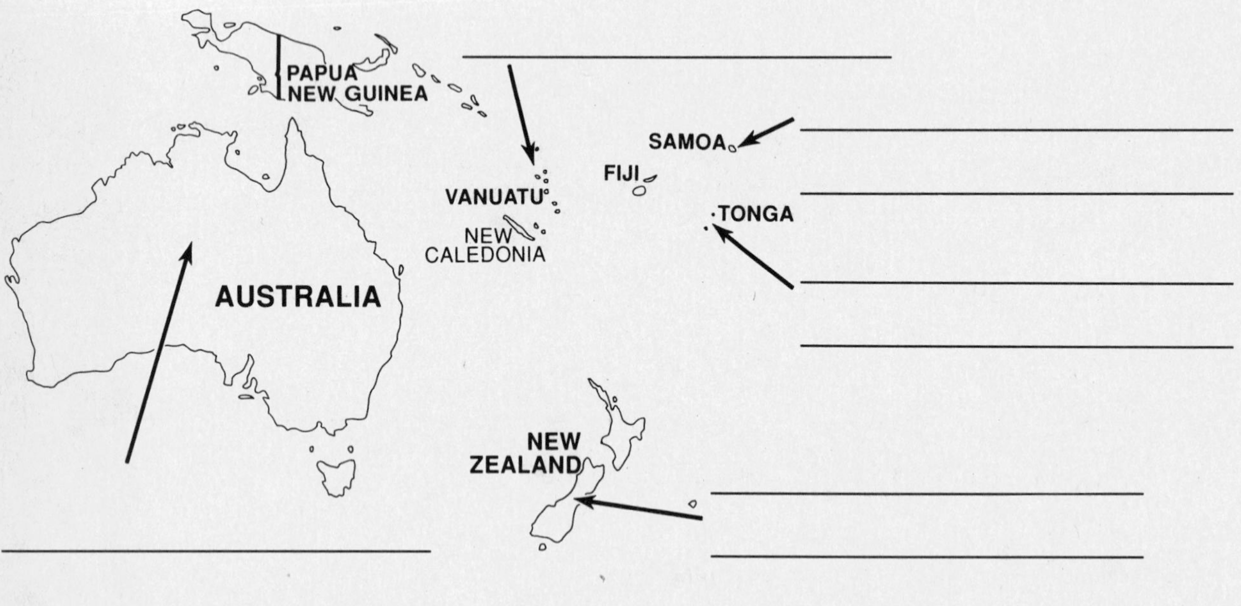

How would you describe the many forms of government in the Pacific region?

Name Use with pages 606–607

Arts and Recreation in the Pacific Region

Follow the directions to complete the activities below. For help, you can refer to pages 606–607 in your textbook.

1. a. Draw a line to the picture that shows one way the Samoans keep their cultural identity alive.

   b. What happens as warriors bend over their oars?

   c. What are some of the chants about?

Sydney Opera House

2. a. Draw a line to the picture that shows where Australians enjoy performances of the fine arts.

   b. What did the Australians hope to show outsiders by building this structure?

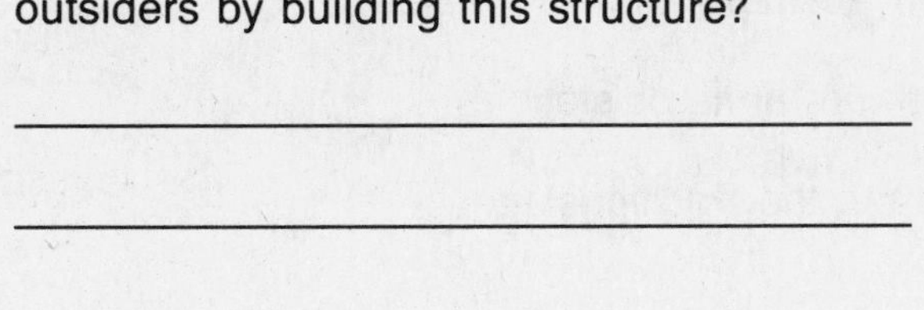

Rugby

Samoan Canoe

3. a. Draw a line to the picture that shows the most popular sport in New Zealand.

   b. What are two other popular New Zealand sports?

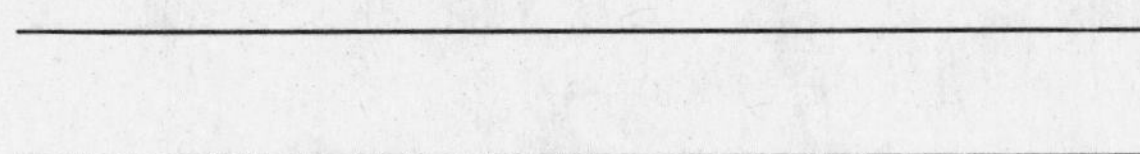

Name Use with pages 612–613

Using New Words

Complete each of the activities below. For help, you can refer to the lessons in Chapter 30 in your textbook.

1. Put an **X** next to each statement that correctly describes a *trust territory.*

______ **a.** A trust territory controls its own government.

______ **b.** A trust territory does not belong to an outside power.

______ **c.** The government of a trust territory is controlled by another country until that country decides the trust territory is ready to govern itself.

______ **d.** A trust territory is a kind of economic system.

______ **e.** An outside power controls the government of a trust territory permanently.

______ **f.** Guam is a trust territory of the United States.

2. Put an **X** next to each statement that is true about *stations.*

______ **a.** Stations are huge ranches where sheep and cattle are raised.

______ **b.** Much of the world's wool is made from sheep on New Zealand stations.

______ **c.** Sheep stations are the only kind of farm found in New Zealand.

______ **d.** Stations are large fruit orchards in Australia and New Zealand.

______ **e.** Only 6 percent of Australians work on farms or stations.

______ **f.** Stations are a form of government in the Pacific islands.

Name	Use with pages 4–13

Using Globes

Use the picture of the globe below to complete the activities on this page. For help, you can refer to pages 4–13 in your textbook.

ARCTIC OCEAN
Prime Meridian
NORTH AMERICA
ATLANTIC OCEAN
PACIFIC OCEAN
SOUTH AMERICA
ANTARCTICA

1. Underline the name of the hemisphere shown on the globe.
   a. Northern
   b. Southern
   c. Eastern
   d. Western

2. Underline the name of each continent in this hemisphere. Then label the continents on the globe.
   a. North America
   b. Antarctica
   c. South America
   d. Europe
   e. Asia
   f. Africa

3. Underline the name of the continent that is entirely in the Northern Hemisphere.
   a. South America
   b. Africa
   c. North America
   d. Asia

4. Underline the name of the imaginary line that separates the Eastern Hemisphere from the Western Hemisphere. Then find it on the globe and label it.
   a. prime meridian
   b. equator

5. Underline the name of each ocean in this hemisphere. Then label the oceans on the globe.
   a. Atlantic Ocean
   b. Pacific Ocean
   c. Arctic Ocean
   d. Indian Ocean

6. Underline the name of the ocean that is entirely in the Northern Hemisphere.
   a. Atlantic Ocean
   b. Pacific Ocean
   c. Arctic Ocean
   d. Indian Ocean

Name	Use with pages 4–13

Distance and Direction on a Map

Use the map of Madagascar and the map scale below to answer the questions. For help, you can refer to pages 4–13 in your textbook.

Cape d'Ambre
Antsiranana
Mozambique Channel
Mahajanga
Maroantsetra
Toamasina
Antananarivo
Morondava
Mananjary
Morombe
ISALO NATIONAL PARK
Manakara
Toliara
N
INDIAN OCEAN
Cape Sainte-Marie
0 150 300 Miles
0 150 300 450 Kilometers

1. If you were traveling from Toamasina to Antsiranana, in which direction would you be traveling?
   north

2. About how many miles is it from Toamasina to Maroantsetra?
   about 190 miles

3. Suppose you wanted to go from Antananarivo to Morondava. In which direction would you be traveling?
   southwest

4. About how many kilometers is it from Antananarivo to Morondava?
   about 450 kilometers

5. About how many miles long is the island of Madagascar?
   about 1,000 miles long

6. About how many kilometers is it from Morombe to the Indian Ocean by the shortest route?
   about 500 kilometers

7. About how many miles long is Isalo National Park?
   about 50 miles

8. In which part of Madagascar is Isalo National Park located?
   northern	southern	eastern	western

Name   Use with pages 4–13

Using Map Symbols

Study the map of Japan and the map key below. Then put an X next to each sentence that makes a true statement according to the information on the map. For help, you can refer to pages 4–13 in your textbook.

ECONOMIC ACTIVITY IN JAPAN

- Cattle
- Fishing port
- Grapes and other fruit
- Industry
- Mandarin oranges
- Mining
- Rice
- Shipbuilding

______ **1.** The major economic activity near the city of Sendai is shipbuilding.

X **2.** Most of Japan's industry is located on the island of Honshu.

______ **3.** Fruit production is the only economic activity on the island of Kyushu.

X **4.** Mt. Daisen is northeast of the city of Kagoshima.

X **5.** Sapporo is about 150 miles north of Aomori.

______ **6.** The main cattle raising areas are on the islands of Hokkaido in the south and Kyushu in the north.

X **7.** The two main crops grown on the island of Hokkaido are fruits and rice.

X **8.** Mandarin oranges are grown mostly in the southern half of Japan.

______ **9.** This map could help you figure out the locations of the most popular tourist attractions in Japan.

X **10.** This map helps you to understand where most of Japan's major economic activities are located.

Name   Use with pages 4–13

Using Map Symbols

Put and **X** next to each question you can answer based on information on the map. Then use the space provided to answer each question you marked with an X. For help, you can refer to pages 4–13 in your textbook.

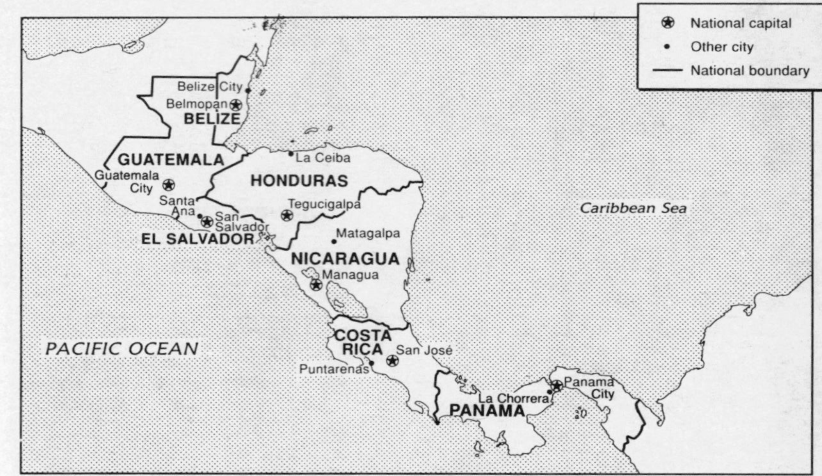

______ **1.** Which country has no mountains, hills, or plateaus? ______

______ **2.** Which country has the most people per square mile? ______

X **3.** What is the capital of Nicaragua? **Managua**

X **4.** Which countries border Costa Rica? **Panama and Nicaragua**

______ **5.** Which country is the most mountainous? ______

X **6.** How many countries make up Central America? **seven**

______ **7.** What crops are grown in Honduras? ______

______ **8.** What is the average temperature in San Salvador for the month of July? ______

Name Use with pages 4–13

Touring Paris

Use the map of Paris below to complete the activities on this page. For help, you can refer to pages 4–13 in your textbook.

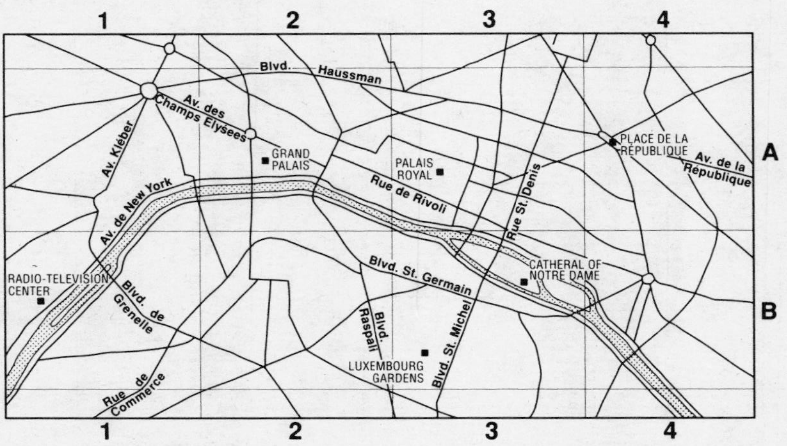

1. Suppose you and your family were planning a trip to Paris. Listed below are the places you intend to visit. Find and circle each place on the map. Then write the number and letter of the square in which it is shown on the map.

Cathedral of Notre Dame: **B–3** Grand Palais: **A–2**

Radio-Television Center: **B–1** Luxembourg Gardens: **B–3**

Place de la Republique: **A–4** Palais Royal: **A–3**

2. Use the map to plan a visit to each place in Paris listed above. Use a colored pencil to draw a line on the map showing the route you would take. Your route should require as little travel as possible. Then, in the space provided, list the places you would visit in the order shown on your route.

Stop 1: ______ Stop 4: ______

Stop 2: ______ Stop 5: ______

Stop 3: ______ Stop 6: ______

Answers will vary but should follow a logical order based on the student's starting point.

Name Use with pages 4–13

Using a Distribution Map

Draw a line under the word or phrase that best completes each sentence. For help, you can refer to pages 4–13 in your textbook.

Srinagar
Delhi
Kanpur
Ahmadabad
Calcutta
Nagpur
Bombay
Hyderabad
Bangalore
Madras

AVERAGE JANUARY TEMPERATURES

Degrees Fahrenheit	Degrees Celsius
Over 75°	Over 24°
65°–75°	18°–24°
55°–65°	13°–18°
45°–55°	7°–13°
Below 45°	Below 7°

1. The kind of map on this page is called a ______ map.
   a. political
   b. <u>distribution</u>
   c. physical

2. The map key on this page shows different ______ categories.
   a. population
   b. <u>temperature</u>
   c. precipitation

3. According to the map, the city of Srinagar has an average January temperature of ______.
   a. <u>below 45°F.</u>
   b. 45°F. to 55°F.
   c. over 24°C

4. According to the map, it is colder in ______ than in Calcutta during January.
   a. Madras
   b. Hyderabad
   c. <u>Delhi</u>

5. According to the map, the coolest part of India during January is in the ______ part of the country.
   a. <u>far northern</u>
   b. southern
   c. southeastern

6. According to the map, the southeastern coast of India has an average January temperature of ______.
   a. <u>over 24°C</u>
   b. 13°C to 18°C
   c. below 7°C

7. According to the map, the average January temperature in Kanpur is ______ the average January temperature in your community.
   a. higher than
   b. lower than
   c. about the same as

8. The symbol for temperatures between 65°F. and 75°F. is ______.
   a. [symbol] b. [symbol] c. [symbol] ______

Name Use with pages 38–44

Using Maps

Use the map on this page to complete the activities below. For help, you can refer to pages 38–44 in your textbook.

1. Locate and label the following regions of the United States and Canada.

Pacific Mountains	Coastal Plains	Arctic Islands
Appalachian Highlands	Interior Plains	Rocky Mountains
Canadian Shield		

2. Name and describe the region of the United States in which you live.
Student responses should accurately describe the region in which they live.

3. Name and describe the region you would most like to visit.
Responses will vary but should demonstrate a knowledge of the geography of the region selected by the student.

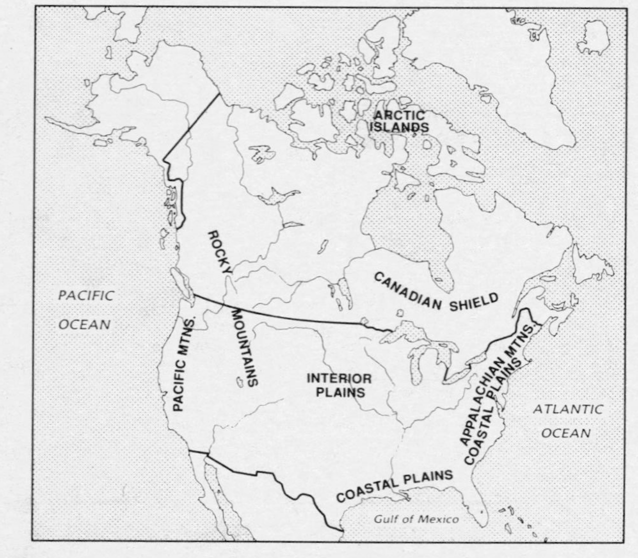

Name Use with pages 45–49

Resources of the United States and Canada

Study the table on this page. Then answer the questions below. For help, you can refer to pages 45–49 in your textbook.

PRODUCTS FROM NORTH AMERICAN RESOURCES

Products	United States	Canada
most important crops	corn, soybeans, wheat	barley, oats, wheat
most valuable mineral products	petroleum, natural gas, coal	petroleum, natural gas, uranium, zinc
amount of lumber produced each year	37,153,000,000 board feet	21,136,000,000 board feet
percent of electricity from hydroelectric power	5 percent	70 percent

1. a. According to the table, which crop is an important product in both countries?
wheat

   b. What natural resource makes an abundance of this crop possible?
rich, arable soil

2. a. According to the table, which country produces more lumber per year?
the United States

   b. What natural resource makes this product possible?
trees, forests

3. Which two mineral products are valuable to both the United States and Canada?
petroleum
natural gas

4. Which country uses hydroelectric power as its main source of electricity?
Canada

5. What are three reasons that the United States and Canada are lands of abundance?
many natural resources
temperate climate
sufficient precipitation

Name Use with pages 50–51

Using Latitude and Longitude

Chen and his family took a trip around the world. In the chart at the bottom of the page are the latitudes and longitudes near ten of the cities they visited. Put a dot on the map to show the approximate location of each city. Then label the city according to the letter in the chart. Finally, connect the dots with a line to show the route that Chen and his family took. For help, you can refer to pages 50–51 in your textbook.

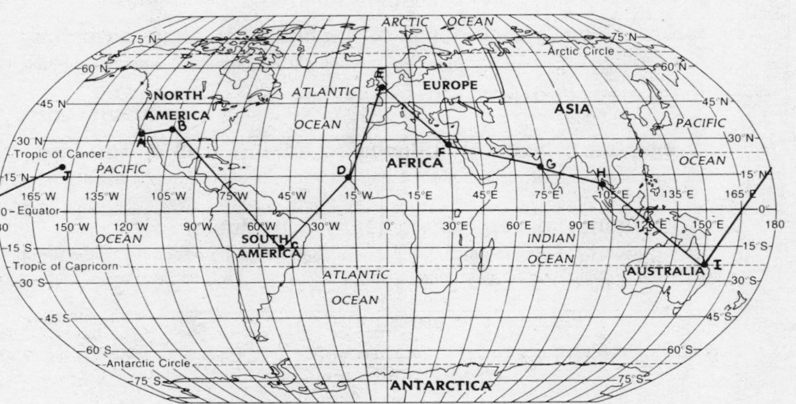

Los Angeles, California	35°N, 118°W	A
Denver, Colorado	40°N, 105°W	B
Brasília, Brazil	16°S, 48°W	C
Dakar, Senegal	15°N, 16°W	D
London, England	52°N, 0°	E
Cairo, Egypt	30°N, 30°E	F
Bombay, India	19°N, 73°E	G
Bangkok, Thailand	13°N, 100°E	H
Sydney, Australia	27°S, 150°E	I
Honolulu, Hawaii	20°N, 155°W	J

Name Use with pages 52–53

Using New Words

Find each of the terms in the box hidden among the letters that follow. Draw a circle around each term you find. The words may be read forward, backward, up, down, or diagonally. For help, you can refer to the lessons in Chapter 1 in your textbook.

hydroelectric power	permafrost	erosion	population density
Continental Divide	temperate	arable	timberline

T E M P E R A T E D S N M N E T V O X L E K A P
C S E C Q A E L O E D W Q K C Q S T R P M N E S
A N I S H Y D R O E L E C T R I C P O W E R O A
C O P Z D T U S P D L E Q C X O E J I U M L R L
D I B P S N O E N I L R E B M I T E G A F R R E
J S E D O K T R K B R O P D V T Z A F R M E L U
P O P U L A T I O N D E N S I T Y R S I F B I K
A R T U R O Q E J K L S T R D Q O C O Z A M L O
D E N L M D T U S V E W N E T S O X L R E I A P
O E D I V I D L A T N E N I T N O C A N T O R K

Write each circled term in the space next to its definition.

Continental Divide 1. an imaginary line that separates rivers flowing eastward and westward across the land

erosion 2. the gradual wearing down of the earth's surface by water and wind

temperate 3. neither too hot nor too cold

timberline 4. the elevation above which trees cannot grow

arable 5. good for farming

population density 6. people per square mile in a given land area

permafrost 7. a layer of soil that is permanently frozen

hydroelectric power 8. electricity generated by the force of rapidly moving water

Name Use with pages 55–59

A Look at Ethnic Groups

Read what Sadie Frowne wrote upon arriving in the United States in 1902. Then answer the questions. For help, you can refer to pages 55–59 in your textbook.

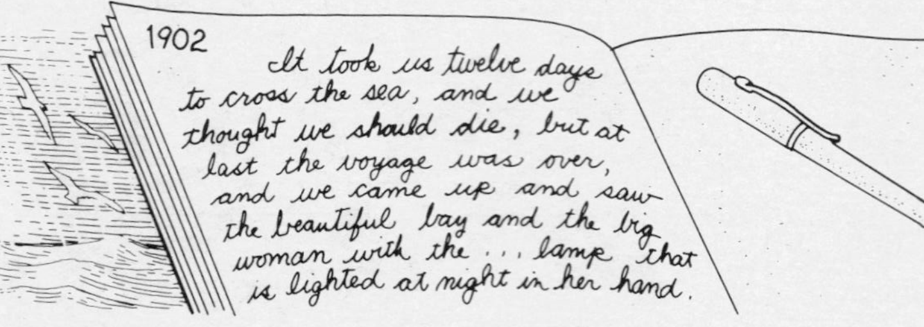

1. Sadie Frowne mentioned a "big woman with the . . . lamp." To whom or what was she referring? **the Statue of Liberty**
2. Sadie Frowne was one of the many Europeans who came to the United States in 1902. From which European countries have many immigrants come to the United States?
   Germany, Italy, Great Britain, Ireland, Austria
3. How has the pattern of immigration changed since the early history of the nation?
   Today the largest groups of immigrants come from Asia and Latin America.
4. Why have people continued to immigrate to the United States?
   People continue to immigrate to the United States in order to find economic, religious, and political freedom.
5. What are two problems that most ethnic groups have faced at some time in their history? **prejudice** **discrimination**
6. How have members of ethnic groups been protected against these problems?
   Laws have been passed to protect people against unfair treatment in jobs, housing, transportation, education, and other areas of life.

Name Use with pages 60–61

Immigrating to the United States

Mr. and Mrs. Slavin want to move to the United States. In the conversation below they are trying to decide how best to make the move. Read the conversation. Then answer the questions that follow. For help, you can refer to pages 60–61 in your textbook.

"We could save enough money to move the entire family all at once," said Mr. Slavin. "But that would take a long time. And we would still need more money to get started in the United States."

"Another way would be to wait until the children have grown up," said Mrs. Slavin. "Then we could move to the United States by ourselves. The children could follow if they wanted to. But that would be many years from now. And besides, I want the children to have the advantages of growing up in the United States."

"Perhaps it would be best if I went to the United States by myself and sent for you and the children later," said Mr. Slavin. "I could get a good job and find a place to live. Then in a year or two you and the children could come. When you arrive, everything would be ready. We would miss each other, but in the end we would all be together in our new country. What do you think?"

1. According to the conversation, what was Mr. and Mrs. Slavin's goal?
   a. to take a vacation in the United States
   b. to move their family to the United States
   c. to save money
   d. to get an education
2. Which three of the following alternatives did Mr. and Mrs. Slavin consider?
   a. Have the entire family move together.
   b. Have everyone in the family but Mr. Slavin move.
   c. Wait until the children grow up before moving.
   d. Have Mr. Slavin move first and send for the family later.
3. How do you think Mrs. Slavin answered the question that Mr. Slavin asked at the end of their conversation? Explain why you think she answered the way she did.
   Answers may vary but student responses should reflect an analysis of the outcome of the alternative they selected to determine its benefits and drawbacks.

Name Use with pages 62–65

Earning a Living in the United States

Use the table below to answer the first three questions on this page. For help, you can refer to pages 62–65 in your textbook.

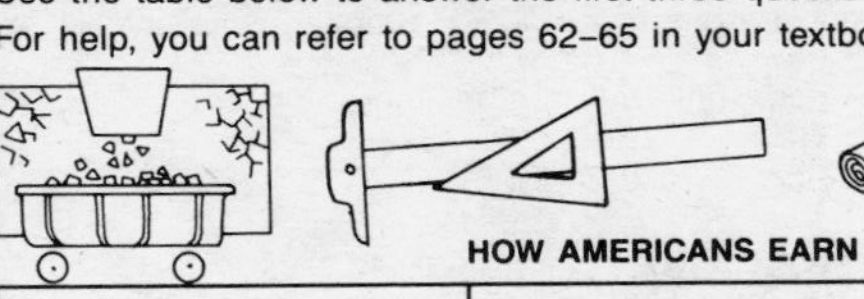

HOW AMERICANS EARN A LIVING

Type of Job	Number of Workers	Percentage of Workers
Services	72,638,000	72%
Manufacturing	19,424,000	19%
Construction	4,661,000	4%
Agriculture	3,750,000	4%
Mining	969,000	1%

1. According to the table, in which type of job do most people work?
   service jobs

   What percent of the people in the United States have these types of jobs?
   72 percent

2. In which type of job do the fewest people work?
   mining

3. About how many people have jobs in agriculture?
   about 3,750,000 people

   How can this relatively small number of people supply food for the nation?
   Many farms are large, and huge machines are used to harvest crops.

4. If you worked in a factory, what type of job would you have?
   a manufacturing job

   About how many people in the United States have these types of jobs?
   about 19,424,000 people

5. What kind of economic system does the United States have?
   capitalist system

   What is an important part of this system?
   free enterprise

6. How does the developed economy of the United States help provide a comfortable way of life for many Americans?
   It involves many different economic activities and makes use of advanced technology.

Name Use with pages 66–69

The Federal Government

Use the pictures on the right to complete the activities on this page. For help, you can refer to pages 66–69 in your textbook.

1. a. Draw a line to the picture that shows the branch of federal government that makes the laws of the nation.

   b. Which two houses make up this branch?
   the House of Representatives
   the Senate

Judicial Branch

2. a. Draw a line to the picture that shows the branch of government that is responsible for carrying out the laws of the United States.

   b. What is the title of the person who heads this branch of government?
   the President

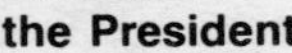

Executive Branch

3. a. Draw a line to the picture that shows the branch of government that interprets the nation's laws.

   b. What court is at the head of this branch of government?
   the Supreme Court

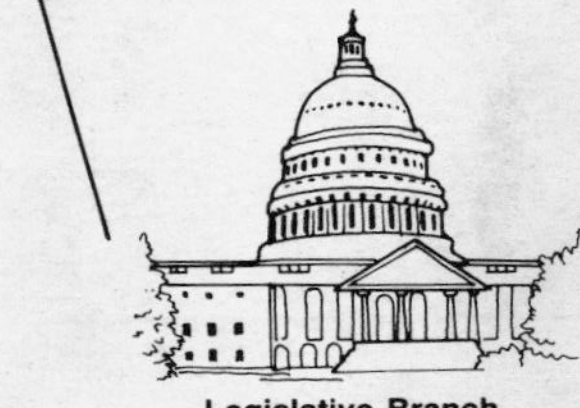

Legislative Branch

4. How is a system of checks and balances built into the system of federal government in the United States? **Student responses should indicate an understanding of how each branch of government limits the powers of the other branches.**

5. How are state governments organized? **Each state has an executive branch headed by a governor, a judicial branch, and a legislative branch.**

Name

Use with pages 70–73

Freedom and the Arts

Use the pictures to answer the questions on this page. For help, you can refer to pages 70–73 in your textbook.

1. Which freedom are these artists exercising?
   freedom of expression
2. How has this freedom affected the arts in the United States?
   Freedom of expression has made the arts in the United States well known throughout the world. Because of this freedom, artists from many nations come to the United States to study and work.
3. Suppose you could participate in one of the events illustrated above. Which one would you choose? **Responses will vary depending upon individual interests.**
4. Which freedom would you be exercising when you choose? **freedom of choice**
5. Do you think freedom of expression and freedom of choice are important? Explain your ideas. **Responses may vary but should demonstrate an understanding of how these freedoms contribute to a rich and varied life in the United States.**

Name

Use with pages 78–79

Using New Words

Write the letter of the term that matches each description below. For help, you can refer to the lessons in Chapter 2 in your textbook.

a. freedom of expression	**f.** free enterprise	**k.** capitalism	**p.** republic
b. checks and balances	**g.** judicial branch	**l.** technology	**q.** export
c. legislative branch	**h.** discrimination	**m.** prejudice	**r.** import
d. developed economy	**i.** federal system	**n.** immigrants	
e. executive branch	**j.** megalopolis	**o.** democracy	

m 1. an unfavorable opinion of a group that is formed unfairly

c 2. the branch of goverment that makes the nation's laws

h 3. the unfair treatment of a person or group by another person or group

j 4. an area of cities and suburbs that is so crowded it looks like one vast city

g 5. the branch of government that interprets the nation's laws

k 6. an economic system in which businesses are owned by individuals or groups rather than by the government

n 7. people who move to a country other than the one where they were born

f 8. the freedom to own property and run a business free of government control

q 9. any item sold to another nation

d 10. an economy that has many different economic activities

l 11. the methods, tools, and machinery used to meet human needs

o 12. a government in which decisions are made by citizens

p 13. a democracy where voters elect officials to represent them in government

r 14. an item bought from another nation

b 15. a government system where each branch limits the powers of the others

i 16. a system of government that divides power between the national government and local governments

e 17. the branch of government responsible for carrying out the laws

a 18. the freedom to express any idea or opinion

Name Use with pages 81–83

Thinking About Canadian Culture

Read the following statements carefully. If a statement is true, write **True** after it. If a statement is false, write **False** after it. Then, in the space provided, write the reasons for your answers. For help, you can refer to pages 81–83 in your textbook.

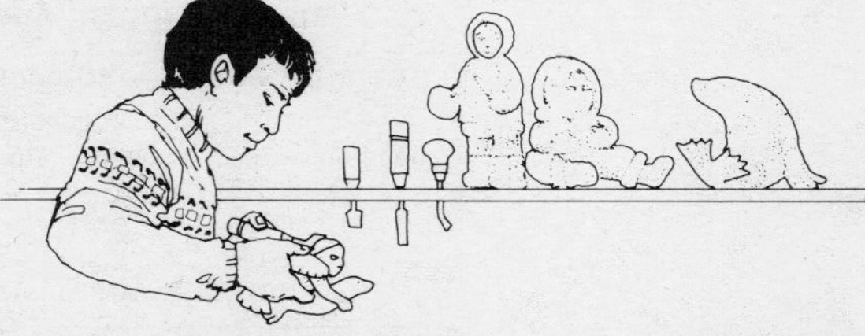

1. The picture above shows an Inuit making a traditional soapstone sculpture. The Inuit were one of the first peoples to settle in the land that is now called Canada.
   True. The Inuit came from Asia to the land that is now called Canada about 6,000 years ago.

2. Today the Inuit are the largest cultural group in Canada.
   False. Today British Canadians are the largest cultural group in Canada.

3. Because Canada was colonized mainly by people from Great Britain, its official language is English. **False. Canada was colonized mainly by people from both Great Britain and France. For this reason Canada has two official languages, English and French.**

4. In the 1960s some French Canadians wanted to break away from Canada.
   True. They felt they had to break away from Canada in order to preserve their culture.

5. Some Canadians worry that the United States may be a threat to their way of life.
   True. The United States has great influence in Canada because most Canadians live close to the United States–Canadian border.

Name Use with pages 86–88

Writing About Canada's Economy

A letter like the one below might have been written by a miner at the Polaris Mine. Read the letter. Then complete the following exercises. For help, you can refer to pages 86–88 in your textbook.

Dear Jed,
Polaris is about the coldest place on earth. I keep my car running 24 hours a day for fear that it won't start again if I turn it off. Half the time it's so cold the tires freeze!
I used to think winters in Toronto were cold. But not after this.
Your frosty pal,
Ben

1. What is the writer describing?
   the climate at the Polaris Mine

2. Why is it so cold at Polaris?
   because it is located north of the Arctic Circle

3. Because of its location, the Polaris Mine is expensive to run. Why is it profitable?
   because the mine produces high-quality ore

4. Besides iron ore, what are two other minerals that help make mining Canada's most important industry?
   nickel, lead, zinc, fossil fuels

5. List two other natural resources important for Canada's economy.
   a. **From its huge forests, Canada produces newsprint.**
   b. **Canada's rich farmland produces wheat.**

6. a. What is acid rain and how is it harmful to the environment?
   Acid rain is rain mixed with chemicals. It pollutes waterways, killing fish and other water life, and damages trees and buildings.

   b. How might the problem of acid rain strain relations between Canada and the United States?
   A great deal of the acid rain in Canada comes from factories in the United States.

Name   Use with page 89

Finding Information in a Library

Suppose you are writing a report about Canada. You need to check some facts in the library. Draw a line from the information you want to the picture that shows where you might find it. In the space provided, give a reason for your answer. For help, you can refer to page 89 in your textbook.

1. You want to check the location of each of Canada's provinces.
   An atlas shows the location of places on a map.

2. You need to find out what the word *separatism* means and how to spell it.
   A dictionary provides the meanings and spellings of words.

3. You want to check the most recent population figures for Canada's largest cities.
   An almanac provides up-to-date facts on many subjects.

4. You need to find some information about Canada's economy.
   An encyclopedia has articles on many useful subjects.

5. You need to find a book on the Inuit.
   A card catalog tells where books in the library are located.

DICTIONARY

ENCYCLOPEDIA

ATLAS

ALMANAC

Name   Use with pages 90–92

A Look at Canada's Government

Complete the activities below. For help, you can refer to pages 90–92 in your textbook.

1. The picture shows Queen Elizabeth II of Great Britain signing the Constitution Act, which gave Canada full independence from British rule. In what year did the signing take place?
   1982

2. What role does the British monarch play in Canada's government today?
   The British monarch is head of the government in name only.

3. In the picture the man looking on is former Prime Minister Pierre Trudeau of Canada. What part does the prime minister play in the national government of Canada?
   The prime minister is the leader of Canada's national government.

4. Which branches of the Canadian government does the prime minister head?
   the executive branch and the legislative branch

5. What is Canada's national legislative branch called? **parliament**

6. What two houses make up the Canadian legislative branch?
   the House of Commons and the Senate

7. How are these two houses different? **The House of Commons is elected by the people. The Senate is appointed by the governor general.**

8. What must the Canadian prime minister do if he or she loses support of the majority of the members of Parliament? **resign**

Name　　　　Use with pages 93–95

Art and Recreation in Canada

Use the pictures on the right to complete the activities on this page. For help, you can refer to pages 93–95 in your textbook.

1. a. Draw a line to the picture that shows one of Canada's artistic traditions.
   b. What is a favorite topic among Canada's many artists?
   nature and the beauty of the Canadian land

2. a. Draw a line to the picture that shows one way Canadians might express their interest in ethnic identity.
   b. Why are Canadians interested in ethnic identity?
   because Canada is a mosaic of cultures

3. a. Draw a line to the picture that shows Canada's national sport.
   b. What other sports event draws thousands of spectators to Alberta every year?
   the Calgary Stampede

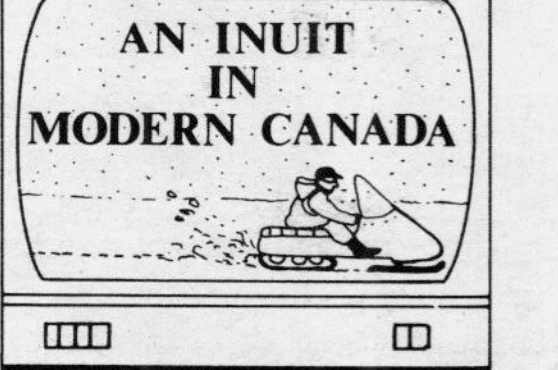

Name　　　　Use with pages 96–97

Using New Words

Use the terms in the box to complete the crossword puzzle below. For help, you can refer to the lessons in Chapter 3 in your textbook.

Commonwealth of Nations	fossil fuels	monarchy	mosaic
parliamentary democracy	separatism	province	
prime minister	acid rain	cabinet	

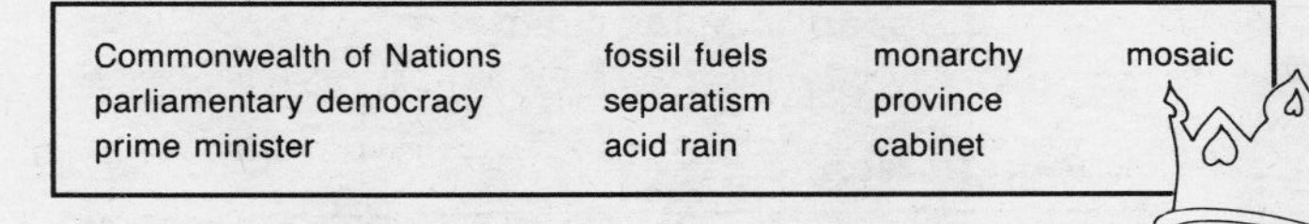

Across

2. coal, petroleum, and natural gas (2 words)
6. a system of government with a national legislature called parliament (2 words)
7. a group of independent nations once ruled by Great Britain (3 words)
9. a governmental body made up of the prime minister and about 30 members from the House of Commons
10. a self-governing area within a nation

Down

1. the leader of the political party that has a majority of members in the House of Commons (2 words)
3. a movement to break away from a country in order to preserve a particular culture
4. a pattern or picture made up of many small pieces of stone or glass
5. a government headed by a hereditary ruler, such as a king or a queen
8. rain mixed with chemicals from burning coal and other fuels (2 words)

Name Use with pages 107–110

Using Maps

Use the map on this page to complete the activities below. For help, you can refer to pages 107–110 in your textbook.

1. a. Locate and label the following land areas.

   Central America

   Caribbean Islands

   South America

   Mexico

   b. Which region do these land areas form?

   Latin America

2. a. Locate and label the following rivers. Then trace each river and its tributaries in blue.

   Amazon Orinoco

   Paraná Paraguay

   b. Which of these rivers forms one of the world's largest river systems?

   the Amazon

3. a. Locate and label the Andes mountains. Then color them brown.

   b. How would you describe the climate in these mountains?

   It is hot during the day and very cold at night.

4. a. Locate and label Lake Titicaca.

   b. What is the area around Lake Titicaca called?

   the altiplano

Name Use with pages 111–114

Climate and Resources in Latin America

Use the picture to answer the first question below. Then answer the following questions. For help, you can refer to pages 111–114 in your textbook.

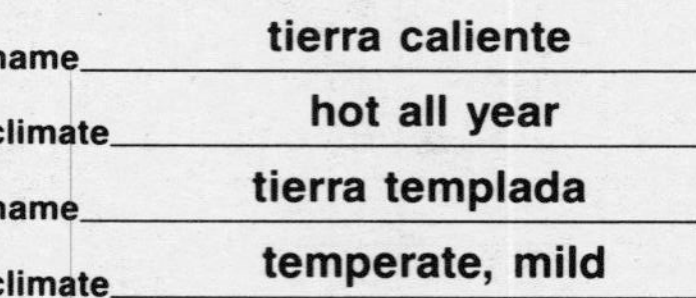

Mount Aconcagua

1. In which of Latin America's three climate zones would you find snow-capped mountain peaks?

   the tierra fría

2. What are Latin America's other two mountain climate zones called? What kind of climate does each have?

   name **tierra caliente**

   climate **hot all year**

   name **tierra templada**

   climate **temperate, mild**

3. Why is it surprising that Latin America's mountainous areas have three climate zones? **because most of Latin America is in the tropics**

4. What two places in Latin America hold world records for rainfall?

   a. World's driest place: **the Atacama Desert in Chile**

   b. World's largest rainy area: **the Amazon River Valley**

5. What natural resource is found in the rain forest of the Amazon River Valley?

   many kinds of trees

6. What are three other important natural resources found in Latin America?

   Possible answers: iron ore, petroleum, gold, silver, tin, emeralds

7. Why are many of these resources said to be "nature's jealously hidden treasures"?

   because many of them are difficult to find

Name Use with page 115

Relating Latitude, Elevation, and Climate

The following statements are based on information in the chart. Read the statements carefully. If a statement is true, write **True** after it. If a statement is false, write **False** after it. Then, in the space provided, write the reasons for your answer. For help, you can refer to page 115 in your textbook.

City and Country	Latitude	Approximate Elevation (ft.)
Mexico City, Mexico	21°N	7,500
Pueblo, Mexico	21°N	7,500
Bogotá, Colombia	5°N	8,500
Buenaventura, Colombia	5°N	500
Quito, Ecuador	equator	15,500
Guayaquil, Ecuador	2°S	sea level

1. You would expect the climate of Mexico City and Pueblo to be similar. **True. Both cities are at about the same latitude and elevation.**
2. Despite the fact that Bogotá is near the equator, you would expect it to have a cold climate. **True. Although Bogotá is near the equator, it is at a high elevation, approximately 8,500 feet.**
3. Because Quito and Guayaquil are both near the equator, you would expect them to have hot climates. **False. Quito is at a very high elevation and would have a cold climate. Guayaquil is at a very low elevation and would have a hot climate.**
4. If you were planning to visit Mexico City and then Bogotá, you would expect to encounter cool climates in both cities. **True. Both are at high elevation and would have cool climates.**
5. The climates of Bogotá and Buenaventura are quite different from each other. **True. Although both cities are at the same latitude, Bogotá is at a much higher elevation and would thus have a much cooler climate.**

Name Use with pages 116–117

Using New Words

Put an **X** next to each statement that gives correct information about the term in boldface type. For help, you can refer to the lessons in Chapter 4 in your textbook.

1. **archipelago**
   - X **a.** An archipelago is a group of islands.
   - X **b.** The Caribbean archipelagos are part of Latin America's mountain system.
   - ___ **c.** Latin America's mountain system is known as an archipelago.
   - X **d.** The Caribbean Islands are made up of small archipelagos.
2. **rain forest**
   - ___ **a.** Much of North America is covered by rain forest.
   - X **b.** A rain forest is a dense tropical forest.
   - X **c.** Most of Latin America's trees grow in the rain forest of the Amazon River Valley.
   - ___ **d.** The rain forests of Latin America are located in the climate zone known as tierra fría.
3. **altiplano**
   - ___ **a.** The Andes mountains are sometimes called the altiplano.
   - X **b.** The altiplano is a high, cold, flat area between two mountain ranges in Bolivia and Peru.
   - X **c.** Many people live in the altiplano area of the Andes mountains.
   - X **d.** Lake Titicaca is on the altiplano.
4. **river system**
   - X **a.** A river system is the land drained by a major river and its tributaries.
   - ___ **b.** South America doesn't have any large river systems.
   - X **c.** The Amazon is one of the world's greatest river systems.
   - ___ **d.** The Andean altiplano is Latin America's second-largest river system.

Name Use with pages 119–122

The Origins of Mexico's Culture

Answer the following questions. For help, you can refer to pages 119–122 in your textbook.

1. The picture above shows the ancient city of Tenochtitlán. Who built the city and where did they build it? **Tenochtitlán was built by the Mexica (whom the Spanish called the Aztecs) where Mexico City stands today.**

2. The Spanish explorer Hernando Cortés thought Tenochtitlán was "the most beautiful city in the world." If he felt this way, why did he destroy it? **Cortés and his followers destroyed Tenochtitlán in order to defeat the Aztecs gathered there.**

3. How did the Spanish conquest of Mexico change the culture and way of life of its people? **The way of life of Mexico's people became a mixture of Spanish and Indian cultures.**

4. What is the ancestry of the Mexican people today? **About 55 percent of the people are mestizos. Another 29 percent are of pure Indian descent. Most of the remaining people are of Spanish ancestry.**

5. Why are most present-day Mexicans Roman Catholic? **The Spanish who conquered Mexico were Roman Catholic. They converted many of the Indians to their religion.**

Name Use with pages 123–125

A Look at Mexico's Economy

Use the graph below to answer the first two questions on this page. Then answer the following questions. For help, you can refer to pages 123–125 in your textbook.

HOW PEOPLE EARN A LIVING IN MEXICO

Commerce, restaurants, and hotels 14%
Construction 7%
Manufacturing industries 12%
Mining 1.5%
Agriculture, forestry, and fishing 27%
Finance 2.5%
Health, social, and personal services 31.5%
Transportation and communications 5%

1. a. According to the graph, what percent of Mexicans work in the agriculture, forestry, and fishing industries? **27 percent**

   b. What two types of farming take place in Mexico? **subsistence farming** **commercial farming**

2. a. According to the graph, what percent of Mexicans work in manufacturing industries? **12 percent**

   b. In which city is most of Mexico's industry located? **Mexico City**

3. What is one reason that Mexico is only partly industrialized? **The ores mined in Mexico were not used to develop the nation's businesses and factories but went instead to other countries.**

4. How did the discovery of large petroleum deposits in Mexico in the 1970s affect Mexico's economy? **The discovery of oil created new industries, such as the petrochemical industry.**

5. How has Mexico's population affected the country's economic growth? **Mexico's population is growing faster than the nation's ability to provide jobs for everyone. As a result, its economic growth has slowed.**

Name Use with pages 126–127

Is It Accurate?

The paragraph below is from a book titled *Latin America and Canada*. The book was published in 1987. Read the paragraph. Then answer the questions that follow. For help, you can refer to pages 126–127 in your textbook.

> Mexico's largest city is its capital, Mexico City. There the nation's roads, railroads, and telephone and telegraph lines all come together. It is the center of Mexico's political, economic, and cultural life. Mexico City is the most important manufacturing center in the country. It is home to about 20 percent of the nation's population, with over 9 million people. By the year 2000, it will probably be the world's largest city.
>
> *by John Jarolimek, recognized authority on social studies, author of several books and articles on teaching and learning social studies, professor at the University of Washington; published by Macmillan*

1. What is the source of the information above? **A book titled *Latin America and Canada***
2. Is the author an expert or well-informed on the topic? How do you know? **Yes. John Jarolimek is a recognized authority in the area and author of several books and articles as well as a university professor.**
3. Does the author have anything to gain by giving inaccurate information on the topic?

   yes (no)
4. Is the information current? How do you know? **The information is probably current because the book was written only a few years ago.**
5. What are two sources you might check to determine the accuracy of the information? **Answers may vary, but should identify sources appropriate to the topic, such as world almanacs, encyclopedias, and newspapers.**
6. Do you think the information is probably accurate? How can you tell? **The information is probably accurate because it is from a good source, written by an expert on the topic, and is reasonably accurate.**

Name Use with pages 128–130

Mexico's Government

Use the terms in the box to complete the diagram of Mexico's government. Then answer the questions that follow. For help, you can refer to pages 128–130 in your textbook.

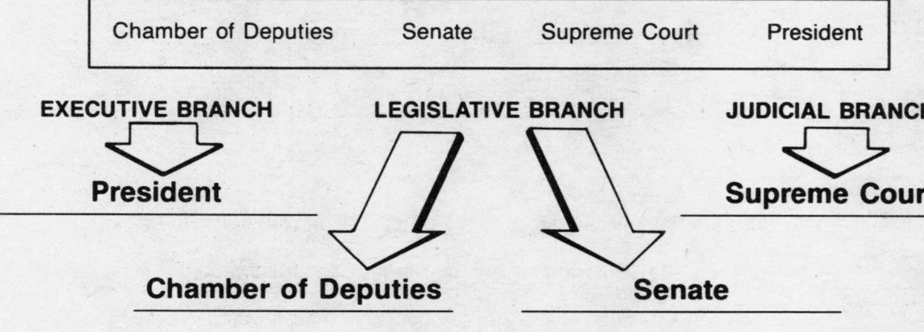

1. According to its constitution, what kind of government does Mexico have? **a representative democracy**
2. What are two powers that the President of Mexico has that the President of the United States does not have? **The president of Mexico can remove local officials from office and change laws with the approval of the Senate.**
3. For what is the Chamber of Deputies responsible? **The Chamber of Deputies passes laws and is responsible for elections.**
4. For what is the Senate responsible? **The Senate approves or disapproves treaties and presidential appointments.**
5. Why was only one strong political party, the PRI, formed in Mexico? **It was formed to include many interests and to prevent different groups from clashing and causing unrest.**
6. Why do critics of the PRI feel it is time for a change? **They believe it is time to make the govcrnment more directly responsible to the people and to allow parties to air their differences in public.**

Name ______ Use with pages 131–133

Art, Culture, and Recreation in Mexico

The pictures below show two features of Mexican culture. Write a caption for each picture. Explain what is shown and how the picture illustrates the combining of Indian and Spanish cultures. Then answer the question that follows. For help, you can refer to pages 131–133 in your textbook.

1. **The game of jai alai shown in the picture had its origins in traditional Indian culture. The game is still one of the most popular sports in Mexico.**

2. **Murals like the one in the picture explore mestizo heritage. The simple lines and bold colors capture the spirit of Mexico's past sufferings and hopes for the future.**

3. How and why has the Mexican government supported traditional Mexican crafts?
The Mexican government has supported traditional Mexican crafts by giving craftsworkers awards and by helping them export their best works. By so doing, Mexico hopes to maintain its traditions, give people income, and produce goods for export.

Name ______ Use with pages 138–139

Using New Words

Write the letter of the term that matches each definition. For help, you can refer to the lessons in Chapter 5 in your textbook.

a. subsistence farming	**e.** mestizo	**h.** petrochemical
b. developing economy	**f.** mural	**i.** civilization
c. commercial farming	**g.** extended family	**j.** campesino
d. metropolitan area		

j 1. a Mexican village farmer with a small plot of land and a very low income

h 2. a chemical that is made from petroleum

i 3. a culture that has developed systems of government, religion, and learning

a 4. farming in which just enough food is grown to feed the families of the farmers

f 5. a work of art on a building wall

e 6. a Mexican of mixed Indian and Spanish ancestry

g 7. a family that contains, in addition to parents and their children, other family members

c 8. large-scale farming in which crops are sold and exported

b 9. a national economy that is only partly industrialized

d 10. an area that includes a large city and its surrounding suburbs and towns

Name ______ Use with pages 141–144

The Origins of Latin American Cultures

Use the pictures on the right to complete the activities on this page. For help, you can refer to pages 141–144 in your textbook.

1. a. Draw a line to the picture that shows something made by the first people to live in Central America.

   b. Which three areas in Central America did these people settle?

   Guatemala

   Belize

   western Honduras

2. a. Draw a line to the picture that shows the second stream of people to come to Central America and the Caribbean.

   b. Which four European countries gained control of the Caribbean Islands?

   England **France**

   Spain **Netherlands**

3. a. Draw a line to the picture that shows the third stream of people to come to Latin America.

   b. Why did these people come to Central America and the Caribbean Islands? **They were brought against their will and forced to work on plantations.**

4. What makes each of the Caribbean Islands unique? **the combination of historical events, customs, and different ethnic groups**

Enslaved Africans brought to the Caribbean Islands

Spanish settlers landing on a Caribbean island

Mayan sculpture

Name ______ Use with pages 145–147

ECONOMY: Central America and the Caribbean

Use the bar graph below to complete the exercises on this page. For help, you can refer to pages 145–147 in your textbook.

MAIN EXPORTS OF THIRTEEN CENTRAL AMERICAN AND CARIBBEAN COUNTRIES

Percentage of Total Exports by Value (0–90)

THE BAHAMAS PETROLEUM PRODUCTS; BARBADOS SUGAR; COSTA RICA BANANAS COFFEE; CUBA SUGAR; DOMINICAN REPUBLIC SUGAR; EL SALVADOR COFFEE; GUATEMALA COFFEE; HAITI COFFEE; HONDURAS COFFEE/BANANAS; JAMAICA ALUMINA AND BAUXITE; NICARAGUA COTTON COFFEE; PANAMA PETROLEUM PRODUCTS; TRINIDAD AND TOBAGO PETROLEUM PRODUCTS CRUDE OIL

1. List the countries that export mineral products.

   the Bahamas **Jamaica**

   Panama **Trinidad and Tobago**

2. List the countries that export mainly agricultural products. Put an * next to those countries that depend heavily on a single crop.

   ***Barbados** **Costa Rica** ***Cuba**

   ***Dominican Republic** ***El Salvador** ***Guatemala**

   ***Haiti** **Honduras** **Nicaragua**

3. Why is it risky for a nation to depend heavily on one crop for its income? **If world prices for that crop fall, or if a natural disaster that affects that crop strikes, the nation will lose the income from the crop.**

4. Why are most manufacturing jobs in Central America and the Caribbean countries related to agricultural products instead of mineral products? **Many of the nations in this part of the world do not have coal or other minerals needed for manufacturing.**

Name ____________ Use with page 148

The Pan-American Highway

The map below shows the Pan-American Highway system. Study the map. Then answer the questions that follow. For help, you can refer to page 148 in your textbook.

1. According to the map, at which three cities in the United States does the Pan-American Highway begin?
   Laredo
   El Paso
   Eagle Pass

2. To which major city do each of these routes lead?
   Mexico City

3. If you traveled on the Pan-American Highway from Mexico City to Managua, Nicaragua, which three major cities would you pass through?
   Guatemala City
   San Salvador
   Tegucigalpa

4. Trace one route you could take from Managua to Brasília in red. Trace a second route you could take in blue. **Routes will vary, but should indicate the student's understanding of the map symbols for cities and roads.**

5. Why is the Pan-American Highway system of great importance to the economies of Latin America and South America? **It provides routes for the transportation of raw materials, agricultural products, and other goods.**

Name ____________ Use with pages 149–151

GOVERNMENT: Central America and the Caribbean

Complete the map by writing phrases from the box in the spaces provided on the map. Each space should have a separate phrase. For help, you can refer to pages 149–151 in your textbook.

commonwealth	part of Britain
overseas area	part of France
dictatorship	part of the United States
colony	independent nation

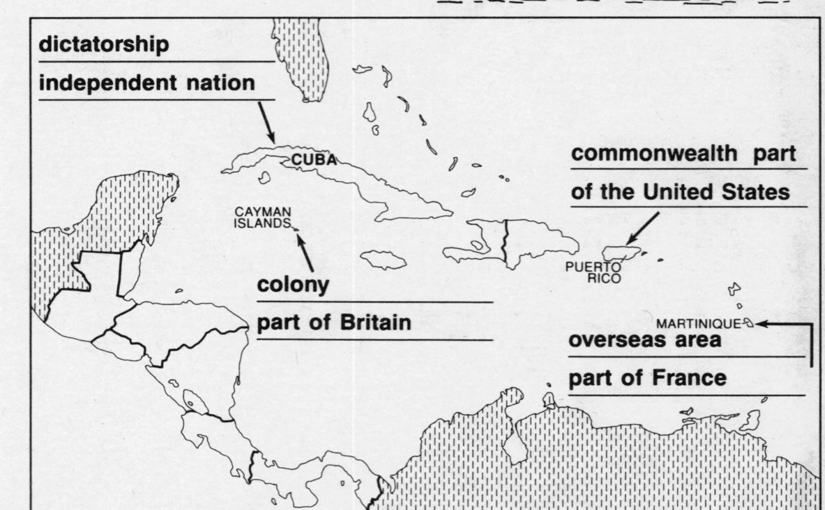

Why does the United States closely watch the events that take place in the Caribbean? **because the area is very near to its borders; the United States has possessions in the region; the United States has an interest in the Panama Canal**

Name Use with pages 154–155

Arts and Recreation in Latin America

Use the pictures below to complete the activities on this page. For help, you can refer to pages 154–155 in your textbook.

1. a. What kind of musical instrument are the people in the picture playing? **steel drums**

   b. On which Caribbean Island was this musical instrument developed? **Trinidad**

   c. What kind of music are the musicians probably playing? **calypso**

   d. What is the origin of calypso music? **Calypso was started in the Caribbean by enslaved Africans who sang while they worked.**

2. a. Which popular sport is being played in the picture? **baseball**

   b. In which Caribbean and Central American nations is this sport played most frequently? **Nicaragua, Cuba, Dominican Republic**

   c. What is remarkable about the Dominican Republic's contribution to this sport? **Over 200 Dominicans play on major and minor league teams in the United States.**

   d. What other sport is a favorite in this part of the world? **soccer**

Name Use with pages 148–149

Using New Words

Use the code to spell the words in the left column. Then write the number of each word next to its definition in the right column. For help, you can refer to the lessons in Chapter 6 of your textbook.

CODE

a = 26	g = 23	m = 20	s = 17	y = 14
b = 1	h = 4	n = 7	t = 10	z = 13
c = 25	i = 22	o = 19	u = 16	
d = 2	j = 5	p = 8	v = 11	
e = 24	k = 21	q = 18	w = 15	
f = 3	l = 6	r = 9	x = 12	

1. 20 26 9 19 19 7 **maroon**
2. 25 26 6 14 8 17 19 **calypso**
3. 25 19 20 20 19 7 15 24 26 6 10 4 **commonwealth**
4. 17 24 25 10 **sect**
5. 2 22 25 10 26 10 19 9 **dictator**
6. 8 6 26 7 10 26 10 22 19 7 **plantation**
7. 19 7 24 25 9 19 8 24 25 19 7 19 20 14 **one-crop economy**

2 a. a style of music developed in the Caribbean by African slaves

1 b. a descendant of enslaved Africans who escaped from the Spanish in the Caribbean

4 c. a religious group that is outside the mainstream of large, organized religion

5 d. a ruler who has total control over a country

6 e. a large farm that grows crops for sale

3 f. a self-governing territory

7 g. an economy that depends on a single crop for income

Name Use with pages 159–161

Some Ethnic Groups in South America

Use the map to complete the activities on this page. For help, you can refer to pages 159–161 in your textbook.

1. Shade and list the two countries in which much of the population is European or of European ancestry.
   Argentina,
   Uruguay

2. Put a star in and list each of the three countries whose population includes many Indians.
   Bolivia,
   Peru,
   Ecuador

3. Outline and list each of the four countries in which the population consists mainly of mestizos.
   Paraguay,
   Venezuela,
   Ecuador,
   Chile

4. Name and briefly describe South America's best-known mestizo group.
   The gauchos of Argentina are cowhands who roam the pampas herding cattle.

5. Briefly explain how the ethnic mix of South America affects its culture.
   Student responses will vary but should indicate an understanding of how the different groups' ways of life have formed the cultures of present-day South America.

Name Use with pages 162–163

Is It Fact or Opinion?

You might read statements similar to the ones below in an article about the Incas. Decide if each statement is a fact, a value judgment, or a reasoned opinion. Circle your choice. Then explain your answer. For help, you can refer to pages 162–163 in your textbook.

1. The Incas are the most interesting people to have lived in South America.
   fact **(value judgment)** reasoned opinion
   explanation: **making a judgment about the worth or quality of something**

2. By the middle of the 1400s, the Incan empire had expanded to occupy more than 2,500 miles (4,200 km) along the western coast of South America.
   (fact) value judgment reasoned opinion
   explanation: **information that can be proved**

3. The Incas built a vast network of roads to link the provinces of their large empire.
   (fact) value judgment reasoned opinion
   explanation: **information that can be proven**

4. The Incan people must have been very creative since they made so many beautiful works of art.
   fact value judgment **(reasoned opinion)**
   explanation: **an opinion supported by evidence or reasons**

5. Because so much of the private and public lives of the Incas revolved around religious practices, priests and other religious leaders must have had great authority.
   fact value judgment **(reasoned opinion)**
   explanation: **an opinion supported by evidence or reasons**

6. Today the Incan ruins are the most interesting things to see in Peru.
   fact **(value judgment)** reasoned opinion
   explanation: **making a judgment about the worth or quality of something**

Name

Looking at the Products of South America

Use the pictures below to complete the activities on this page. For help, you can refer to pages 164–167 in your textbook.

1. a. Which South American country is the leading exporter of this product?
   Ecuador

   b. What cash crop is grown in Colombia and Brazil?
   coffee

2. a. In which part of South America might these animals be raised?
   the pampas

   b. What two crops are also grown in this area?
   cotton **wheat**

3. a. From which South American country might these leather goods have come?
   Argentina

   b. What do most South American manufacturers process?
   Most South American manufacturers process, or treat, agricultural products.

4. a. Which South American country used this major resource to help its economic development?
   Venezuela

   b. Why was basing its economy on this one product risky?
   When world oil prices fell, Venezuela's economy was hurt.

Name

A Look at the Dictatorship of Juan Perón

The headline and article below are from *The New York Times,* September 20, 1955. Read the article and answer the questions that follow. For help, you can refer to pages 170–171 in your textbook.

PERÓN'S REGIME IS OVERTHROWN; JUNTA WILL MEET WITH REBELS; CROWDS HAIL FALL OF DICTATOR

BUENOS AIRES, Tuesday, Sept. 20–The Government of President Juan D. Perón fell last night.

A four-man junta of army generals assumed command of the forces that had fought unsuccessfully to keep General Perón in power. He had been master of Argentina since Oct. 17, 1945, and its President for nine years. . . .

The junta quickly entered into negotiations to end the four-day civil war. Army and Navy units had joined in the rebellion and forced the resignation of the President, the Cabinet and other authorities. . . .

There was no news about the whereabouts of President Perón tonight. Some reports had him in . . . the Paraguayan Embassy in Buenos Aires.

1. According to the article, who was Juan Perón and what happened to him?
   Juan Perón was president of Argentina, and he was overthrown by army generals.

2. According to the headline, how did Argentinians feel about the fall of Perón's dictatorship?
   They were glad Perón's dictatorship had ended.

3. According to the article, how long had Perón been president of Argentina?
   almost ten years

4. How did Perón maintain power in Argentina?
   by creating labor unions, schools, and new industries

5. At the same time Eva Perón encouraged workers to give money to government programs, what did Juan Perón do?
   He took control of the press, businesses, labor unions, and the army.

6. Who ruled Argentina after Perón's death?
   dictators

Name　　　　　　　　　　　　　　　　Use with pages 172–173

A Look at South American Traditions

Use the pictures on the right to complete the activities on this page. For help, you can refer to pages 172–173 in your textbook.

1. **a.** Draw a line to the picture that shows one of South America's famous poets.

   b. What are some of the topics most often described by South American poets?

   ethnic identity, environment, and poverty

2. **a.** Draw a line to the picture that shows one of South America's most famous celebrations.

   b. What national dance is featured at this celebration?

   the samba

   c. What is the origin of this dance?

   It has African roots.

3. **a.** Draw a line to the picture that shows one of South America's most famous soccer players.

   b. What are some other popular sports in South America?

   baseball, tennis, polo, jai alai

Carnaval in Rio de Janeiro

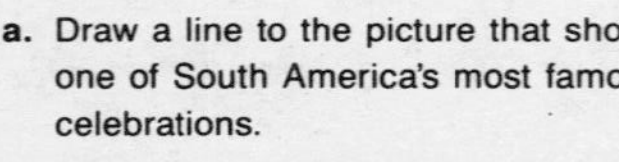

João Nunes de Oliveira

Pablo Neruda

Name　　　　　　　　　　　　　　　　Use with pages 174–175

Using New Words

Complete each of the exercises below. For help, you can refer to the lessons in Chapter 7 in your textbook.

1. Put an **X** next to each statement that correctly describes a gaucho.
   - X **a.** A gaucho is a member of one of South America's best-known mestizo groups.
   - X **b.** A gaucho is a cowhand who roams the pampas herding cattle.
   - ___ **c.** A gaucho is a farmer who lives high in the Andes.

2. Put an **X** next to each statement that correctly describes a caudillo.
   - ___ **a.** A caudillo is a South American mestizo group.
   - X **b.** A caudillo is a local South American military leader.
   - X **c.** A caudillo may become powerful enough to form an army.

3. Put an **X** next to each statement that correctly describes junta.
   - X **a.** A junta is a group of military officers that run a country.
   - ___ **b.** Junta is the name of a South American dictator.
   - ___ **c.** A junta is a South American farmer.

4. Put an **X** next to each statement that correctly uses the word coup.
   - X **a.** A coup is the sudden overthrow of a government.
   - X **b.** Enemies of Juan Perón overthrew him in a coup.
   - ___ **c.** Perón's wife helped him by forming a coup.

5. Put an **X** next to each statement that correctly uses the term per capita income.
   - X **a.** The average yearly income for each person in a country is called per capita income.
   - ___ **b.** Taxes are called per capita income in some countries.
   - X **c.** Venezuela's per capita income rose when oil was discovered there.

Name

Use with pages 183–187

Using Maps

Use the map on this page to complete the activities below. For help, you can refer to pages 183–187 and the atlas on page 629 in your textbook.

1. Locate and label the following bodies of water.

   Atlantic Ocean
   English Channel
   Mediterranean Sea
   North Sea
   Baltic Sea

2. Locate and label the following peninsulas. Then color each one as indicated.
   - **a.** Jutland Peninsula—brown
   - **b.** Scandinavian Peninsula—red
   - **c.** Italian Peninsula—green
   - **d.** Balkan Peninsula—blue
   - **e.** Iberian Peninsula—yellow

3. Locate and label the following islands.

   British Isles
   Sardinia
   Corsica
   Sicily

4. List the countries that make up the Low Countries. Then color this area orange.

   Netherlands Belgium Luxembourg

5. Why is Western Europe called "a land of peninsulas and islands"?

   because the shape of the land can be divided into peninsulas and islands

Name

Use with pages 188–189

Understanding Map Projections

The map below is called a Robinson projection. Put an **X** next to each sentence that makes a true statement about the map. For help, you can refer to pages 188–189 in your textbook.

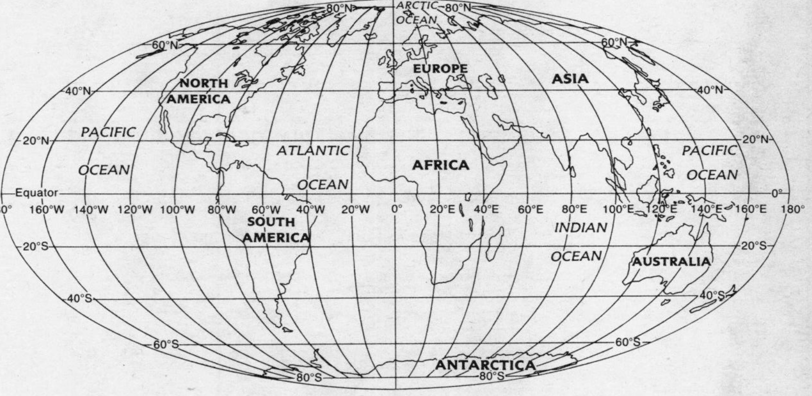

X 1. The map above is an example of an equal-area projection.

___ 2. As you move toward the poles on this map, distances and shapes become distorted.

___ 3. This kind of map is useful to navigators of ships because they can use it to draw their ships' courses in straight lines.

X 4. The projection of this map shows sizes and shapes of continents fairly accurately, and distances are nearly correct.

X 5. The projection of this map is useful for comparing different places on the earth.

___ 6. North is always directly toward the top of this map.

___ 7. A Mercator projection would show the shapes of the continents more accurately than they are shown on this map.

X 8. On this map all the lines of longitude are curved except the prime meridian.

Name Use with pages 192–197

Writing About Western Europe

Use the space provided to answer the questions in each box. Arrange your answers in paragraphs. Your paragraphs will be a summary of important ideas from the lesson. For help, you can refer to pages 192–197 in your textbook.

- Which factors cause the mild climate of the Atlantic coast of Europe?
- What kind of climate does the northern part of Western Europe have? Why?
- What kind of climate does the southern part of Western Europe have? Why?

The Gulf Stream brings warm water from the Gulf of Mexico to the Atlantic coast of Europe. These ocean waters heat up in summer and cool off in winter more slowly than the land does, creating a mild climate. In the northern part of Western Europe, the moderating effect of the Gulf Stream and the Atlantic Ocean are not nearly as strong. As a result, the winters are long, cold, and snowy. Two mountain ranges in the southern part of Western Europe, the Alps and the Pyrenees, prevent Atlantic breezes from reaching this area. This makes the summers mostly sunny and dry. The winters are usually mild or even warm.

- What happened to most of the forests that once covered Western Europe?
- What threatens the forests that are left?
- What makes Western Europe a good region for growing crops?
- Why are Western Europe's rivers and waterways important?

Many of the forests that once covered Western Europe were cut down to make room for farms. Today the forests that remain are threatened by logging and by acid rain. Western Europe's mild climate and rich soil make it a good region for growing crops. Its rivers and waterways provide transportation and shipping routes for even the landlocked countries of Luxembourg, Switzerland, and Austria.

Name Use with pages 198–199

Using New Words

Complete each of the activities below. For help, you can refer to the lessons in Chapter 8 in your textbook.

1. Put an **X** next to each statement that correctly uses the word *landlocked*.

   ____ **a.** A landlocked country is one that is surrounded by water on three sides.
   X **b.** A landlocked country is one that is entirely surrounded by land.
   X **c.** Luxembourg, Switzerland, and Austria are the three landlocked countries of Western Europe.
   ____ **d.** Good inland waterways are of little use to a landlocked country.
   ____ **e.** Great Britain is a landlocked country.
   X **f.** The Rhine River begins in the landlocked country of Switzerland.

2. Put an **X** next to each statement that correctly uses the word *fjord*.

   X **a.** A fjord is a deep, narrow inlet of the sea between high cliffs.
   X **b.** The western coast of Norway is a good place to see a fjord.
   ____ **c.** A fjord is a large lake formed by retreating glaciers.
   ____ **d.** The landlocked countries of Western Europe are good places to see a fjord.
   ____ **e.** A fjord is often located far from the sea.
   X **f.** A fjord must be located along the coast of a country.

3. Write a sentence containing both the words *fjord* and *landlocked*.

   Example sentence: You will never see a fjord in a landlocked country.

Name

Use with pages 201–203

The People Who Came to the British Isles

Use the sentences in the box to complete the time line. Then answer the questions that follow. For help, you can refer to pages 201–203 in your textbook.

Stonehenge was built.
The Celts came to the British Isles.
The Romans invaded the British Isles.
The Anglo-Saxons invaded Britain.
The Normans invaded England.

Stonehenge was built. 2000 B.C.

Celts came to British Isles. 800 B.C.

Romans invaded British Isles. A.D. 43

Anglo-Saxons invaded Britain. 450

Normans invaded England. 1066

2000 | 1500 | 1000 | 500 | 500 | 1000 | 1500 | 2000

B.C. ← → A.D.

1. Who built Stonehenge?
   the first people to settle the British Isles
2. According to the time line, about how long after Stonehenge was built did the Celts invade the British Isles?
   about 1,200 years
3. About how long were the Celts in the British Isles before the Romans invaded?
   about 850 years
4. Who were the Anglo-Saxons?
   warriors from northern Europe who invaded Britain
5. Where did the Normans come from?
   the western part of France known as Normandy
6. Today where do the largest groups of newcomers to Great Britain come from?
   from India, Pakistan, West Indies—countries once ruled by Britain

Name

Use with pages 204–205

Reading Time Zone Maps

Use the time zone map below to complete the sentences. For help, you can refer to pages 204–205 in your textbook.

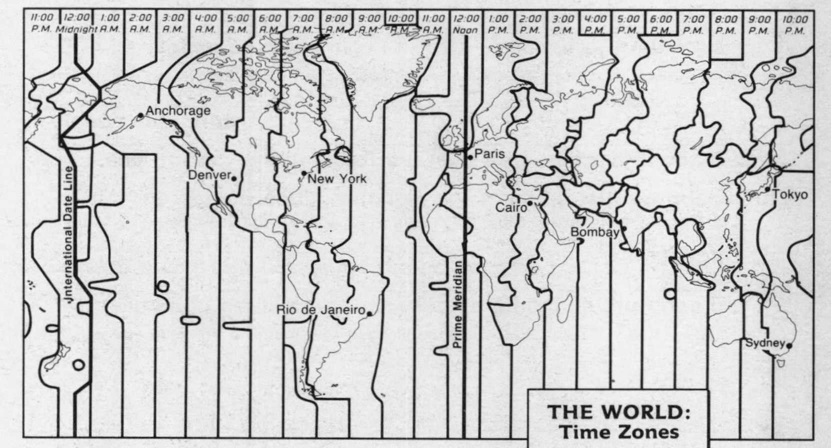

1. The line that marks the boundary between one day and the next is called the **International Date Line**.
2. If you travel east across this line, today becomes **yesterday**.
3. If you travel west across this line, today becomes **tomorrow**.
4. If you were traveling east from New York to Bombay, you would pass through **ten** time zones.
5. When it is noon on Monday in Paris, it is **4:00 A.M.** on **Monday** in Denver.
6. When it is 6:00 A.M. on Wednesday in Anchorage, it is **1:00 A.M.** on **Thursday** in Sydney.

Name Use with pages 206–208

Taking a Look at the British Economy

Answer the following questions. For help, you can refer to pages 206–208 in your textbook.

1. The picture above shows the inside of a British factory during the Industrial Revolution. How did factories like this change the way things were produced? **Jobs that were once done by hand were now done by machine. Products that once were made at home or in small workshops were now produced in factories like this one.**
2. How did the economies of Great Britain and the Republic of Ireland differ during the Industrial Revolution? **The Industrial Revolution made Great Britain the economic leader of the world. The economy of the Republic of Ireland developed at a much slower pace.**
3. How has the economy of Great Britain changed since the days of the Industrial Revolution? **Great Britain is no longer the world's leading industrial nation. People in other countries can produce goods more cheaply than the British can.**
4. What economic problems does Britain face today? **Its natural resources are limited. In addition, British factories now find it hard to compete against the more modern factories in other countries.**
5. Which newly discovered natural resources in Great Britain are likely to be the key to Britain's economic future? **oil and natural gas**

Name Use with pages 209–211

The Government of Great Britain

Answer the questions below. For help, you can refer to pages 209–211 in your textbook.

1. The picture shows King John of England signing the Magna Carta. In which year did the signing take place? **1215**
2. What was the Magna Carta? **a document, or charter, limiting the power of Britain's monarch**
3. What role does the monarch play in Britain's government today? **The monarch carries out many public functions but does not play a direct role in making public policy.**
4. How does the British constitution differ from most other constitutions in the world today? **The British constitution is not a single written document. Instead, it consists of important laws and charters adopted over many centuries.**
5. What are the names of the two houses that make up the British Parliament? **House of Lords** **House of Commons**
6. What is the title of the person who heads the Parliament? **prime minister**
7. Who becomes the prime minister? **the leader of the political party with the most seats in Parliament**
8. How has the British system of government influenced other democracies in the world? **Many of the world's democracies are modeled after it.**

Name Use with pages 212–213

Arts and Recreation in Great Britain

Use the names of people and sports in the box to answer the map questions below. Then answer the following question. For help, you can refer to pages 212–213 in your textbook.

William Shakespeare	James Joyce	Robert Burns
Dylan Thomas	soccer	golf

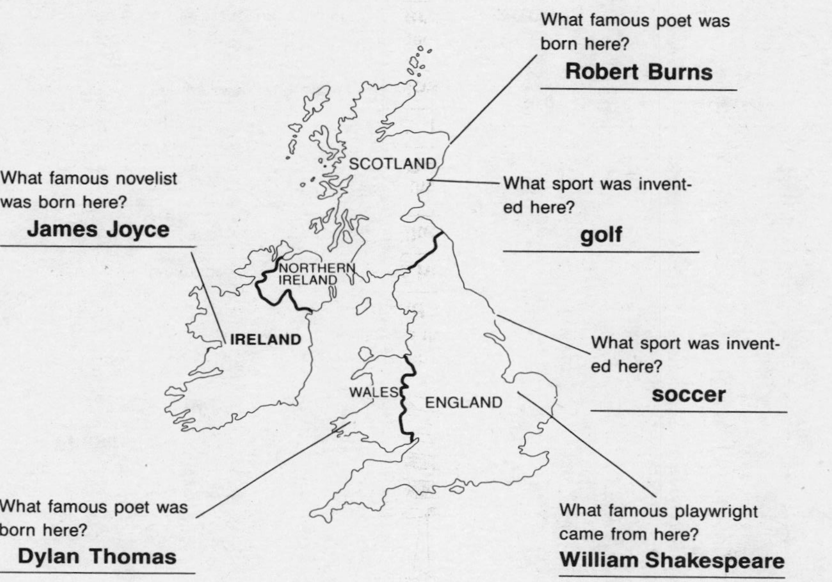

What famous poet was born here? **Robert Burns**

What famous novelist was born here? **James Joyce**

What sport was invented here? **golf**

What sport was invented here? **soccer**

What famous poet was born here? **Dylan Thomas**

What famous playwright came from here? **William Shakespeare**

What are three ways in which the great writers of Britain and Ireland have influenced the world? **They helped to invent the novel. They wrote many great plays, poems, and novels. They gave the world the English language.**

Name Use with pages 214–215

Using New Words

Choose a term from the box to answer each question. Some terms may be used more than once. For help, you can refer to the lessons in Chapter 9 in your textbook.

constitutional monarchy	welfare state
Industrial Revolution	nationalize
mixed economy	Magna Carta

1. Which term describes the government of Great Britain? **constitutional monarchy**
2. Which term would you use to refer to the period in the 1800s when factories began manufacturing most products? **Industrial Revolution**
3. Which term would you use to refer to the practice of placing industries under the control of government? **nationalize**
4. What is the name of the document that limited the powers of the British monarchy? **Magna Carta**
5. Which term describes the economy of the United Kingdom? **mixed economy**
6. Which term would you use to describe a country that takes the responsibility for the well-being of all its citizens? **welfare state**
7. Which term would you use to refer to an economy consisting of both private enterprise and government-run businesses? **mixed economy**
8. Which term would you use to describe a government that has both a monarch and a constitution? **constitutional monarchy**

Name　　　　　　　　　　　　　　　　Use with pages 217–220

France and the Low Countries

Follow the directions to do the exercises below. For help, you can refer to pages 217–220 in your textbook.

1. List three groups of people who invaded the region shown on the map between 58 B.C. and A.D. 900.
   Possible answers:
   Celts, Franks,
   Romans, Vikings
2. Shade the region of the map where you might hear an ancient Celtic language spoken today.
   Brittany
3. Put a star in the region where you might hear English-sounding names. **Bordeaux**
   How did such names come about here? **for 300 years Bordeaux was ruled by the English**
4. Put a triangle in the area where people speak Basque. **Pyrenees**
5. Belgians speak three different languages. What are they?
   French　　**Dutch (Flemish)**　　**German**
6. Why do you think so many different languages are spoken in the region of France and the Low Countries? **Student responses may vary but should demonstrate an understanding of how the invasion of this region by many different people resulted in many different languages being spoken.**

Name　　　　　　　　　　　　　　　　Use with pages 221–223

Economies of France and Low Countries

Imagine that you took a trip through France and the Low Countries. Here are some of the photographs you put in your scrapbook. Complete the captions below the pictures. For help, you can refer to pages 221–223 in your textbook.

I saw many fields like these in the **Netherlands**. Dutch **flowers** and **bulbs** are exported all over the world. At the world's largest flower market at Aalsmeer, farmers sell more than **12 million** flowers every day.

I spotted this ship in one of the Low Countries. Wide, navigable **rivers** flow from the heart of **Western Europe**, through this region, into the **North Sea**. The transportation network also consists of many **roads**, **railroads**, and **airports**.

I spent several afternoons just relaxing in this **outdoor café** in the city of **Paris**. **Service** industries such as tourism play an important part in the **economies** of France and the **Low Countries**.

This supersonic jet was assembled in **France**. Several cities in southern France also produce **satellites**, **missiles**, and sophisticated **weapons**.

Name　　　　Use with pages 224–225

Using Maps with Different Scales

Use the maps below to answer the questions that follow. For help, you can refer to pages 224–225 in your textbook.

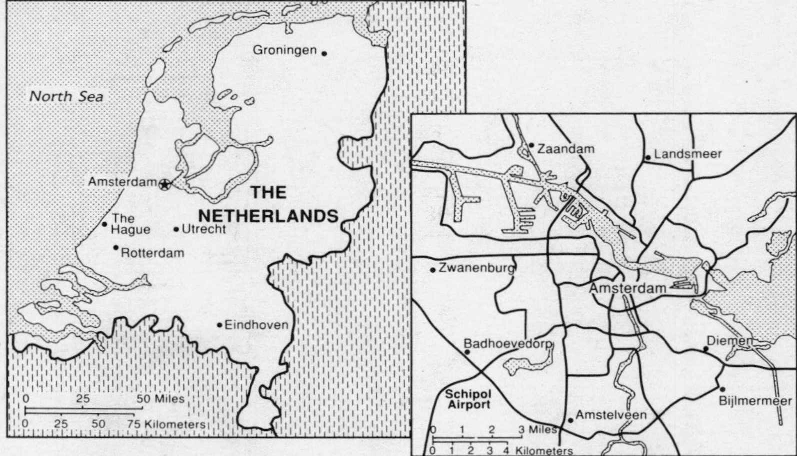

1. Which country does the small-scale map show?
   the Netherlands
2. What is the scale on the large-scale map?
   ¾ inch = 3 miles
3. Which part of the small-scale map is shown on the large-scale map?
   the area around Amsterdam
4. What is the scale on the small-scale map?
   1 inch = 50 miles
5. What does the large-scale map show that the small-scale map does not show?
   It shows more detail of the area around Amsterdam. It shows more cities and towns.
6. Suppose you were planning a vacation in a part of the Netherlands near Amsterdam. Which map would be more helpful? Why?
   The large-scale map would be more helpful because it provides more detailed information about the area.

Name　　　　Use with pages 226–227

Comparing Governments

Draw a line under the word or phrase that best completes each sentence. For help, you can refer to pages 226–227 in your textbook.

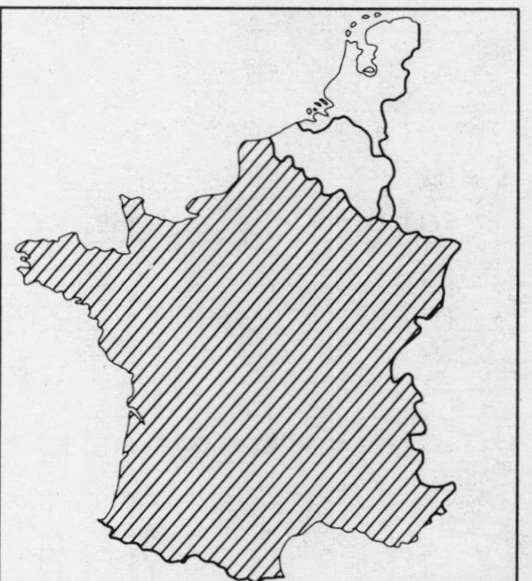

1. The current government of this country is called ______.
   a. a constitutional monarchy
   b. the Fifth Republic
   c. a dictatorship
2. This country's government is headed by a ______.
   a. monarch
   b. dictator
   c. president
3. In this country most of the important decisions are made by the ______.
   a. president
   b. National Assembly
   c. king or queen
4. The governments of these countries are all ______.
   a. constitutional monarchies
   b. republics
   c. dictatorships
5. The head of state in each of these countries is a ______.
   a. monarch
   b. dictator
   c. president
6. In these countries most of the important decisions are made by the ______.
   a. president
   b. parliament
   c. king or queen

Name Use with pages 228–229

People in the Arts and in Sports

Each picture below shows a person who has contributed to the arts or sports of France and the Low Countries. Draw a line from each picture to its correct description. Then complete each description with the correct word or words. For help, you can refer to pages 228–229 in your textbook.

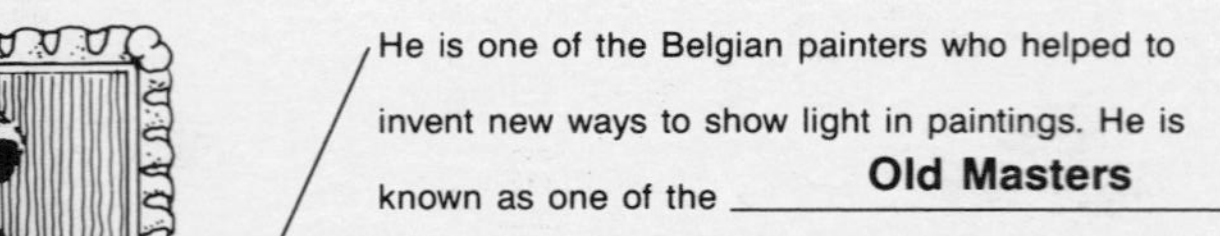

He is one of the Belgian painters who helped to invent new ways to show light in paintings. He is known as one of the **Old Masters**.

He is a Dutch painter who lived during the late 1800s. In 1988 his painting of **sunflowers** sold for almost $40 million.

He is a famous French painter of the late nineteenth century. He helped to develop a style of painting known as **impressionism**.

He has been a Belgian contender in the Tour de France. He has won this famous bicycle race **five** times.

Name Use with pages 230–231

Using New Words

Use the words in the box to complete the crossword puzzle below. For help, you can refer to the lessons in Chapter 10 in your textbook.

Tour de France	vineyard	polder
Impressionism	European Community	canal
guest worker	premier	dike

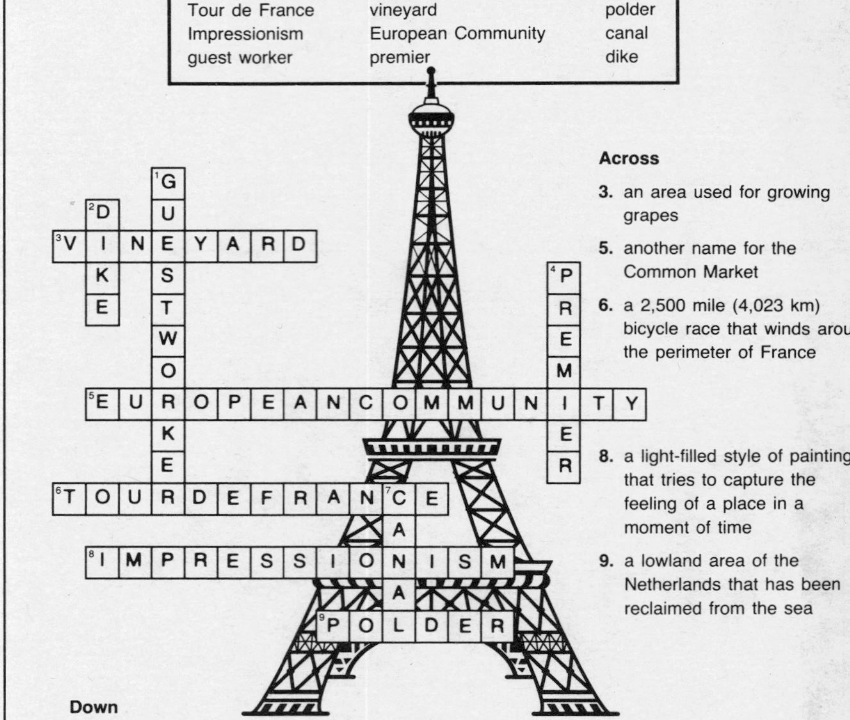

Across

3. an area used for growing grapes
5. another name for the Common Market
6. a 2,500 mile (4,023 km) bicycle race that winds around the perimeter of France
8. a light-filled style of painting that tries to capture the feeling of a place in a moment of time
9. a lowland area of the Netherlands that has been reclaimed from the sea

Down

1. an immigrant who has moved to France in search of work
2. a huge wall built to keep water away from the land
4. what the prime minister is called in France
7. a waterway that is dug for boat travel

Name

Use with pages 233–236

Taking a Look at Central Europe

Follow the directions and answer the questions below. For help, you can refer to pages 233–236 in your textbook.

GERMANY
Berlin
LIECHTENSTEIN
AUSTRIA
Vienna
SWITZERLAND
A L P S
green

1. Locate and label the following countries on the map.
   Germany
   Switzerland
   Austria

2. Locate the Alps and color them green.

3. a. Locate and label the largest city in Central Europe. **Berlin**
   b. Why was this city once a divided city? **because, until 1989, half was in West Germany and half in East Germany; the Berlin Wall separated them.**

4. How and when did reunification come about in Germany?
   Germany became reunified in 1990 after a movement for democracy swept through Europe; East Germans overthrew their government.

5. a. Locate and label the capital of Austria.

   b. Do most Austrians live in cities, such as the capital, or in rural areas?
   in cities and large towns

6. What two characteristics are common for most people of Central Europe?
   the German language; the Christian religion

Name

Use with pages 237–239

Thinking About Central Europe's Economy

Read the following statements carefully. If a statement is true, write **True** after it. If a statement is false, write **False** after it. Then, in the space provided, write the reasons for your answer. For help, you can refer to pages 237–239 in your textbook.

1. The picture above shows what most of Germany looked like at the end of World War II. The German people were never able to recover from such devastation.
   False. The East Germans under communism developed the most advanced economy in Eastern Europe and, in only 20 years, West Germany changed from a ruined land into a prosperous nation.

2. Since 1990 the Germans have found it easy to bring their two economies back together.
   False. It will cost billions of dollars and it has already cost nearly half the jobs in eastern Germany.

3. Today Germany's Ruhr Valley is Europe's biggest industrial center.
   True. Today the Ruhr Valley is crowded with coal and iron mines, oil refineries, chemical plants, and heavy industries.

4. The Swiss and Austrian peoples have low standards of living because their countries have few natural resources and little arable land.
   False. Despite few resources and little arable land, Switzerland has the highest standard of living in Europe, and Austria's economy benefits from tourism and industry.

5. Air and water pollution are a serious problem for the countries of Central Europe.
   True. Pollution is one price the region has had to pay for industrialization.

Name Use with pages 240–241

The Governments of Central Europe

Use the table to answer questions 1 to 4. Then answer the question that follows. For help, you can refer to pages 240–241 in your textbook.

CENTRAL EUROPEAN GOVERNMENTS

Part of Government	West Germany	Austria	Switzerland
two-house legislature	Bundestag	Nationalrat	Federal Assembly
head of state	president	president	president
head of government	chancellor	chancellor	Federal Council
local division of government	lander	province	canton

1. According to the table, how are the Bundestag, Nationalrat, and Federal Assembly similar?
   They are all two-house legislatures.
2. What is the head of state in each of the countries called?
   the president
3. What is the difference between the head of government in Switzerland and the head of government in Austria and Germany?
   A Federal Council, which is a group, heads the government in Switzerland. A chancellor heads the government in Germany and Austria.
4. a. How are lander, provinces, and cantons alike?
   They are all local divisions of government.

   b. In which country is pure democracy at work in its local division of government? Describe how it works.
   In Switzerland. Citizens hold regular meetings to make decisions on all local issues.
5. Why is the city of Geneva in Switzerland the headquarters of many world organizations?
   because Switzerland is officially a neutral country

Name Use with pages 242–243

Identifying a Biased Statement

Read each of the passages. Then follow the directions and answer the questions. For help, you can refer to pages 242–243 in your textbook.

Passage A

The Ruhr Valley is one of the largest industrial centers in Europe. Production from the region's factories has helped to make Germany one of the leading industrial nations of the world. But not without a price. The Ruhr is also one of the most polluted areas in Europe. Germany is taking steps to curb the pollution, but it will take time, money, and a serious commitment to solve the problem without seriously damaging Germany's economy.

Passage B

A heavy blanket of smog hangs over the entire Ruhr Valley. It is one of the most horrifying sights you can imagine. The greedy corporations responsible for the pollution care only about profits, not about the health of the nation's people. The German government must put an end to this national disgrace. Pollution generated by the region's industries must be stopped at once, no matter what the cost.

1. Recall the definition of bias. Write it here. **Bias is a one-sided, or slanted, presentation of information.**
2. Underline any loaded or emotionally charged words or phrases in either passage. Underline any words or phrases that are exaggerations.
3. Which passage presents only one side of the issue? passage A **(passage B)**
4. Which passage presents a one-sided view or impression about the pollution problem in the Ruhr Valley? passage A **(passage B)**
5. Which passage do you think is a biased statement? passage A **(passage B)**
6. State the bias. **The writer of passage B shows a bias for immediately ending the pollution problem in the Ruhr Valley without considering the impact on the nation's economy.**

Name Use with pages 244–245

Arts and Recreation in Central Europe

Use the pictures on the right to complete the exercises below. For help, you can refer to pages 244–245 in your textbook.

1. **a.** Draw a line to the picture that shows one way Central Europe celebrates its musical heritage.

   b. Who are three well-known composers from Central Europe whose music is celebrated in this way?

   Mozart

   Beethoven

   Wagner

2. **a.** Draw a line to the picture that shows one way Central Europeans enjoy the outdoors.

   b. What are three other popular outdoor sports in Central Europe?

   rock climbing

   skiing

   bicycling

3. **a.** Draw a line to the picture that shows one way Central Europeans celebrate the harvest

   b. What are some of the things people do at festivals?

   People listen to brass bands, dress in colorful costumes, and eat delicious foods.

Name Use with pages 246–247

Using New Words

Follow the directions to find each hidden term. Then write the definition of the term on the line below the letters. For help, you can refer to the lessons in Chapter 11 in your textbook.

1. Cross out the letters b, o, r, s, u
   ~~s~~ d ~~u~~ i ~~b~~ a ~~o~~ l e ~~r~~ c t **dialect**
   local variation of a language

2. Cross out the letters d, g, i, s
   ~~d~~ c ~~s~~ h ~~i~~ a n ~~i~~ c e ~~g~~ l l o r **chancellor**
   what the head of government in Germany and Austria is called

3. Cross out the letters b, i, o, s
   ~~s~~ n ~~b~~ e ~~o~~ ~~s~~ u t ~~i~~ r a ~~i~~ l **neutral**
   refusing to take sides in any dispute

4. Cross out the letters a, c, k, r, s
   ~~s~~ p o ~~a~~ l l ~~c~~ u ~~r~~ ~~a~~ t i ~~r~~ o ~~k~~ n ~~s~~ **pollution**
   dirty and impure elements in the environment

5. Cross out the letters d, g, i, m
   ~~i~~ h ~~g~~ o l ~~d~~ o c ~~d~~ a u s ~~m~~ t **Holocaust**
   the killing of more than 6 million Jewish people by Germany and its allies during World War II

6. Cross out the letters b, k, d, h, l
   r ~~l~~ e u ~~d~~ n i f ~~k~~ i c ~~h~~ a t i ~~b~~ o n **reunification**
   being united again

7. Cross out the letters d, h, k, s, u
   ~~s~~ c a ~~d~~ n ~~d~~ t ~~h~~ o n ~~k~~ ~~u~~ **canton**
   a small political unit, like a state or province

Name　　　　Use with pages 249–252

The Southern European Countries

Answer the questions and complete the activities below. For help, you can refer to pages 249–252 in your textbook.

1. On the map below locate and label the following countries.

   Italy

   Spain

   Greece

   Portugal

2. What is this region called?

   Southern Europe

3. On the map below locate and label the following cities.

   Barcelona

   Rome

   Athens

4. From which of these cities did the ancient Romans once rule?

   Rome

5. On the map below shade in the countries where most of the people belong to the Roman Catholic Church. List them below.

   Spain, Portugal, Italy

6. To which religion do most of the people in the remaining country belong?

   the Greek Orthodox Church

7. Outline each of the three countries where languages based on Latin are spoken. List them below.

   Spain

   Italy

   Portugal

8. Which Southern European country has a language that is written in a different alphabet from those of the other three?

   Greece

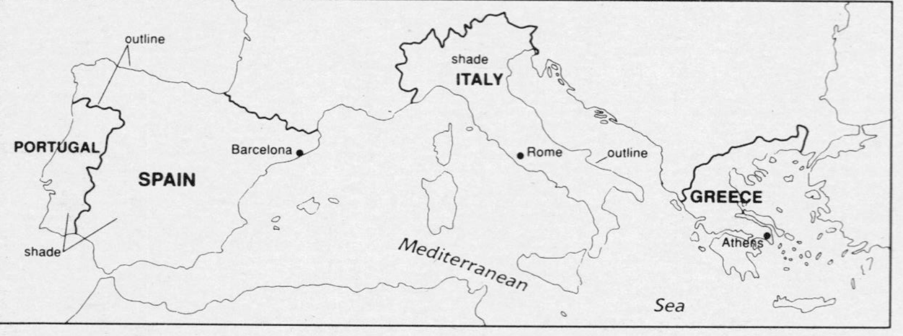

Name　　　　Use with page 253

Reading Graphs and Charts

Study the bar graph and the chart below. Then answer the questions that follow. For help, you can refer to page 253 in your textbook.

AREA OF THE FOUR MAIN COUNTRIES OF SOUTHERN EUROPE

thousands of sq. mi.

0 20 40 60 80 100 120 140 160 180 200

Portugal Greece Italy Spain

Source: World Almanac, 1989

1. a. What does the bar graph show?

   areas of the four main countries of Southern Europe

   b. What does the horizontal axis of the graph show?

   the name of each country

   c. What does the vertical axis show?

   the area of each country

   d. According to the graph, which Southern European country has the largest area?

   Spain

2. a. According to the title, what does the chart show?

   the population and area of the four main countries of Southern Europe

   b. According to the chart, which country has the smallest area?

   Portugal

   c. Does this country also have the smallest population? If not, which country does?

   No. Greece has the smallest population.

3. If you wanted to compare information at a glance, would you use a chart or a bar graph? Circle your answer.

   chart　　(bar graph)

POPULATION AND AREA OF THE FOUR MAIN COUNTRIES OF SOUTHERN EUROPE

country	population	area (sq. mi.)
Greece	10,048,000	51,146
Italy	57,439,000	116,303
Portugal	10,240,000	36,390
Spain	39,784,000	194,896

4. If you wanted to know actual figures, would you look at a chart or a bar graph? Circle your answer.

   (chart)　　bar graph

Name Use with pages 254–256

Writing About Southern Europe's Economy

The travel brochure below tells about some of the things you might see and do in Southern Europe. Complete the brochure by filling in the blanks. For help, you can refer to pages 254–256 in your textbook.

Explore the Wonders of Southern Europe

Bask in the sun along the beautiful **Mediterranean** shore. Take a side trip to the village of Marbella on the **Spanish** coast. While in Athens, wander through the ancient remains of the **Parthenon**. Explore the ancient Forum on your visit to **Rome**. Everywhere you go you will see the splendid architecture of **churches**, **cathedrals**, **palaces**, and **towers.**.

As you travel through the countryside, you you will pass by the small farms that grow some of the sweetest **oranges** and **tangerines** in the world. Other crops produced in the region include **wheat**, **barley**, **nuts**, and **cotton**.

In **Turin** you can take a tour of the **Fiat** assembly lines. Every year more than one **million** cars are assembled here. Some of the finest leather goods in the world are made in factories in **Italy**, **Portugal**, and **Spain**.

If you arrived in Southern Europe by ship, the ship you were on may have been built by one of the shipping **families** that make the Greek island of **Oinoussai** their home. Greek shipowners control the largest **merchant** **fleet** in the world.

Name Use with pages 257–260

Thinking About Today's Governments

Answer the questions below. For help, you can refer to pages 257–260 in your textbook.

Greece

1. a. What kind of government does this country have?
   parliamentary democracy
   b. How many houses does parliament have? Circle the answer.
   (one) two
   c. What is the head of government called?
   the prime minister

Italy

2. a. What kind of government does this country have?
   parliamentary democracy
   b. How many houses does parliament have? Circle the answer.
   one (two)
   c. Who runs the government from day to day?
   the prime minister

Portugal

3. a. What kind of government does this country have?
   parliamentary democracy
   b. How many houses does parliament have? Circle the answer.
   (one) two
   c. Who shares executive power?
   president, prime minister

Spain

4. a. What kind of government does this country have?
   parliamentary democracy
   b. How many houses does parliament have? Circle the answer.
   one (two)
   c. Who is head of state?
   a monarch

The Heritage of Southern Europe

Use the maps on the right to complete the activities below. For help, you can refer to pages 261–263 in your textbook.

1. a. Draw a line to the map of the country where the world's oldest dramas were written.
   b. What are the names of three poets who wrote these plays?
   Aeschylus
   Euripides
   Sophocles

2. a. Draw a line to the map of the country where the Renaissance began.
   b. What was the goal of the artists of this period?
   to create an image of the ideal human being
   c. Which Renaissance artist painted the inside of the Sistine Chapel?
   Michelangelo

3. a. Draw a line to the map of the country in which famous pilgrimages have been made for almost 2,000 years.
   b. What does this pilgrimage celebrate?
   the feast day of Santiago, the patron saint of Spain

Learning New Words

Look at the box containing the Morse Code. The Morse Code uses dots and dashes to stand for the letters of the alphabet. Use the code to figure out the words that follow. For help, you can refer to the lessons in Chapter 12 in your textbook.

A	B	C	D	E	F	G	H	I
•—	—•••	—•—•	—••	•	••—•	——•	••••	••
J	K	L	M	N	O	P	Q	R
•———	—•—	•—••	——	—•	———	•——•	——•—	•—•
S	T	U	V	W	X	Y	Z	
•••	—	••—	•••—	•——	—••—	—•——	——••	

d 1. **S I E S T A**
••• •• • ••• — •—

a 2. **R E N A I S S A N C E**
•—• • —• •— •• ••• ••• •— —• —•—• •

f 3. **T E R R O R I S M**
— • •—• •—• ——— •—• •• ••• ——

c 4. **A U T O N O M Y**
•— ••— — ——— —• ——— —— —•——

b 5. **C O A L I T I O N**
—•—• ——— •— •—•• •• — •• ——— —•

e 6. **P I L G R I M A G E**
•——• •• •—•• ——• •—• •• —— •— ——• •

Match the definitions below with the words above. Write the letter of each definition on the line before the appropriate word.

a. a period of great activity in the arts beginning in the 1300s and 1400s

b. a temporary union between different political parties that agree to work together for a common purpose

c. the right of self-government

d. a period of rest taken during the middle of the afternoon

e. a journey that people make to a sacred place

f. the use of violence and the threat of violence to frighten people

Name Use with pages 271–273

The People of Scandinavia

Look at the picture and bar graph, then answer the questions. For help, you can refer to pages 271–273 in your textbook.

1. The picture shows a Viking warrior. Who were the Vikings?
The Vikings were seafarers who lived in Scandinavia hundreds of years ago.

2. How do the people of Scandinavia today differ from their Viking ancestors?
The Vikings were warlike seafarers. Today, the Scandinavians work at developing their own land and resources.

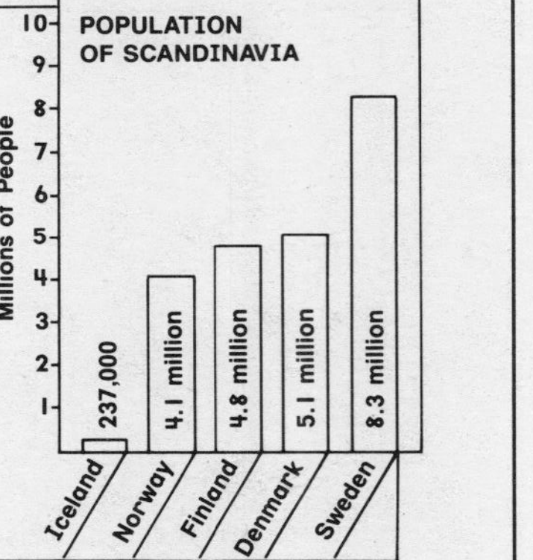

3. According to the graph, which Scandinavian country has the smallest population?
Iceland

4. Which has the largest population?
Sweden

5. How is the size of Scandinavia's population an advantage?
Scandinavia's small population helps the Scandinavians get things done efficiently.

6. What ties the Scandinavian people together? **Most Scandinavians are tied together by languages and close-knit families.**

Name Use with pages 274–276

The Resources and Economy of Scandinavia

Use the map to complete the first five activities. Then answer the questions that follow. For help, you can refer to pages 274–276 in your textbook.

1. Draw a fish on the two countries where the fishing industry has played an important role in the economy.
Norway, Iceland

2. Draw an oil barrel on the country that has Western Europe's largest fields of offshore oil and natural gas.
Norway

3. Draw a tree on the two countries that have for hundreds of years based their economies on their huge forests.
Finland, Sweden

4. Draw a factory on the country that is the most industrialized nation in Scandinavia.
Sweden

5. Draw a chair on the country that is renowned for its furniture, glassware, and toys.
Denmark

6. How does the economy of Scandinavia today differ from the economy of the past?
In the past most Scandinavians earned their living either by fishing, farming, or lumbering. Today most workers are in services, mining, or factory work.

7. Why have the economies of the Scandinavian countries prospered?
The Scandinavian economies have prospered because of cooperation between government and business, farming cooperatives, and cooperation among the different Scandinavian countries.

Name Use with pages 277–279

Taking a Look at Scandinavian Governments

Answer the questions below. For help, you can refer to pages 277–279 in your textbook.

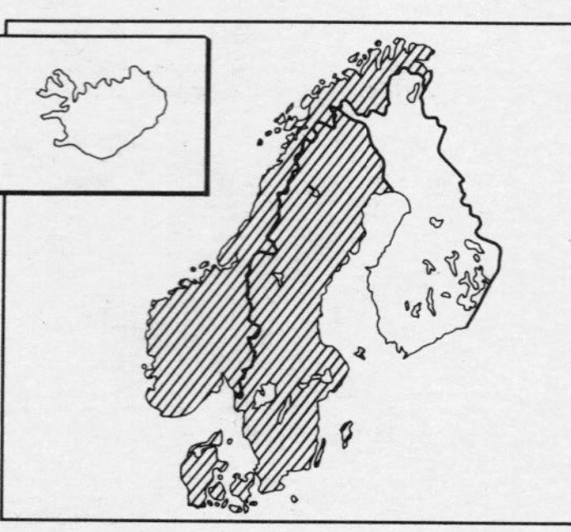

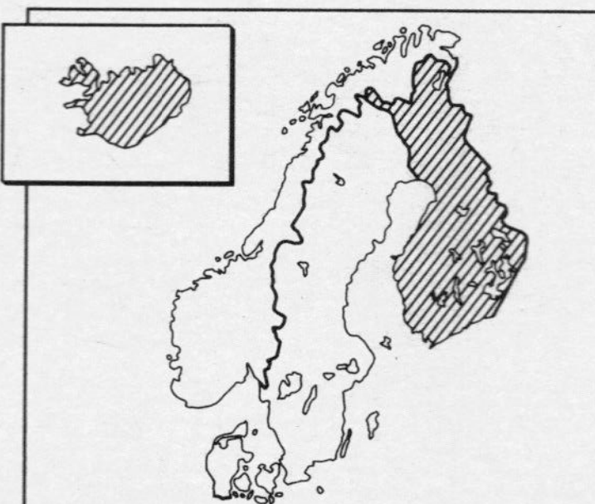

1. What form of government do these countries have?
   constitutional monarchies
2. How many houses make up the legislature in each of these countries?
   one
3. Who elects the head of the executive branch of government?
   the parliament
4. What is the head of government called?
   the prime minister
5. What form of government do these countries have?
   republics
6. How do the governments of these countries differ from those of Sweden, Norway, and Denmark?
   They each have a president, but neither has a monarch.
7. How are the governments of these countries like those of Sweden, Norway, and Denmark?
   They each have a parliament and a prime minister.
8. Why are the taxes in the Scandinavian countries so high? **Because the governments provide necessary services for their citizens through far-reaching welfare programs.**

Name Use with pages 280–281

Recognizing Point of View

Read the passages below. Then read the questions that follow and underline the answer to each question. For help, you can refer to pages 280–281 in your textbook.

The Swedish welfare state has come close to creating the ideal society. For example, just about everyone enjoys free medical service. The government loans newly married couples money for home furnishings. Every employed person is guaranteed a four-week vacation with pay. Swedes who lose their jobs receive generous unemployment benefits. After retirement most Swedes receive substantial retirement pensions. Sweden's welfare system takes the worry out of living.

1. Which of the following statements is a fact?
   a. The Swedish welfare system has come close to creating an ideal society.
   b. Just about everyone receives free medical service.
   c. Sweden's welfare system takes the worry out of living.
2. What information does the writer leave out?
   a. The Swedes pay the highest taxes in the world.
   b. After retirement, most Swedes receive substantial retirement pensions.
   c. Most Swedes receive free medical services.
3. What is the writer's point of view?
   The Swedish welfare system is good for its citizens.

The Swedish welfare state looks good on paper, but the price is too high. Sweden's tax rates are the highest in the world. Some people have to pay more than 75 percent of their earnings to the government. Many people believe that individuals should have the right to spend their money and plan for the future in the way they see fit. In my opinion the welfare state takes too much power from the people and places it in the hands of the government.

4. Which of the following statements is a fact?
   a. The Swedish welfare state looks good on paper, but the price is too high.
   b. Sweden's tax rates are the highest in the world.
   c. People have the right to spend their money and plan for the future in the way they see fit.
5. What information does the writer leave out?
   a. The Swedish government ensures the well-being of its citizens.
   b. Sweden's taxes are the highest in the world.
   c. Sweden's welfare state is very expensive.
6. What is the writer's point of view?
   The welfare state takes too much power from the people.

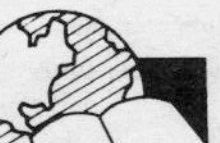

Name

Use with pages 282–283

Arts and Recreation in Scandinavia

Complete the activities below. For help, you can refer to pages 282–283 in your textbook. The excerpt below is from the Poem entitled "Voluspa" on page 1, *Poems of the Elder Edda,* translated by Patricia Terry. Copyright © 1990 by the University of Pennsylvania Press. Reprinted by permission of Patricia Terry and the publisher.

Then all the gods
 Met to give judgment,
The holy gods
 Took counsel together;
They named night
 and the waning moon,
They gave names
 To morning and midday,
Afternoon and evening,
 Ordered time by years.

1. The verse above is from an ancient **Edda.** What were Eddas and what did they tell about? **Eddas were long poems created by the Vikings. They told stories about early Scandinavian gods.**

2. What are the ancient **sagas** of Iceland and what do they tell about? **The sagas of Iceland are a long group of stories that tell about the history of that country.**

3. List three modern Scandinavian writers who have carried on this long tradition of storytelling. Tell what each wrote about.

WRITER	WROTE ABOUT
Henrik Ibsen	**wrote plays about the problems of contemporary men and women**
Selma Lagerlöf	**updated the folktales she heard as a child**
Sigrid Undset	**explored the history of her country and examined contemporary life**

Name

Use with pages 284–285

Thinking About New Words

Answer each question in the space provided. For help, you can refer to the lessons in Chapter 13 in your textbook.

1. What is a **diversified economy?** **A diversified economy is one that produces a wide range of goods.**

   Why do most Scandinavian countries now have diversified economies? **Skill, hard work in developing new resources, and modern factories have enabled most Scandinavian countries to now have diversified economies.**

2. Almost 200 years ago, Sweden created a special officer called an **ombudsman**. What does an ombudsman do? **An ombudsman receives complaints by citizens who are not satisfied with a government service or action. He or she informs government representatives about the problem and tries to persuade them to make changes.**

3. What is the difference between a Viking **Edda** and an Icelandic **saga**? What does each tell about? **A Viking Edda is a long poem that tells about the early Scandinavian gods. An Icelandic saga is a long story that tells about the history of that country.**

4. If you lived in Scandinavia, you might do business through a **cooperative**. What is a cooperative? **A cooperative is a business organization owned by its members.**

   How does a retail cooperative help consumers? **Retail cooperatives are owned by consumers. The consumers save money because items in the stores are sold at the cost the store paid to purchase them.**

Name Use with pages 293–297

Using Maps

Use the map on this page to complete the exercises below. For help, you can refer to pages 293–297 in your textbook.

1. Locate and label the Ural Mountains. These mountains mark the boundary between which two continents?
   Europe and Asia
2. Locate and label these rivers. Then trace the rivers in blue.
   Volga River Danube River
3. Locate and label the West Siberian Plain. What feature of its environment would make the West Siberian Plain an unpleasant place to live?
   the fact that it is frozen for most of the year
4. Locate and label Central Asia. Color the area brown. Why is Central Asia so dry?
   because the mountains to its south block the rain-bearing clouds that would bring rain

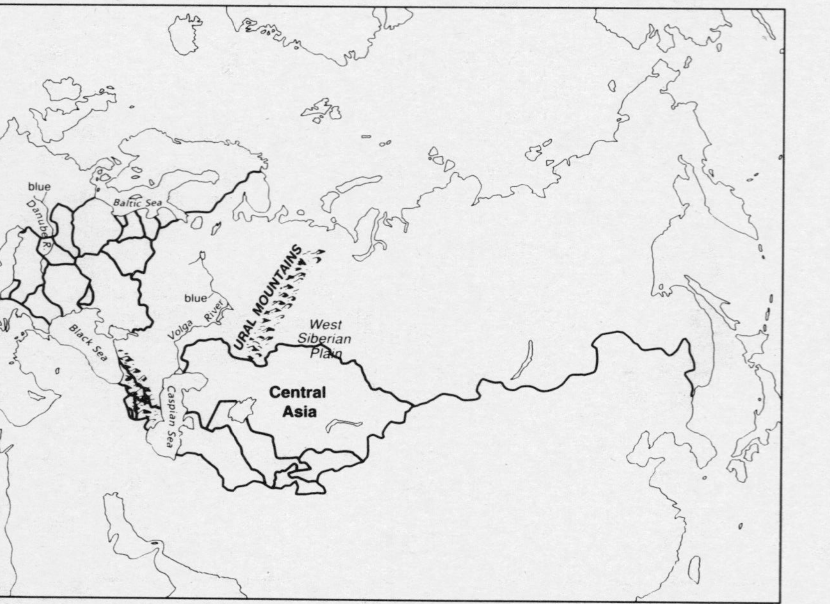

Name Use with pages 298–300

Identifying Climates and Natural Resources

Study the pictures at the right. On the line beneath each picture write the letter of the place or places from the column at the left where you might find this scene. You may use a letter more than once or not at all. For help, you can refer to pages 298–300 in your textbook.

a. Romania
b. Siberia
c. steppes
d. Poland
e. taiga
f. Ukraine
g. Russia

evergreen forest: a, b, d, e, g

snowy landscape: a, b, d, f, g

wheat fields: c, f, g

oil fields: b, a, g

Describe the two climate zones in Eastern Europe and Northern Asia.

Eastern Europe and the western part of Northern Asia have temperate climates with warm to hot summers and mild to cold winters. In Siberia and northern Eastern Europe the climate consists of short, cool summers and long, cold winters.

Name ______ Use with page 301

Reading Climographs

Study the climograph below. Then answer the questions. For help, you can refer to page 301 in your textbook.

AVERAGE PRECIPITATION AND TEMPERATURES IN ST. PETERSBURG

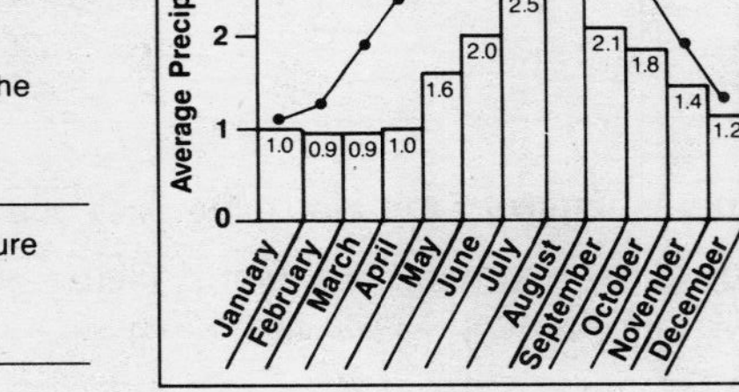

1. a. What does the bar graph of the climograph show?
   average monthly precipitation in St. Petersburg

   b. What does the line graph show?
   average monthly temperature of St. Petersburg

2. a. During which month is there the most precipitation?
   August

   b. What is the average temperature during this month?
   60°

3. a. During which two months is there the least precipitation?
   February and March

   b. Which of the two months is generally cooler?
   February

4. a. Suppose you were to visit St. Petersburg in July. How would you describe the weather?
   warm and rainy

   b. During which month do you think St. Petersburg has the most favorable weather? Why?
   Answers should include information about the temperature and precipitation in the month selected.

Name ______ Use with pages 302–303

Thinking About New Words

Put an **X** next to each statement that gives correct information about the word in boldface type. Then complete the activity that follows. For help, you can refer to the lessons in Chapter 14 in your textbook.

1. **steppes**

X a. Steppes are dry, treeless, grassy plains south of the taiga.
____ b. Steppes are vast regions of evergreen forests south of the tundra.
X c. Steppes cover much of Russia, Ukraine, and parts of Eastern Europe.
X d. The steppes of Europe contain some of the world's finest soil.
____ e. The steppes stretch all the way from Finland to the Pacific Ocean.
X f. Today the steppes of Northern Asia are a major grain-growing area.

2. **taiga**

____ a. The Eastern European countries are covered mostly by taiga.
X b. The taiga is a vast region of evergreen forests located south of the tundra.
____ c. The taiga is a dry, treeless, grassy plain located south of the steppes.
____ d. The taiga is one of the richest farming areas in the world.
X e. The taiga stretches all the way from Finland to the Pacific Ocean.
X f. Russia's vast regions of evergreen forests are located in the taiga.

Use the words *taiga* and *steppes* in a single sentence.

Example sentence: The taiga is a heavily forested region while the steppes are dry, treeless, grassy plains.

Name ____ Use with pages 305–309

Taking a Look at Ethnic Groups

Read the following statements carefully. If a statement is true, write **True** after it. If a statement is false, write **False** after it. Then, in the space provided, write the reasons for your answer. For help, you can refer to pages 305–309 in your textbook.

1. Russia is part of a large country called the Soviet Union.
   False. In late 1991 the Soviet Union ceased to exist. Russia and the other republics of the Soviet Union are now independent countries.

2. The largest ethnic groups in the region are the Uzbeks and Kazakhs.
   False. The Russians, Ukrainians, and Byelarusians make up nearly three fourths of the population in the region.

3. The people of Russia and its neighboring countires are now free to worship as they please.
   True. Since the end of the Soviet Union, the governments in this region no longer discourage religion. There are Christians, Muslims, and Jews in the region.

4. In Russia women make up an important part of the work force.
   True. About 85 percent of women of working age have jobs outside the home.

5. Even though there is no longer a Soviet Union in the region, education has changed little.
   False. The schools are still there, but each government will run the schools as they choose. There is no longer a Soviet government requiring children to learn to believe in communism.

Name ____ Use with pages 314–317

Economies of Russia and Its Neighbors

The headlines below might have been written about the economies of Russia and its neighbors. Answer the questions about each headline. For help, you can refer to pages 314–317 in your textbook.

Command Economy Slows Down

a. What is a command economy? **an economy in which the government makes most of the decisions**

b. What problems did people in the Soviet Union face under their command economy?
There were not enough consumer goods produced; workers were not motivated to do well in their work since they would be paid anyway; quality was often poor.

Gorbachev Seeks Change

a. What did Gorbachev call his plan of reforms? **perestroika**

b. How was Boris Yeltsin's plan different? **Yeltsin's plan would have brought changes much more quickly; he wanted to shock the economy into the free-enterprise system**

Commonwealth of Independent States Faces Many Challenges

a. In about what year would this headline have been written? **1991**

b. Why was the Commonwealth of Independent States set up?
to help Russia and its neighbors link their economies in ways that would be helpful to make the transition from communism

c. What were three economic challenges faced by the C.I.S.?
Who would own the factories? How would electricity be shared? What would become of pensions owed people from jobs done in the former Soviet Union?

Name _______ Use with pages 320–323

Using a Map

Use the map to complete the activities below. For help, you can refer to pages 320–323 in your textbook.

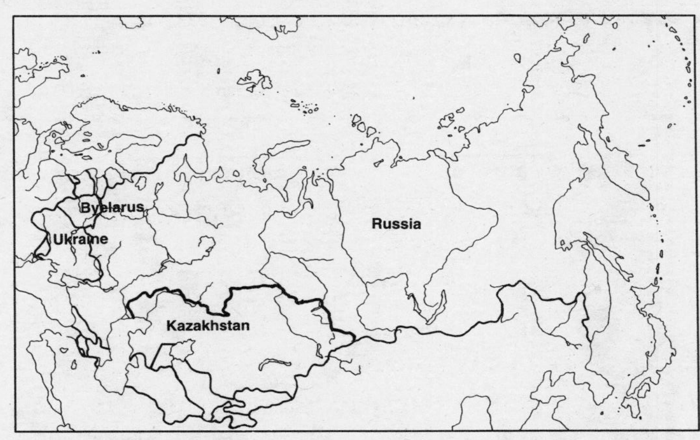

1. Which country took the Soviet Union's seat in the Security Council of the United Nations? **Russia**
   Label the country and color it green.
2. In which country are C.I.S. headquarters located? **Byelarus**
   Label it and color it brown.
3. The C.I.S. was started by Russia, Byelarus, and **Ukraine**.
   Label the third country and color it purple.
4. Which was the first non-Slavic country to join the C.I.S.? **Kazakhstan**
   Label it and color it yellow.
5. Label at least three other countries on the map.
6. What ideas of Lenin's were practiced in the Soviet Union until 1989?
   The government ran most economic affairs. The Communist Party controlled the government.

Name _______ Use with pages 324–325

Drawing Conclusions

Put an **X** next to each conclusion you can draw from information in each of the boxes. For help, you can refer to pages 324–325 in your textbook.

- Whatever the size of the Russian family, both the men and the women usually work.
- About 85 percent of all Russian women of working age have jobs outside the home.
- Russian women hold many different kinds of jobs, from street cleaner to judge.
- About 75 percent of all Russian physicians are women.

____ **a.** As many women as men work in Russia.

____ **b.** Women have all the important jobs in Russia.

X **c.** In Russia most women of working age have jobs.

X **d.** Women are an important part of the Russian work force.

- Before the Soviet Union became 15 independent countries, the government controlled almost all economic and government decisions.
- Today 15 independent countries are each working to create mixed or free-enterprise economies.
- The C.I.S., set up in 1991, is a loose organization of most of the countries that used to be bound together by the Soviet Union.
- Leaders in each of the 15 countries were elected by their people.

X **a.** Enormous changes have come to the economies and governments of Russia and its neighbors.

____ **b.** The people of the former Soviet Union are glad they now have their own countries.

____ **c.** The 15 countries of the former Soviet Union are working together to solve their problems.

____ **d.** Russia, through the C.I.S., still dominates its neighbors.

Name ______ Use with pages 326–327

Arts and Recreation in Russia

Label each picture with a phrase from the box. Then answer the questions that follow. For help, you can refer to pages 326–327 in your textbook.

the father of Russian literature	won Nobel Prize for Literature in the 1950s
great Russian novelist of the 1800s	composed *The Nutcracker*

composed *The Nutcracker*

great Russian novelist of the 1800s

won Nobel Prize for Literature in 1950s

the father of Russian literature

1. In the past, what effect did the Soviet government have on the arts? **Student responses may vary but should demonstrate an understanding of how strict government control of the arts was.**

2. How did Mikhail Gorbachev's policy of glasnost affect the arts in the Soviet Union in the late 1980s? **Student responses may vary but should indicate that glasnost brought about less government control of the arts.**

Name ______ Use with pages 328–329

Thinking About New Words

Write the letter of the term that matches each definition below. For help, you can refer to the lessons in Chapter 15 in your textbook.

a. Soviet	**d.** command economy	**g.** censor
b. consumer goods	**e.** perestroika	**h.** glasnost
c. capital goods	**f.** reform	
	i. Commonwealth of Independent States	

e 1. the name of Mikhail Gorbachev's plan for economic reform in the Soviet Union

a 2. the name for people who lived in the former Soviet Union

g 3. to prevent something from being published

c 4. products that are used by other industries rather than by individuals

h 5. the name of Mikhail Gorbachev's policy of openness

d 6. a system in which the government makes most economic decisions

b 7. products, such as stoves, refrigerators, and clothes, that are used by individuals

i 8. an organization formed to promote cooperation among the countries that were once part of the Soviet Union

f 9. to make a change for the better

Name Use with pages 331–334

The People of Eastern Europe

Use the graphs to answer the questions. For help, you can refer to pages 331–334 in your textbook.

1. According to the top graph, which is the largest ethnic group in Czechoslovakia?

Czechs

2. Name two other Eastern European countries that have large Slavic groups.

Poland, Yugoslavia

3. According to the bottom graph, which religion has the most followers in Czechoslovakia?

Roman Catholicism

4. In which Eastern European country are almost all people Roman Catholic?

Poland

5. Why are there so few Jews in Eastern Europe?

because so many were killed during the Holocaust

6. Until the late 1980s how did the governments in Eastern European countries treat religion?

They tried to discourage it.

ETHNIC GROUPS IN CZECHOSLOVAKIA

Group	Percent
Czechs	71%
Slovaks	29%

RELIGIONS IN CZECHOSLOVAKIA

Religion	Percent
Roman Catholic	50%
Other	28%
Protestant	20%
Orthodox	2%

Source: 1992 Please Almanac

Name Use with pages 335–338

The Resources of Eastern Europe

Use the map to complete the activities. Then answer the questions that follow. For help, you can refer to pages 335–338 in your textbook.

1. Draw a piece of coal in the country where high-quality coal is mined.
Students should identify Poland.

2. Draw a spice jar in the country where paprika is a specialty.
Students should identify Hungary.

3. Draw a rose where rose petals are a specialty.
What are the rose petals used for?
Students should identify Bulgaria; to make perfume

4. Draw a symbol for money in three countries where real progress is being made toward changing to a free market system.
Students should identify Poland, Hungary, and Czechoslovakia

5. How was agriculture organized while Eastern European countries were satellites of the Soviet Union?
in collectives, where the government owned all the farms and people worked in groups together to farm a certain area

6. In one sentence, state the main idea of the Lesson 2.
Enormous changes have come to the economies of the countries in Eastern Europe.

Name Use with pages 339–342

Interviewing a Czech Leader

Suppose you had a chance to interview Vaclav Havel, first president of Czechoslovakia. You might ask him questions similar to those below. Use the space provided to write the answers you think Mr. Havel might give. For help, you can refer to pages 339–342 in your textbook.

Interviewer: What were some of the important events in your life before you were elected president?

Mr. Havel: **I wrote plays, was sent to jail for opposing government, and rallied people in opposition to Soviet control**

Interviewer: What was the main change that resulted from the fall of the communist government in your country?

Mr. Havel: **The people now have freedom to make decisions about their lives.**

Interviewer: Have democracy and freedom come to all the countries in Eastern Europe?

Mr. Havel: **not equally; for example, Czechoslovakia, Poland, and Hungary allow more freedom than do Romania and Bulgaria.**

Interviewer: What was the Warsaw Pact? What happened when it ended?

Mr. Havel: **The Warsaw Pact was a military alliance among the Soviet Union and its satellites; when it ended the Soviets began pulling their troops out of the countries in Eastern Europe.**

Interviewer: Was the change to freedom and democracy in neighboring countries always peaceful?

Mr. Havel: **No, in Romania several hundred people were killed and the former leader was executed.**

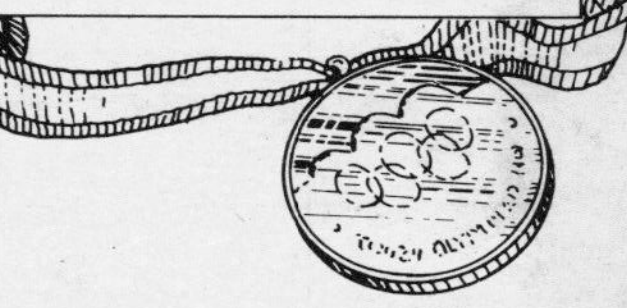

Name Use with pages 343–344

The Arts and Recreation of Eastern Europe

Answer the questions below. For help, you can refer to pages 343–344 in your textbook.

1. Look at the picture. From which Eastern European country did this composer come?
   Poland

2. What did this composer use as themes for much of his music?
   Eastern European folk music

3. Which other Eastern European composer was inspired by the music of his homeland?
   Anton Dvořák, Béla Bartók

The chart gives information about the Summer Olympics in 1988, the last Olympics before the many political changes that came to Eastern Europe in the late 1980s. Use the chart to answer these questions.

SUMMER OLYMPICS 1988
TOP TEN MEDAL HOLDERS

Country	Total Medals
USSR	132
East Germany	102
United States	94
West Germany	40
Bulgaria	35
South Korea	33
China	28
Romania	24
Great Britain	24
Hungary	23

4. Which four Eastern European countries were among the top ten medal holders for the 1988 Summer Olympics?
   East Germany, Bulgaria, Romania, Hungary

5. What was the main reason for the success of the athletes of these countries?
   There was a national emphasis on sports.

6. How might political changes since 1988 change the outcome of later Olympics?
   The countries hope to continue to excel in sports, but with so many economic changes, it might be difficult to support sports in the same way.

Name ______ Use with page 345

Reading a Newspaper Article

In June 1991 Soviet troops withdrew from Hungary. The paragraphs below might have appeared in a newspaper article describing the event. Label the headline and dateline. Then answer the questions. For help, you can refer to page 345 in your textbook.

headline

dateline

SOVIET TROOPS LEAVE HUNGARY

Budapest, June 30—The last Soviet troops pulled out of Hungary this month, ending almost 47 years of occupation. The pullout followed months of dizzying changes in Hungary, where the first multi-party elections were held last October.

Reaction to the Soviet pullout was positive. One university student remarked, "Finally we are free to run our own lives, without interference from outside forces."

Soviet troops had been stationed in Hungary since 1956, when they were called in to crush an anti-Soviet uprising in the country.

1. The article might have appeared on page one of a newspaper. What kind of article is it?
   news article
2. What is the article about?
   the pullout of Soviet troops from Hungary after a 47-year occupation
3. Where did the event take place?
   Budapest
4. When did the event take place?
   the month ending June 30
5. In which kind of article might you read an editor's opinion about the pullout of Soviet troops?
   an editorial

Name ______ Use with pages 346–347

Thinking About New Words

Use the code to figure out the words and write each word under its code in the left column. Then write the number of each word next to its meaning in the right column. For help, you can refer to the lessons in Chapter 16 in your textbook.

CODE

z = a	w = g	t = m	q = s	n = y
13 = b	10 = h	7 = n	4 = t	1 = z
y = c	v = i	s = o	p = u	
12 = d	9 = j	6 = p	3 = v	
x = e	u = k	r = q	o = w	
11 = f	8 = l	5 = r	2 = x	

1. 7 z 4 v s 7 z 8 v q t — **nationalism**
2. q z 4 x 8 8 v 4 x — **satellite**
3. y n 5 v 8 8 v y — **Cyrillic**
4. r p s 4 z — **quota**
5. o z 5 q z o 6 z y 4 — **Warsaw Pact**
6. 13 p 11 11 x 5 1 s 7 x — **buffer zone**

3 a. the alphabet used by the Russian language

6 b. a region between two hostile powers

4 c. a limit on the type and amount of a product that can be sold or produced

1 d. a strong love of one's country or ethnic group

2 e. a country that "revolved" around the Soviet Union

5 f. a military alliance of the Soviet Union and its satellites that ended in 1991

Name

Use with pages 355–359

The Middle East and North Africa

Use the map on this page to complete the activities below. For help, you can refer to pages 355–359 in your textbook.

1. a. Locate and label the following peninsulas.

   Sinai Peninsula Anatolia
   Arabian Peninsula

   b. Which peninsula connects the continents of Africa and Asia?

   Sinai Peninsula

2. a. Locate and label the Sahara Desert. Then color it brown.

   b. What group has developed the special skills needed to survive in the desert?

   The Bedouins (desert dwellers)

3. Locate and label the following bodies of water.

   Mediterranean Sea Red Sea
   Persian Gulf

4. a. Locate and label the following rivers. Then trace the rivers in blue.

   Nile River Tigris River
   Euphrates River

   b. Why are the areas along these rivers densely populated?

   because they provide fertile soil and water for irrigation

5. a. Locate and label the following cities.

   Riyadh Jerusalem

   b. Which of these cities grew up around a desert oasis?

   Riyadh

Name

Use with pages 360–361

Reading Contour Maps

Use the contour map of Cyprus below to answer the questions. For help, you can refer to pages 360–361 in your textbook.

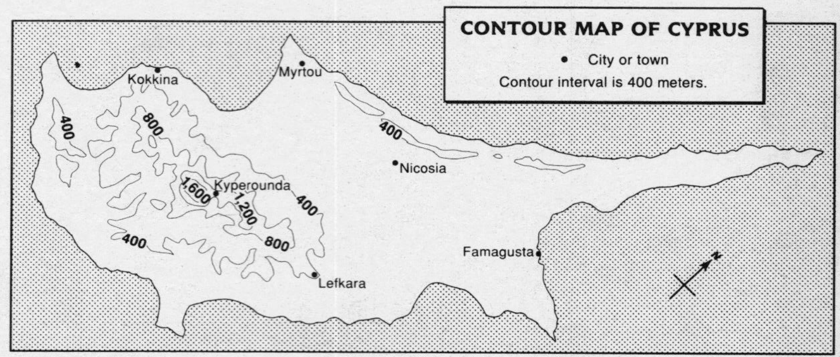

1. What is the elevation of Lefkara?

   about 400 meters above sea level

   How do you know?

   Lefkara is within the 400-meter contour line

2. Is the land around Kyperounda steep or level?

   steep

   How do you know?

   the contour lines are close together

3. List the cities on the map whose elevation is between sea level and 400 meters.

   Kokkina, Myrtou, Nicosia, Famagusta

4. Which part of Cyprus is more level, the western part or the eastern part?

   the eastern part

   How do you know?

   by the pattern and spacing of the contour lines

Name Use with pages 362–365

Looking at Natural Resources

The bar graph below shows the major oil-producing countries in the Middle East and North Africa. Use the graph to answer the first three questions on this page. Then answer the following questions. For help, you can refer to pages 362–365 in your textbook.

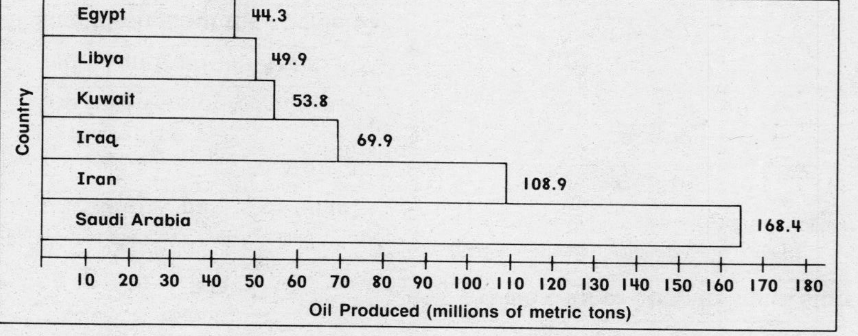

1. According to the graph, which country produces the most oil in the Middle East?
   Saudi Arabia

2. What are three other Middle Eastern countries shown on the graph? List them according to the amount of oil they produce.
   Iran **Iraq** **Kuwait**

3. What two North African countries are shown on the graph?
   Libya **Egypt**

4. Where does most of the Middle East's oil lie? **Most of the Middle East's oil lie beneath the lands bordering on the Persian Gulf.**

5. About which percent of the petroleum used in the world today comes from the Middle East?
   about one third

6. Which natural resource would many people in the Middle East and North Africa consider more valuable than oil? Why? **Water.** **In this arid region water is so scarce that farmers rely upon rivers for irrigation. Little of the land can be farmed.**

Name Use with pages 366–367

Thinking About New Words

Each of the words listed in the box below is hidden among the letters that follow. Draw a circle around each word you find. The words may be read forward, backward, up, down, or diagonally. For help, you can refer to the lessons in Chapter 17 in your textbook.

irrigation	aquifer	petroleum	arid
desert	oasis	qanat	

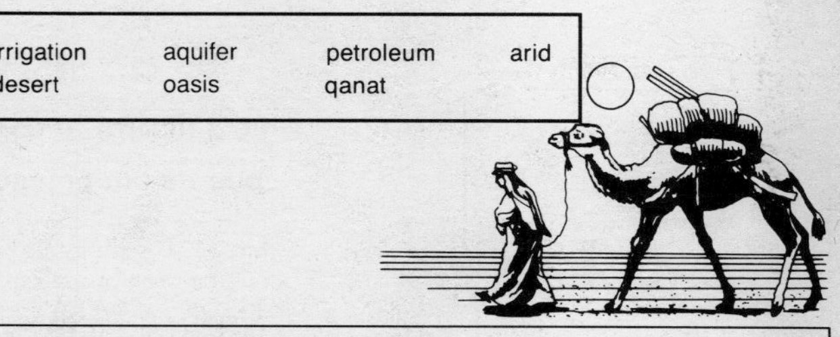

L U T S S Q P R E F U G E E T P H M L K I O C A
T B N O I T A G I R R I D I O Z C Y D C F J P W
D K T A S B A Z R M R E F I U Q A M T Q E T Q R
F D C Q A Y Z E A T R N P R O B T Y R A R S D E
C A R A O N O U E L B S C K D Z T R E K N J L K
I T O P Q J R S K C L P E I C K N B E E K A M O
C E I W C K E A H P E T R O L E U M H S E L Q Y
E T A D R D M S D P N A N M T E V X O E E J A D
U A O Q S O E Z L T W U E C A Z B K M E Q D E N
T Z A K S E D U D Z H N Y F E U R D I W S L A O

Write each circled word in the space next to its definition.

petroleum 1. oil

aquifer 2. an underground layer of rock that holds or carries water

oasis 3. a green, fertile, well-watered spot in a desert

qanat 4. massive underground tunnels built in Iran to carry water

arid 5. very dry

desert 6. a dry, sandy region with very little plant life

irrigation 7. the watering of dry land by means of streams, canals, or pipes

Name Use with pages 369–372

The People of the Middle East

Review the picture on this page. Then answer the questions below. For help, you can refer to pages 369–372 in your textbook.

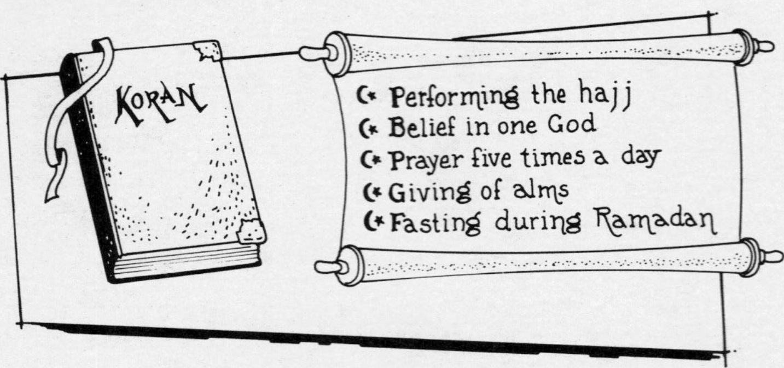

1. The religious book and the list of beliefs show above form the basis of the major religion in the Middle East. What is the name of that religion?
   Islam
2. What is the list of beliefs called?
   the five pillars of Islam
3. How was this religion spread throughout the Middle East?
   The followers of Muhammad carried Islam from the Arabian Peninsula throughout the Middle East.
4. What are two Middle Eastern countries where most of the people are Muslims, but are not Arab?
   Turkey
   Iran
5. What are some special rules that apply to women in Saudi Arabia?
   In Saudi Arabia, women cannot drive cars or shop in some stores.
6. What are two Middle Eastern countries where many of the people are Christians?
   Cyprus
   Lebanon
7. In which Middle Eastern country are most of the people Jewish?
   Israel
8. What role does religion play in the lives of most people in the Middle East?
   Responses should indicate that the lives of most of the people are organized around religion.

Name Use with pages 373–376

Observing Contrasts in the Middle East

Use the pictures on the right to complete the activities on this page. For help, you can refer to pages 373–376 in your textbook.

1. **a.** Draw a line to the picture that shows the product that is most important to the economies of many Middle Eastern countries.
   b. Which Middle Eastern country has a highly developed economy without dependence on this product?
   Israel
2. **a.** Draw a line to the picture that shows a modern way of farming in the Middle East.
   b. By contrast, what kinds of methods are used on many traditional farms in the Middle East?
   labor-intensive methods
3. **a.** Draw a line to the picture that shows one effect of the war in the Persian Gulf.
   b. What effect did this action have on the environment and on Kuwait's oil production?
   The fires polluted the air and stopped much of Kuwait's oil production.
4. How is the economy of the Middle East both modern and traditional?
   Most of the people of the Middle East earn their living in the traditional ways of commerce and farming. Yet, money from oil has changed the economies of some of the countries of this region.

Israeli Kibbutz

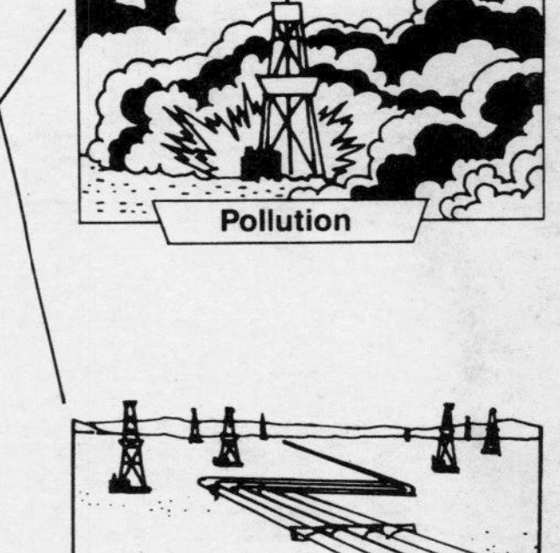

Middle East Oil

Name Use with pages 377–379

Comparing Governments of the Middle East

Draw a line under the word or phrase that best completes each sentence. For help, you can refer to pages 377–379 in your textbook.

1. The man pictured above is the ______ of Oman.
   a. premier
   b. president
   c. absolute ruler
2. Oman has no constitution and ______.
   a. no elections
   b. no strong leaders
   c. no tradition of democracy
3. Turkey, a Muslim country, has a ______ form of government.
   a. democratic
   b. weak
   c. religious
4. The governments of most Muslim countries are based on ______ law.
   a. Jewish
   b. Christian
   c. Islamic
5. The woman pictured above was the ______ of Israel.
   a. premier
   b. president
   c. absolute ruler
6. Israel has a ______ government.
   a. strong, centralized
   b. weak, federal
   c. parliamentary
7. The government of Israel is influenced by ______ law.
   a. Jewish
   b. Christian
   c. Muslim
8. The citizens of Israel have democratic rights and ______.
   a. free elections
   b. an absolute ruler
   c. no religious freedom

Name Use with pages 380–381

Comparing Maps

Use the maps of Egypt below to answer the questions that follow. For help, you can refer to pages 380–381 in your textbook.

MAP A
Distribution of Farm Products

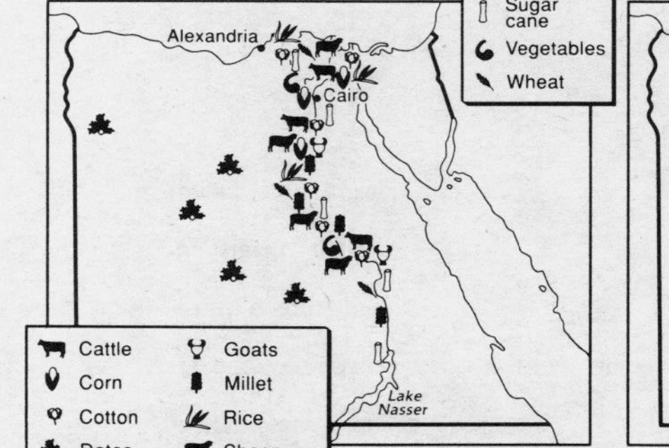

MAP B
Major Oases

Alexandria
Cairo
Siwa Oasis
Baharia Oasis
Farafra Oasis
Dahkla Oasis
Kharga Oasis
Nile River
Lake Nasser

1. What do the two maps show?
   Map A: distribution of farm products in Egypt
   Map B: major oases in Egypt
2. According to Map A, what are three crops grown in the region of the Nile Delta? sugar cane, corn, wheat, rice, cotton, vegetables
3. What two kinds of farm animals are raised in this area?
   cattle and sheep
4. What is the only crop grown away from the Nile River?
   dates
5. Compare Map A with Map B. What two factors seem to determine where farm products are grown in Egypt?
   the Nile River
   the location of oases
6. What farm product is grown around Egypt's major oases?
   dates

Name Use with pages 382–383

The Arts in the Middle East

Use the pictures below to complete the activities on this page. For help, you can refer to pages 382–383 in your textbook.

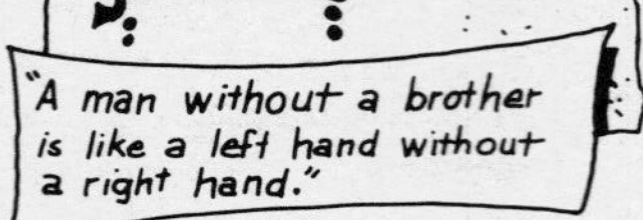

1. a. What is the form of writing in this picture called?
calligraphy

b. What is one collection of Middle Eastern tales that may have been recorded in this form of writing?
Arabian Nights

c. Where might you see writing like this today? **in the Koran and other Arabic and Muslim works and as decoration on the walls of buildings**

2. a. Along with intricate designs, what else do you see in this picture of an Islamic mosaic?
trees, clouds, flowers

b. Why aren't animals and people depicted in most Islamic art?
Islam discourages showing animals and humans in order to prevent people from praying to idols.

c. Where might you see some of the finest Islamic designs today?
on mosques and carpets

Name Use with pages 384–385

Thinking About New Words

Write the letter of the term in the box that matches each description below. For help, you can refer to the lessons in Chapter 18 in your textbook.

a. labor-intensive	**e.** kibbutz	**i.** moshav
b. absolute ruler	**f.** bazaar	**j.** Islam
c. calligraphy	**g.** Islamic republic	
d. hajj	**h.** sharia	

d 1. the Arabic word for the pilgrimage that Muslims make to the city of Mecca

j 2. a religion based on the teachings of Muhammad

c 3. a type of Arabic writing that features graceful, flowing lines

g 4. the term for a nation ruled by Islamic law

a 5. using many people rather than machinery to do work

i 6. an Israeli cooperative farm

b 7. one with complete power whose authority cannot be challenged

f 8. an outdoor market

h 9. Islamic law

e 10. an Israeli collective farm

Name　　Use with pages 387–390

The People of North Africa

The graph below shows Egypt's population in the past and what the population is likely to be in the future. Review the graph and then answer the questions that follow. For help, you can refer to pages 387–390 in your textbook.

EGYPT'S POPULATION GROWTH

Population (millions): 100, 90, 80, 70, 60, 50, 40, 30, 20, 10

Year: 1975, 1980, 1985, 1990, 1995, 2000, 2005, 2010, 2015, 2020, 2025

1976 36.6; 1988 50.3; 1990 52.7; 1995 58.9; 2000 65.2; 2025 97.4

1. According to the graph, what has been happening to Egypt's population?
   It has been growing at a rapid rate.

2. What does the graph show will happen to Egypt's population in the future?
   It will continue to grow rapidly.

3. What are some of the problems that the people of North Africa share because of the rapidly growing population?
   Most of the cities are overcrowded, and food shortages are common.

4. How has improved health care influenced the explosive growth of North Africa's population?
   North Africans are now living longer than they did before.

5. In which ways does Islam affect the people of North Africa?
   Islam shapes the way the people live, work, and play. It also has a strong effect on the government, education, and customs of North Africa.

6. How do many people in North Africa feel about influences from European cultures?
   They want to cut all ties to their European past and return to a stricter form of Muslim life.

Name　　Use with pages 391–393

The Economy of North Africa

Complete the map by writing the phrases from the box in the spaces provided on the map. Each space should have a separate phrase. Then answer the questions that follow. For help, you can refer to pages 391–393 in your textbook.

grew enough food for its people until the 1980s
major oil producing countries
second-largest industrialized nation in Africa
Aswan High Dam provides water for irrigation

grew enough food for its people until the 1980s

second-largest industrialized nation in Africa

MOROCCO
TUNISIA
ALGERIA
LIBYA
EGYPT
WESTERN SAHARA
Nile River

Aswan High Dam provides water for irrigation

major oil producing countries

1. Why must most of the countries of North Africa import food? **Responses may vary but should demonstrate an understanding that there is little usable farmland in North Africa and that as the population increases, this land is also being used for other things such as housing, business, and roads.**

2. On what does the economic future of North Africa depend? **The way the people of the region use their water and oil resources**

Name ________ Use with pages 398–399

The Assassination of Anwar Sadat

The headlines and articles below are from the October 7, 1981, issue of *The New York Times*. Read the headlines and articles and then answer the questions that follow. For help, you can refer to pages 398–399 in your textbook.

SADAT ASSASSINATED AT ARMY PARADE AS MEN AMID RANKS FIRE INTO STANDS; VICE PRESIDENT AFFIRMS 'ALL TREATIES'

Israel Stunned and Anxious; Few Arab Nations Mourning

WORRY IN JERUSALEM

JERUSALEM, Oct. 6—Israel, which had such a high stake in the survival of President Anwar el-Sadat, reacted with stunned anxiety today to the assassination in Cairo.

A fear for the peace treaty between Egypt and Israel dominated all emotions.

JUBILATION IN BEIRUT

BEIRUT, Lebanon, Oct. 6—There was no mourning in most of the Arab world today for President Anwar el-Sadat of Egypt, whose separate peace with Israel had led to his isolation.

Public jubilation was reported in the streets of Syria, Iraq, and Libya. . . .

1. According to the articles, who was Sadat and what happened to him?
   Sadat was the president of Egypt and was assassinated while he watched an army parade.
2. According to the articles, how did many of the Arab countries feel about what happened to Sadat? **There was no mourning in most of the Arab World. Syria, Libya, and Iraq were jubilant.**
3. According to the articles, what had isolated Sadat from the other Arab countries?
   He had signed a separate peace treaty with Israel.
4. According to the articles, why was Israel worried about the assassination?
   Israel was afraid something might happen to the peace treaty it had signed with Egypt.

Name ________ Use with pages 400–401

Asking the Right Questions

Use the picture and caption below to complete the activity that follows. For help, you can refer to pages 400–401 in your textbook.

Berbers in a Marrakesh market.

Suppose a friend of yours had recently returned from a trip to Morocco. As you looked through his photographs of the trip, you came across the one shown above. You knew nothing about the Berbers except what was written under the picture. Yet you became interested in them as a topic of study. Place an X next to each question that would help you to learn more about the topic.

X a. Who are the Berbers?

X b. Where did the Berbers come from?

____ c. What kinds of things can you buy in a Marrakesh market?

X d. Why were Berbers in a Marrakesh market?

____ e. In which part of Africa is Morocco?

X f. How and where do most Berbers live?

____ g. What is the population of Morocco?

X h. How long have there been Berbers in Morocco, and are there Berbers in other parts of the world?

X i. Why is the woman in the picture wearing a veil?

X j. What are some Berber customs and religious practices?

____ k. What is the major religion of the people of North Africa?

____ l. Who are the people that operate the markets in Marrakesh?

Name Use with pages 402–403

Islamic Influence on the Arts and Recreation

Briefly explain how Islam influences each of the activities shown below. For help, you can refer to pages 402–403 in your textbook.

ARTISTIC AND RECREATIONAL ACTIVITIES	ISLAMIC INFLUENCE 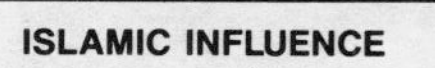
	Paintings are often traditional with religious themes. Wall paintings of pilgrimages are a very popular form of North African folk art.
Literature	One of the favorite themes is the importance of keeping Islamic traditions alive in a constantly changing world.
	Religious holidays are the most important days of the year for Muslims. Presents are exchanged on Muhammad's birthday. The holy month of Ramadan is observed.
	Television programming in North Africa is interrupted to allow Muslims time to pray.

Name Use with pages 404–405

Using New Words

Use the code in the box to figure out each word. For help, you can refer to the lessons in Chapter 19 in your textbook.

CODE

a = ○	g = ▽	l = ◡	q = ●	v = ◠
b = □	h = ✳	m = ■	r = !	w = ⧄
c = △	i = ¿	n = ꓶ	s =)	x = ∴
d = ➔	j = ◡	o = ◠	t = ◪	y = ⊠
e = ☽	k = ?	p = ▼	u = ¡	z = ☾
f = ▲				

b 1. f e l l a h i n

d 2. R a m a d a n

c 3. c o l o n i a l i s m

a 4. m u e z z i n

In the space before each decoded word above, write the letter of each definition it matches.

a. a crier who announces each of the five times every day when Muslims are supposed to pray

b. an Egyptian farmer

c. the control of a country as a colony by another country

d. the most holy month of the Muslim year

Name Use with pages 415–418

A Look at Sub-Saharan Africa

Read the directions and complete the map activities below. For help, you can refer to pages 415–418 in your textbook.

1. Locate and label the following regions of Sub-Saharan Africa. Then color each region as indicated.
   a. West Africa—brown
   b. East and Equatorial Africa—green
   c. Southern Africa—orange
2. Locate and label the following landforms.
   Mount Kilimanjaro Mount Kenya
   Zaire Basin Ethiopian Highlands
3. Locate and label Madagascar.
4. Locate and label the Great Rift Valley. Then color it red.
5. Locate and label the following bodies of water. Color the lake and trace the rivers in blue.
   Lake Victoria Niger River
   Zaire River Nile River

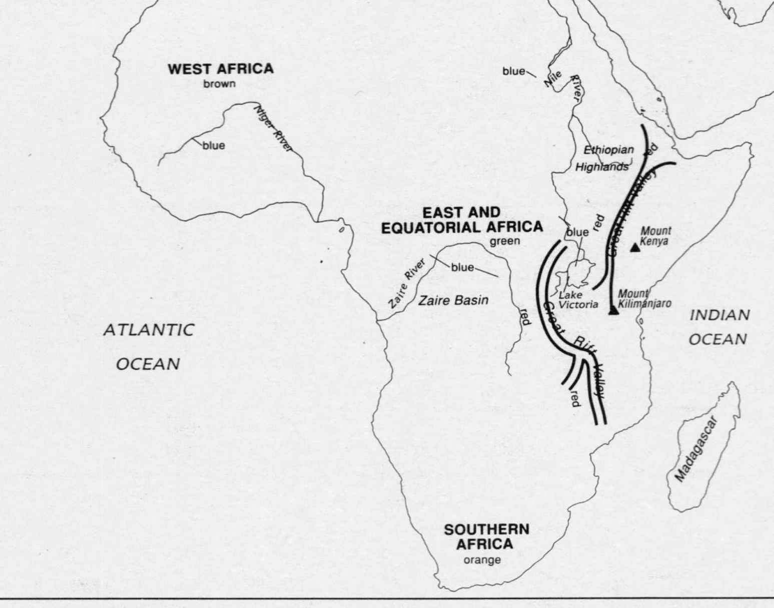

Name Use with page 419

Figuring Distances

Study the chart below. Then answer the questions that follow. For help, you can refer to page 419 in your textbook.

Road Distances in Miles	Jinga	Kampala	Mombasa	Nairobi	Tanga
Jinga		50	668	364	764
Kampala	50		718	414	814
Mombasa	668	718		304	96
Nairobi	364	414	304		401
Tanga	764	814	96	401	

1. What is the chart above called?
   a mileage chart
2. For what purpose is this kind of chart used?
   finding the distances between cities
3. How far is it from Kampala to Nairobi?
   414 miles
4. Would you travel farther going from Kampala to Nairobi or going from Nairobi to Jinga?
   going from Kampala to Nairobi
5. Using a car, which trip could you most likely take in a day—from Nairobi to Jinga or from Mombasa to Tanga?
   from Mombasa to Tanga
6. If you traveled by car from Jinga to Nairobi, on to Tanga, and then on to Mombasa, how many miles would you drive?
   861 miles
7. Are the distances you found on the chart by land or by air? How do you know?
   They are by land because a label on the chart says they are "road distances."
8. How could you use a map to find the same information that you found on the chart?
   You could use the scale bar on a map to measure the distances between cities.

Name Use with pages 420–423

The Resources of Sub-Saharan Africa

Read the following statements carefully. If a statement is true, write **True** in the space provided. If a statement is false, write **False** after it. Then write the reason for your answer. For help, you can refer to pages 420–423 in your textbook.

1. The picture above shows a herd of migrating animals at a drinking hole on the African savanna. Migrating wildlife is an important resource in Sub-Saharan Africa.
   True. Tourists come from all over the world to see African wildlife in its natural setting.

2. The entire African savanna is densely populated. **False. About one fourth of the savanna has very few people because the tsetse fly breeds there.**

3. In some areas of the savanna, people can raise grain crops. **True. In areas of the savanna that have enough rain, residents can raise crops like millet or corn.**

4. The rain forest of Sub-Saharan Africa provides many products and natural resources.
   True. The rain forest provides coffee, rubber, palm oil, and other products. Timber from such trees as mahogany, teak, ebony, cedar, and walnut is also a major resource of the rain forest.

5. Sub-Saharan Africa has very few mineral resources. **False. Sub-Saharan Africa is a storehouse of minerals. Copper, iron, gold, uranium, diamonds, manganese and many other minerals have been found in the region.**

Name Use with pages 424–425

Thinking About New Words

Answer each question in the space provided. For help, you can refer to the lessons in Chapter 20 in your textbook.

1. What is a **rift valley**? **A rift valley is a narrow valley with steep sides formed millions of years ago by cracks in the earth's crust.**

   What is the name of the large area of rift valleys in Sub-Saharan Africa?
   the Great Rift Valley

2. What is an **escarpment**? **An escarpment is a steep cliff at the edge of a plateau.**

   What happens when a river flows over an escarpment? **A river flowing over an escarpment creates a waterfall.**

3. Why did sailors refer to the winds of Sub-Saharan Africa as **trade winds**?
   The winds determined which way trading ships could sail.

4. What is the **harmattan** and how does it affect the climate in Sub-Saharan Africa?
   The harmattan is a wind that carries dry, dusty air from the Sahara to Sub-Saharan Africa, where it creates a hot, dry season.

5. What is a **savanna** and how much of the African continent is covered by it?
   A savanna is a broad grassland containing scattered trees and shrubs. The savanna covers more than one fourth of Africa.

6. What is a **basin**? **A basin is a large, bowl-shaped dip in the land.**

   Why is the huge Zaire Basin sometimes called "The Heart of Africa"?
   because this place of dense rain forests, swamps, and winding rivers is at the center of Africa

7. What is a **drought**, and how have droughts affected many of the people of Africa?
   A drought is a lack of rain over a period of time. Millions of Africans have died because of droughts.

Name _______________ Use with pages 427–431

Influences on West African Cultures

Study the picture and answer the questions below. For help, you can refer to pages 427–431 in your textbook.

1. The picture above shows what a mosque might have looked like in West Africa hundreds of years ago. How and when did Islam reach this part of Africa?
   Islam reached West Africa more than 1,000 years ago when Arab and Berber traders brought Muslim ideas across the Sahara from North Africa.

2. How has the religion of Islam influenced the cultures of West Africa today?
   Today Islam is the major religion in most of West Africa.

3. a. What happened in the 1500s that had a major influence on West African cultures?
   Europeans reached West Africa in the 1500s and began to establish colonies.

   b. What was the result of this event? **For many years most West African countries were ruled as colonies by European powers.**

   c. How has this influenced the cultures of West Africa today? **Today the most frequently spoken European languages are English, French, and Portuguese. Many black West Africans speak one of these languages in addition to the language of their particular ethnic group.**

4. How did the tradition of cooperation develop in West African cultures? How important is this tradition? **Long ago West Africans developed strict rules for working together so that families could survive in their harsh lands. Cooperation became more important than individual success.**

Name _______________ Use with pages 432–434

Some Methods of Farming in West Africa

Follow the directions to answer the questions below. For help, you can refer to pages 432–434 in your textbook.

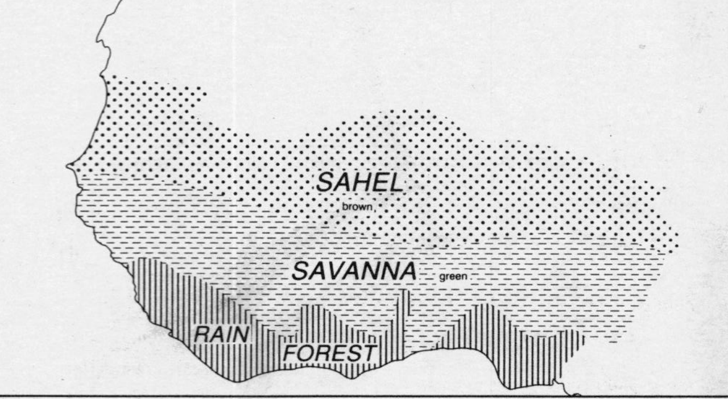

1. a. On the map above locate the region where desertification is occurring. Then color it brown.

   b. Why is desertification increasing?
   Drought, too much grazing, and the cutting down of trees and bushes leaves nothing to hold the soil and it blows away.

   c. What may happen to this region if desertification continues?
   The Sahel may become part of the Sahara.

2. a. On the map above locate the region where people practice shifting cultivation. Then color it green.

   b. What are two ways in which shifting cultivation is practiced?
   allowing some fields to rest
   slash-and-burn farming

   c. What is required for shifting cultivation to be successful?
   a lot of land

3. What are four crops produced by shifting cultivation in West Africa?
   millet **cassava** **yams** **peanuts**

Name Use with pages 435–438

A Look at a West African Government

Study the table and answer the questions below. For help, you can refer to pages 435–438 in your textbook.

FACTS ABOUT GAMBIA

Population: 773,000 (est. 1988)
Official Language: English
Major Religions: 90% Islam, 10% Christian and traditional
Ethnic Groups: Mandingo (41%), Fulani (14%), Wolof (13%), Serahuli (10%), Jola (8%), Other (14%)
Independence Day: February 18, 1965
Type of Government: Republic
Head of State: President elected to a five-year term
Major Political Parties: People's Progressive party
United party
National Convention party

1. a. According to the table, what kind of government does Gambia have?
a republic

b. What kinds of governments do most other West African countries have?
either one-party systems or military governments

2. What is the Head of State of Gambia called?
the president

3. How does a person become Head of State in Gambia?
He or she is elected.

4. a. According to the table, how many major ethnic groups are in Gambia?
five

b. What challenge do so many ethnic groups present to the governments of West Africa?
building national unity

5. How many major political parties does Gambia have?
three

6. In your opinion, is Gambia more or less democratic than most other West African countries? Give a reason for your answer.
Responses may vary, but students should indicate that Gambia, unlike most West African countries, has regular elections and several political parties.

Name Use with page 439

Distinguishing Fact from Opinion

Read the selection below. Then follow the directions and answer the questions. For help, you can refer to page 439 in your textbook.

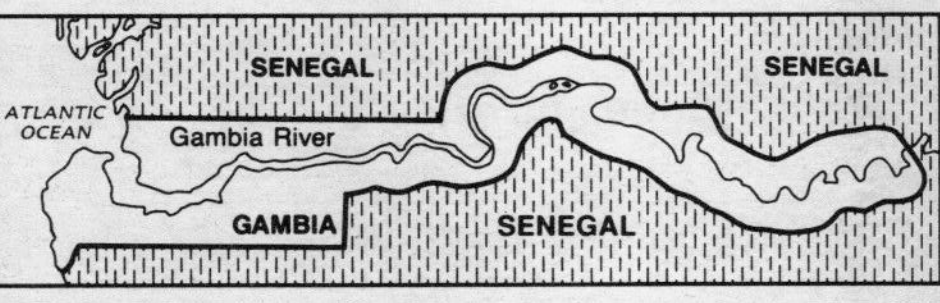

Gambia is the smallest independent country in Africa. I've always thought that the shape of Gambia is unusual. It is about 200 miles long but only from 10 to 40 miles wide. As it winds its way into the continent of Africa, it is surrounded by the country of Senegal. The entire length of Gambia follows the Gambia River, which is the major means of transportation through its interior. Gambia is planning to build a bridge and dam complex so that the river can be used for irrigation. I feel the dam will greatly benefit the Gambian people. It should allow them to grow more crops along the river's banks. In 1982 Gambia and Senegal established an organization for mutual cooperation. I believe this is one of the best things the two countries could have done.

1. Underline the sentences in the selection that state facts.

2. List two reasoned opinions stated in the selection. Then list the evidence the author gives to support each opinion.

reasoned opinion: **I've always thought that the shape of Gambia is unusual.**

supporting evidence: **It is about 200 miles long but only from 10 to 40 miles wide.**

reasoned opinion: **I feel the dam will benefit the Gambian people.**

supporting evidence: **It should allow them to grow more crops along the river's banks.**

3. Which reasoned opinion is supported by the map of Gambia?
I've always thought that the shape of Gambia is unusual.

Name Use with pages 440–441

Arts and Recreation in West Africa

Use the pictures on the right to complete the exercises below. For help, you can refer to pages 440–441 in your textbook.

1. a. Draw a line to the picture that shows West Africa's oral tradition.
   b. Who are the most famous West African storytellers?
   the griots
   c. What role do they play in many groups?
   They are the praise singers and historians.

2. a. Draw a line to the picture that shows how many West Africans mark the main events in human life.
   b. What is the main musical instrument used for these events?
   the drum

3. a. Draw a line to the picture that shows how West Africans traditionally called the gods and spirits to talk to humans.
   b. What materials may be used in the making of West African masks?
   Wood, metal, clay, ivory, feathers, leather, shells, and many other materials.

Mouse may seem small and unimportant, yet she goes all places and sees all things.

Name Use with pages 446–447

Thinking About New Words

Choose a term from the box to answer each question. For help, you can refer to the lessons in Chapter 21 in your textbook.

slash-and-burn farming	lineage	desertification
shifting cultivation	clan	oral tradition
griot	oba	talking drums

1. Which term refers to a West African storyteller? **griot**
2. Which term refers to a West African ruler? **oba**
3. Which term describes a way of farming that involves clearing the land by burning? **slash-and-burn farming**
4. Which term describes literature and history that are passed down from person to person by the spoken word? **oral tradition**
5. Which term would you use to refer to drums that imitate the sound of human speech? **talking drums**
6. Which term describes a group of families that are descended from the same ancestor? **clan**
7. Which term would you use to refer to a kind of farming that allows some fields to rest while others are planted? **shifting cultivation**
8. Which term best describes what is happening to the Sahel of West Africa? **desertification**
9. Which term would you use to refer to a line of direct descent from an ancestor? **lineage**

Name Use with pages 449–452

Migration into East and Equatorial Africa

The chart below lists some of the major groups of people that migrated throughout East and Equatorial Africa. Read the list of groups. Then complete the chart by filling in the columns. For help, you can refer to pages 449–452 in your textbook.

MIGRATION INTO EAST AND EQUATORIAL AFRICA

Migrating Group	Area of Migration	Influence and Skills
Bantus	The Bantus migrated south and east from Cameroon on the west coast southeast into Equatorial Africa. In time the Zaire Basin became the center of Bantu kingdoms.	Bantu-speaking people form the largest ethnic groups in Equatorial Africa and the southern part of East Africa.
Arab Muslims	Muslim traders set up trading posts on the East Coast of Africa. Dar es Salaam, Tanzania, was founded by Arabs.	Arab Muslims introduced the Arabic language and the religion of Islam. They also introduced important food crops.
Kushites	The Kushites migrated south from Ethiopia into the fertile plateaus of the present-day countries of Uganda, Kenya, and Tanzania.	The Kushites were skilled farmers.
Nilotes	The Nilotes migrated south from the Nile River Valley into present-day Sudan. They roamed over the dry lands of East and Equatorial Africa.	The Nilotes knew how to grow grains and keep livestock alive in very dry climates.
Europeans	During colonial days, Europeans ruled most of East and Equatorial Africa.	They introduced European languages and customs.

Name Use with pages 453–455

The Economy of East and Equatorial Africa

Read the following statements carefully. If a statement is true, write **True** after it. If a statement is false, write **False** after it. Then, in the space provided, write the reasons for your answer. For help, you can refer to pages 453–455 in your textbook.

1. The picture above shows the tradition of cattle herding among the people of East and Equatorial Africa. To these people, cattle are much more than just a source of food. **True. Cattle are not just a source of food. They are a status symbol—a sign of a person's wealth and importance.**

2. Many of the people in East and Equatorial Africa are nomadic herders of cattle, moving their herds from one area to another. **True. They move their herds back and forth across the savanna area of Sudan, Ethiopia, Djibouti, Somalia, and Kenya.**

3. The area of cattle herding has plenty of rainfall and an abundance of vegetation for grazing. **False. Even in the best of times the savanna is often harsh and dry. It is not quite a desert, yet water and vegetation are scarce in many parts of the savanna.**

4. In the southern areas, the people farm land that is usually owned by wealthy individuals. **False. Most people are subsistence farmers, and land may be owned by the clan, an extended family, or members of the village.**

5. To become more developed economically, the countries of East and Equatorial Africa need to take several costly steps all at once. **True. All the countries need better transportation systems and more dams to produce hydro-electric power. They also need more educated workers.**

Name Use with pages 458–460

Governments in East and Equatorial Africa

Use the lines below the box to answer the questions in the box. Write your answers as complete sentences and arrange them in paragraphs. When you finish, you should have a brief summary of the typical government in the area, as well as a requirement for change. For help, you can refer to pages 458–460 in your textbook.

- How do most East and Equatorial African leaders feel about democratic rights for their people?
- What kinds of governments have the countries of this region had?
- How many candidates are on the ballot in most elections?
- How has power usually changed hands in these countries?
- What changes are coming to this region?
- What do many people think must happen before the governments of East and Equatorial Africa will change?
- Why do these people think future governments will be better?

Most East and Equatorial African leaders feel that forming stable governments is more important than guaranteeing democratic rights to their people. The governments of this area have had one-party systems or dictatorships. In most elections only one candidate is on the ballot. Power has usually changed only when a leader died or was overthrown in a coup. However, the countries in the region are moving to end one-party rule. Many people in East and Equatorial Africa believe that things will change only when young people who are not familiar with colonialism become adults. They think that this new generation of independent citizens will be better able to govern themselves.

Name Use with pages 461–462

Looking at an Oral Tradition

The song, saying, and proverb below are from the oral tradition of the people of East and Equatorial Africa. On the lines provided, briefly explain what each means to you. For help, you can refer to pages 461–462 in your textbook.

In the time when Dendid created all things,
He created the sun,
And the sun is born, and dies, and comes again.
He created the moon,
And the moon is born, and dies, and comes again;
He created the stars,
And the stars are born, and die, and come again;
He created man,
And man is born, and dies, and does not come again.

–Old Dinka Chant

Answers should indicate an understanding of the song's references to the cycles of nature and the finality of death.

Somewhere the Sky touches the Earth,
and the name of that place is the End.

–A Kamba Saying

To stumble is not to fall down but
to go forward.

–A Swahili Proverb

Responses will vary but should suggest that for the Kamba, the world ends somewhere out there where the sky touches the earth.

Responses will vary but should indicate that the proverb suggests people can learn from their mistakes.

Name Use with page 463

Making a Graph from a Chart

Make a line graph from the information in the chart. Use a different color for each point on your graph. Then use your graph to answer the questions that follow. For help, you can refer to page 463 in your textbook.

POPULATIONS OF TWO AFRICAN CITIES

Country	Population in Millions						
	1960	1965	1970	1975	1980	1985	1990
Lagos, Nigeria	0.7	1.0	1.4	2.1	2.8	3.7	3.9
Casablanca, Morocco	1.1	1.3	1.5	1.9	2.2	2.7	3.2

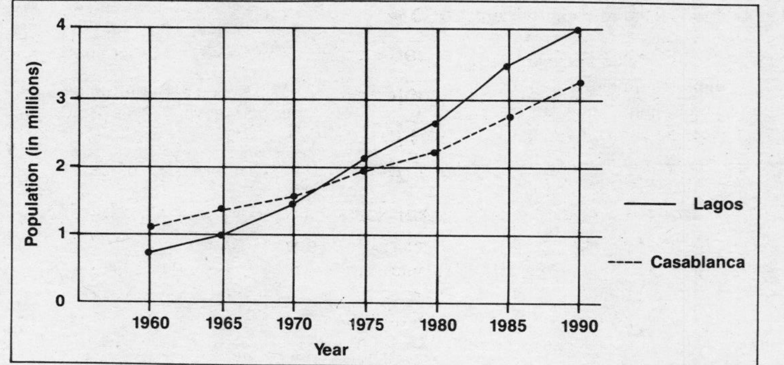

1. Has the population of each city decreased or increased since 1960? decreased **(increased)**
2. Which city had the larger population in 1960? **(Casablanca)** Lagos
3. Which city had the larger population in 1990? Casablanca **(Lagos)**
4. Which city's population grew faster between 1960 and 1990? Casablanca **(Lagos)**

   How can you tell? **The slope of the line is steeper.**
5. Is it easier to compare the population growth of the two cities in the graph or in the chart? Give a reason for your answer. **in the graph because you can see the change of population growth at a glance**

Name Use with pages 464–465

Thinking About New Words

Each of the terms listed in the box below is hidden among the letters that follow. Draw a circle around each term you find. The words may be read forward, backward, up, down, or diagonally. For help, you can refer to the lessons in Chapter 22 in your textbook.

migration	Swahili	famine	malnutrition
civil war	proverb	barter	

```
P O K U E L A S P A E O R R L I L A R O P M B E
R L R N K E M E M F C I V I L W A R Z I R A U W
E L X R O I G F S O T A C X D U A E K P O O V R
C N T Z Y O O S N O A T D I O O Q T E C V A E V
I D I A L I E M I G R A T I O N O C L P E T N X
E W S M T E O R K B O N S D L A K R A E R E N T
I L I H A W S E D A O E P A N B O J S A B U E I
R E S R L F A E D U O T R Q A D I O B K N T I Y
A S E Q H D S O L R M V I L U D P Z S R Z K C P
N O I T I R T U N L A M R O S I O Z S E T C A C
```

Write each circled word in the space next to its definition.

civil war 1. a war between people of the same country

migration 2. a movement of groups of people into new lands

proverb 3. a short, popular saying that illustrates a truth

malnutrition 4. a condition that occurs when people have too little food

famine 5. the widespread and extreme shortage of food

Swahili 6. one of the most common languages in East and Equatorial Africa

barter 7. to swap one thing for another

Name Use with pages 467–470

The People of Southern Africa

Follow the directions and answer the questions that follow. For help, you can refer to pages 467–470 in your textbook.

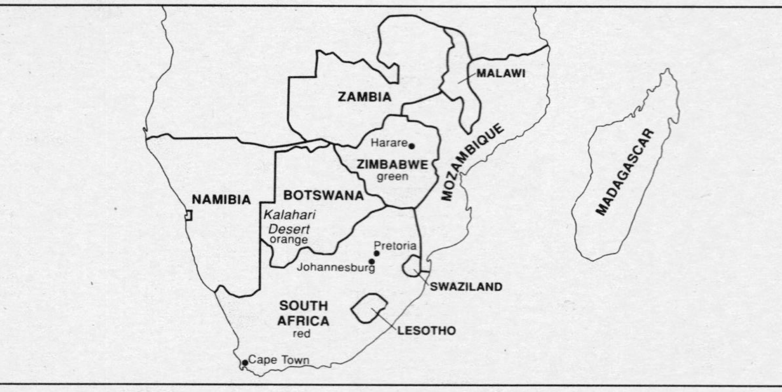

1. On the map above, locate and label the countries of Southern Africa.

Botswana	Lesotho
Madagascar	Malawi
Mozambique	Namibia
Swaziland	Zimbabwe
South Africa	Zambia

2. On the map above, locate and label the area where most Bushmen lived until recently. Then color the area orange.
   Kalahari Desert of Botswana

3. a. From what group are the majority of people in Southern Africa descended?
   the Bantu

   b. When did this group migrate into the lands of the Bushmen?
   between 500 and 800 years ago

4. a. Locate the only country in Southern Africa that is ruled by a white minority. Then color the country red.

   b. How are different racial groups treated in this country?
   Until recently, apartheid kept people separated from each other.

5. a. Locate a country that is ruled by its black majority. Then color it green.

   b. What is one way this country tries to promote understanding between its different ethnic groups?
   Students study the languages of people who belong to other ethnic groups.

Name Use with pages 471–473

The Economies of Southern Africa

Answer the questions below. For help, you can refer to pages 471–473 in your textbook.

AVERAGE YEARLY INCOMES IN SOME SOUTH AFRICAN COUNTRIES

Country	Average Income per Year (U.S. dollars)
Mozambique	$160
Zimbabwe	$260
Zambia	$390
Botswana	$900
South Africa	$1560

1. The graph shows the average amount of money that people in the countries of Southern Africa earn in a year. In which of these countries do people earn the least amount of money?
   Mozambique

2. What two factors have contributed to this low per capita income?
   civil war
   famine

3. In which country shown on the graph do whites and blacks work equally and peacefully together?
   Zimbabwe

4. How do most people make a living in this country?
   from farming

5. According to the graph, in which country do people have the highest income?
   South Africa

6. What two mineral resources does this country have in vast abundance?
   gold and diamonds

7. How do the incomes of white miners and black miners differ in South Africa?
   White miners often earn three to five times more than black miners.

8. Which country shown on the graph has one fourth of the world's copper?
   Zambia

Name Use with pages 474–477

A Look at Apartheid

The graph below shows the categories of races in South Africa. After studying the graph, complete the activities that follow. For help, you can refer to pages 474–477 in your textbook.

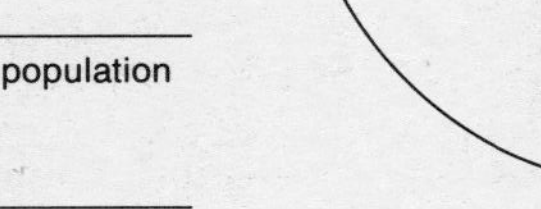

1. How many racial categories had been created by the South African system of apartheid? **four**
2. Which category is the largest? **black Africans**
3. Which racial category is firmly in control of the South African government? **whites**

   About what percentage of the population does this category make up? **14 percent**
4. What did many countries and international organizations do to protest the apartheid system? Give an example. **They passed sanctions against South Africa. For example, other nations did not allow South African athletes to compete in most world sports events because the majority of South African teams were separated by race.**
5. What changes began to take place in South Africa by 1990? **The state of emergency was declared over, and many apartheid laws were repealed.**

Name Use with page 478

Recognizing Bias

Read the accounts below of the "state of emergency" declared by the South African government in 1986. Then complete the activities that follow. For help, you can refer to page 478 in your textbook.

ACCOUNT A

In response to recent anti-apartheid demonstrations and protests, the South African government has placed the country under a state of emergency. The state of emergency gives the government the power to arrest and hold people without charge. The government has also limited news reporting and expelled journalists from several foreign countries. The government has taken these steps because it believes that excessive news coverage only makes the matter worse.

ACCOUNT B

In response to recent anti-apartheid demonstrations, the repressive white government of South Africa has assumed dictatorial power by placing the country under a state of emergency. Under the state of emergency the government has jailed tens of thousands of peaceful demonstrators and terrorized their leaders. It has also suppressed reporting of the protests and expelled any foreign journalists daring to report what is really happening.

1. Which account do you think shows bias? **Account B**
2. What are some clues that alerted you to the bias? **Answer may vary, but student responses should identify phrases such as "repressive white government," "assumed dictatorial power," "terrorized leaders," "suppressed reporting," and "daring to report what is really happening" as examples.**
3. Describe the bias in your own words. **Answers may vary, but student responses should indicate that the bias is against the South African government or in favor of the anti-apartheid demonstrators.**

Name   Use with pages 479–481

Arts and Recreation in Southern Africa

You might see the announcements on this page in almost any Southern African country. Read each one. Then answer the questions. For help, you can refer to pages 479–481 in your textbook.

1. a. What is the music called that is performed by the group in the top announcement?
   township music

   b. How was this music created?
   by mixing traditional African music with popular American and British songs heard on the radio

Ladysmith Black Mambazo

Enjoy the sound of South Africa as performed by this popular group.

2. a. What kinds of instruments does the group in the middle announcement use?
   They use only instruments invented in Africa.

   b. What is the main instrument used by this group called?
   a mbira

AMAMPONDO

The traditional instruments of Southern Africa as you've never heard them before.

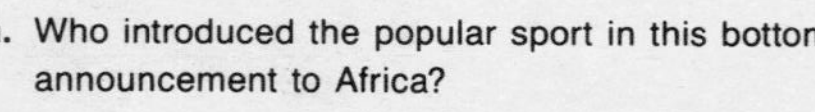

3. a. Who introduced the popular sport in this bottom announcement to Africa?
   the British

   b. What group ended its 21-year ban against competition by South African athletes in 1991?
   the International Olympic Committee

SOCCER OUTLIVES APARTHEID

South Africa Reenters World Competition.

Name   Use with pages 482–483

Learning New Words

Look at the box containing the Morse Code. The Morse Code uses dots and dashes to stand for the letters of the alphabet. Use the code to figure out the words and write each word on the lines provided. For help, you can refer to the lesson in Chapter 23 in your textbook.

A	B	C	D	E	F	G	H	I
•—	—•••	—•—•	—••	•	••—•	——•	••••	••
J	K	L	M	N	O	P	Q	R
•———	—•—	•—••	——	—•	———	•——•	——•—	•—•
S	T	U	V	W	X	Y	Z	
•••	—	••—	•••—	•——	—••—	—•——	——••	

c 1. **S A N C T I O N S**
••• •— —• —•—• — •• ——— —• •••

d 2. **V E L D**
•••— • •—•• —••

a 3. **T O W N S H I P**
— ——— •—— —• ••• •••• •• •——•

e 4. **M B I R A**
—— —••• •• •—• •—

b 5. **A P A R T H E I D**
•— •——• •— •—• — •••• • •• —••

Match the definitions below with the words above. Write the letter of each definition in the space before the appropriate word.

a. a racially segregated urban area in South Africa

b. the system used in South Africa for keeping racial groups separated

c. actions taken against a country by other nations to try to get the country to change

d. the vast, dry, treeless plateau that covers much of South Africa

e. an African finger piano made of metal or bamboo strips tied to a wood bowl

Name Use with pages 491–495

Southern and Eastern Asia

Use the map and follow the directions to complete the activities below. For help, you can refer to pages 491–495 in your textbook.

1. Locate and label the subcontinent of India.
2. Color the area of the Gobi and Takla Makan deserts brown.
3. Draw a red circle around the Indonesian archipelago.
4. Draw a green circle around the Philippine archipelago.
5. Locate and label the following rivers.

   Huang River Chang River

   Ganges River Mekong River

   Indus River
6. Locate and label the Pamir Knot.
7. Color the area of the North China Plain and the Tibetan Plateau orange.

Name Use with pages 496–497

Thinking About Great-Circle Routes

Use the maps to answer the questions and complete the activities that follow. For help, you can refer to pages 496–497 in your textbook.

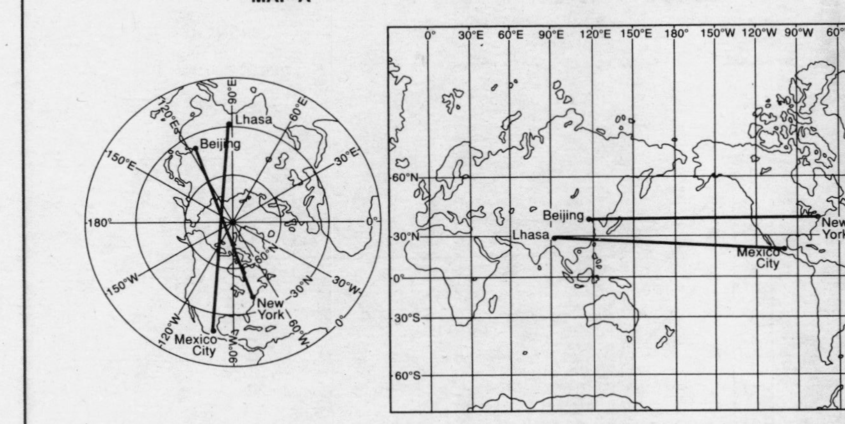

Circle the correct answer to each question.

1. Which map shows a great-circle route between New York and Beijing? 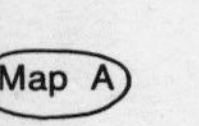 Map A Map B
2. Which map shows the shortest route between New York and Beijing? 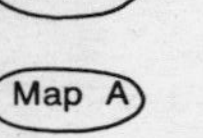 Map A Map B
3. Draw a straight line from Mexico City to Lhasa on each map. Suppose this line shows your route of travel. Which map shows the longer route? Map A 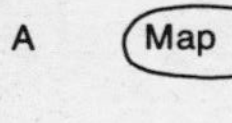 Map B
4. What kind of line would show a great-circle route between Mexico City and Lhasa on Map B?  curved straight

Name　　　　　　　　　　　　Use with pages 498–501

Climate in Southern and Eastern Asia

Study the maps and answer the questions. For help, you can refer to pages 498–501 in your textbook.

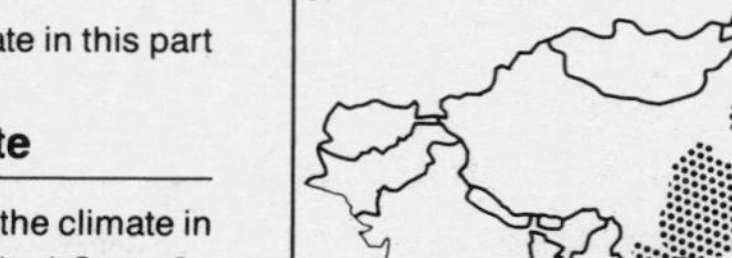

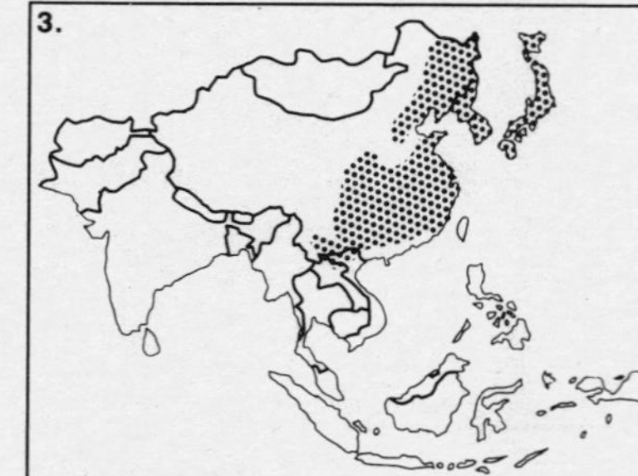

1. **a.** What kind of climate does most of this part of Asia have?
   tropical

   b. What is the major seasonal feature of this region?
   the monsoons

2. **a.** What kind of climate does this part of Asia have?
   cold and dry

   b. Why is this region cold and dry?
   It is cold because it is located at high elevations. It is dry because the mountains block most of the rain.

3. **a.** What is the major climate in this part of Asia?
   temperate

   b. How is this climate like the climate in the eastern part of United States?
   It has four seasons like the eastern United States.

Name　　　　　　　　　　　　Use with pages 502–503

Using New Words

Each of the terms listed in the box below is hidden among the letters that follow. Draw a circle around each term you find. The words may be read forward, backward, up, down, or diagonally. For help, you can refer to the lessons in Chapter 24 in your textbook.

subcontinent	monsoons	loess
alluvial soil	terraces	

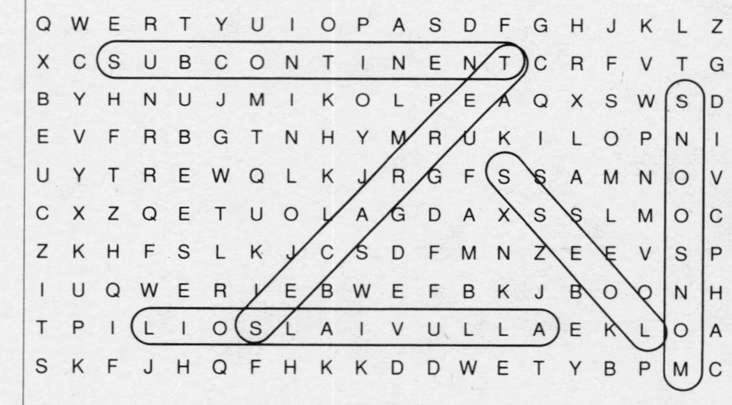

Q W E R T Y U I O P A S D F G H J K L Z
X C S U B C O N T I N E N T C R F V T G
B Y H N U J M I K O L P E A Q X S W S D
E V F R B G T N H Y M R U K I L O P N I
U Y T R E W Q L K J R G F S S A M N O V
C X Z Q E T U O L A G D A X S S L M O C
Z K H F S L K J C S D F M N Z E E V S P
I U Q W E R I E B W E F B K J B O O N H
T P I L I O S L A I V U L L A E K L O A
S K F J H Q F H K K D D W E T Y B P M C

Write each circled word in the space next to its definition.

monsoons 1. heavy rains brought on by seasonal winds

terraces 2. large steps that have been carved into hillsides for the raising of crops

alluvial soil 3. soil deposited by a river as it flows

loess 4. yellowish, fertile soil that has been deposited by the wind

subcontinent 5. a large landmass that is smaller than a continent

Name Use with pages 505–513

The People of South Asia

Study the table. Then answer the questions that follow. For help, you can refer to pages 505–513 in your textbook.

THE PEOPLE AND RELIGIONS OF SOUTH ASIA

Country	Major Religion	Population Density	Major Occupation Percentage of Workers
Afghanistan	Islam	65/per sq. mi.	68% farming/10% industry
Bangladesh	Islam	2,028/per sq. mi.	74% farming/11% industry
Bhutan	Buddhism	84/per sq. mi.	95% farming
India	Hinduism	658/per sq. mi.	70% farming/19% industry
Maldives	Islam	1,756/per sq. mi.	80% fishing and farming
Nepal	Hinduism	334/per sq. mi.	91% farming
Pakistan	Islam	335/per sq. mi.	53% farming/10% industry
Sri Lanka	Buddhism	692/per sq. mi.	46% farming/27% industry

source: *World Almanac, 1989*

1. According to the table, what are the three major religions in South Asia?

Hinduism

Buddhism

Islam

2. How did religious differences contribute to the formation of Pakistan?

Conflict between Hindus and Muslims in India led to the partition of India and creation of Pakistan.

3. According to the table, what is the major occupation of South Asians?

farming

4. According to the table, which South Asian country has the highest population density?

Bangladesh

5. How has a high population density contributed to a low standard of living for many South Asians?

Having so many people makes it hard for a country to grow enough food for everyone.

6. What is being done to ease the problems of famine and malnutrition in South Asia?

New irrigation systems are being built, and new kinds of crops are being raised.

Name Use with pages 514–517

The Governments of South Asia

Complete the map by writing phrases from the box in the spaces provided on the map. Each space should have a separate phrase. For help, you can refer to pages 514–517 in your textbook.

a socialist government	among the world's last monarchies
an Islamic country	gained independence with India's help
a threatened island democracy	the world's largest democracy

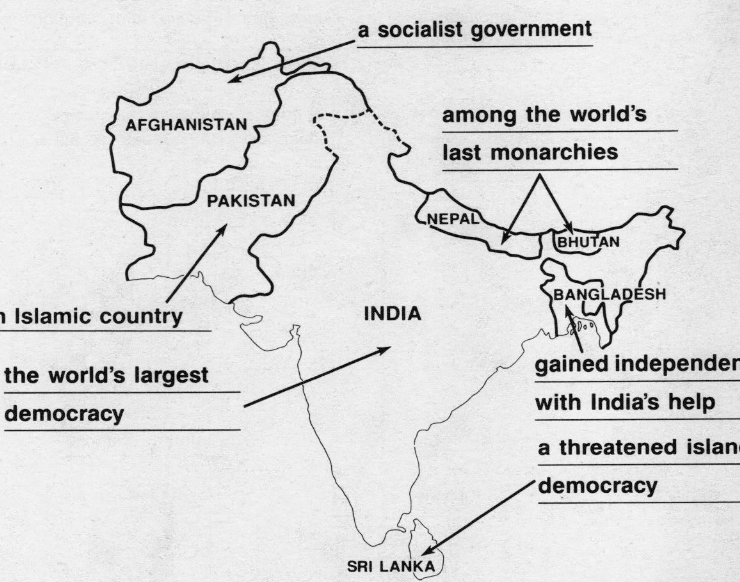

What have the nations of South Asia done to preserve their independence?

They have banded together with other small countries in a worldwide movement of nonaligned nations.

Name Use with page 518

Determining Point of View

Read the selection to complete the activities that follow. For help, you can refer to page 518 in your textbook.

Anyone visiting India should put the city of Agra at the top of his or her list of things to do and places to see. Agra is one of India's oldest cities and is famous for the Taj Mahal. The Taj Mahal may be the most beautiful building in the world. It was built in the 1600s by Emperor Shah Jahan as a memorial to his wife. The city of Agra is also famous for its gold lace and inlaid mosaics that are made mostly by hand. A visit to Agra is the best way to introduce yourself to the history, life, and customs of India.

1. List three sentences from the selection that are statements of fact.
   a. **Agra is one of India's oldest cities and is famous for the Taj Mahal.**
   b. **It was built in the 1600s by the Emperor Shah Jahan as a memorial to his wife.**
   c. **The city is also famous for its gold lace and inlaid mosaics that are made mostly by hand.**
2. List three sentences that are statements of opinion.
   a. **Anyone visiting India should put the city of Agra at the top of his or her list of things to do and places to see.**
   b. **The Taj Mahal may be the most beautiful building in the world.**
   c. **A visit to Agra is the best way to introduce yourself to the history, life, and customs of India.**
3. What is the writer's point of view? **Agra is one of the first places a visitor to India should see.**

Name Use with pages 519–521

Arts and Recreation in South Asia

Study the pictures. Then follow the directions to answer the questions that follow. For help, you can refer to pages 519–521 in your textbook.

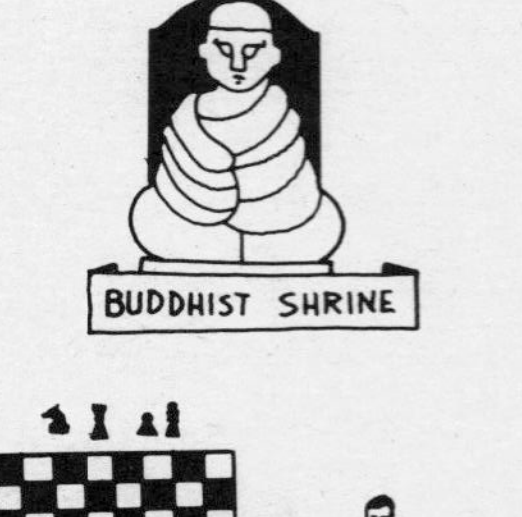

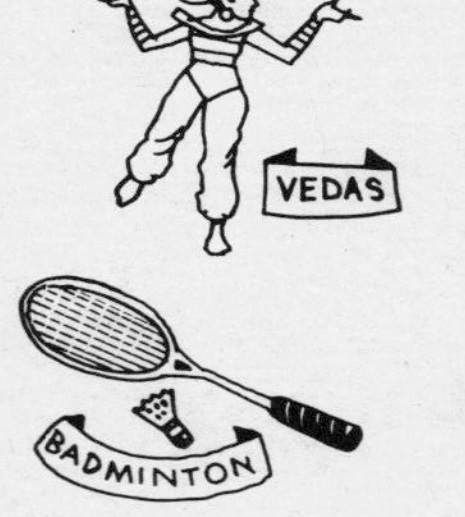

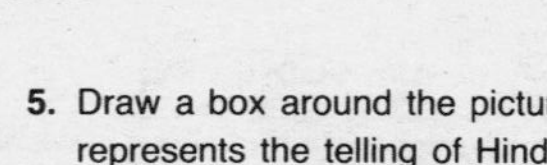

1. Circle the pictures that represent things from Indian culture that have spread to other parts of the world.
   yoga, badminton, polo, chess
2. Shade the picture that represents Islamic influence in art and architecture.
   Taj Mahal
3. Draw a triangle around the picture that represents Buddhist influence in art and architecture.
   Buddhist shrine
4. Put an **X** on the picture that represents a popular recreational activity imported from Britain.
   cricket
5. Draw a box around the picture that represents the telling of Hindu tales.
   Vedas
6. What plays a major role in the arts and recreation of South Asia?
   religion
7. What is meant by a cultural exchange between South Asia and other parts of the world?
   South Asia has imported some things from other cultures and has given much of its culture to other parts of the world.

Name Use with pages 522–523

Using New Words

Use the words in the box to complete the puzzle below. For help, you can refer to the lessons in Chapter 25 in your textbook.

nonaligned nations	Hinduism	Vedas
Green Revolution	Brahmans	yoga
cottage industry	Sikhism	
partition	caste	

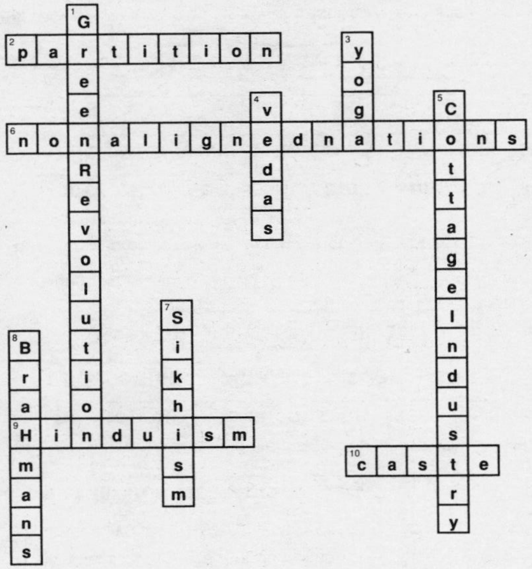

Across

2. division
6. countries that do not want to take sides in the struggles between the world's superpowers
9. the religion that grew out of the legends and customs of the Aryans
10. a social group that identifies people according to the occupation of their ancestors

Down

1. changes in South Asian farming techniques that have resulted in larger harvests
3. a way of training body and mind through exercise and meditation
4. a collection of Hindu writings
5. manufacturing that takes place inside people's homes
7. a religion combining some elements of Hinduism and Islam
8. the priestly caste of ancient India

Name Use with pages 525–528

People and Tradition in East Asia

Follow the directions to complete the activities below. For help, you can refer to pages 525–528 in your textbook.

1. **a.** Draw a line to the picture of the person who helped to establish the tradition of family loyalty in China.
   b. After the communists took power, with what did they try to replace family loyalty?
   loyalty to the state

2. **a.** Draw a line to the picture of the person who is believed to have been the founder of Daoism in East Asia.
   b. What does Daoism teach?
   People should accept their fate calmly.

3. **a.** Draw a line to the picture of the person who began Buddhism.
   b. What did this person come to be called?
   Buddha
   c. What does Buddhism teach?
   Suffering is caused by desire and selfishness.

4. **a.** Draw a line to the picture that shows the person who wanted China to break with the past.
   b. What system of government did he establish in China?
   communism

Name ____________ Use with pages 529–531

The Economies of East Asia

The headlines below might have been written about the economies of East Asia. Answer the questions about each headline. For help, you can refer to pages 529–531 in your textbook.

CHINA LOOSENS GRIP ON PRIVATE ENTERPRISE

a. During which years would this headline have been written? **in the late 1970s**

b. Why did China's leaders decide to allow limited private enterprise?
Answers may vary but should indicate that China's leaders believed that limited free enterprise would help solve China's food problem.

c. Was China's new economic program successful? Explain your answer.
The program was successful. More food and other goods were produced and sold on the open market.

CHINA SLOWS CHANGE TO PRIVATE ENTERPRISE

a. During which years would this headline have been written? **in the late 1980s**

b. List two problems that caused the government of China to tighten its control over private enterprise.
Under private enterprise some parts of China had too many goods, while other areas had severe shortages. Many prices had risen steeply.

EAST ASIA WORKS ECONOMIC MIRACLES

a. Which countries and colony of East Asia would this headline describe?
Hong Kong, Taiwan, South Korea

b. Why did these countries and colony produce goods more cheaply than other countries?
because their workers' wages were low

c. How did the people in these countries make their economies successful?
by rapidly increasing their trade with other countries

Name ____________ Use with pages 532–534

The Governments of East Asia

Look at the map and follow the directions to answer the questions below. For help, you can refer to pages 532–534 in your textbook.

1. Put an **X** on the countries that have communist governments.
China, Mongolia, North Korea

2. Shade the countries that have republican forms of governments.
South Korea, Taiwan

3. Circle the area that is a colony. What will happen to this colony in 1997?
Hong Kong
It will be returned to China.

4. What led to the present systems of government in China and Taiwan?
civil wars

5. What led to the present systems of government in North Korea and South Korea?
After World War II communist troops held the northern part of Korea. South Korea was occupied by American troops.

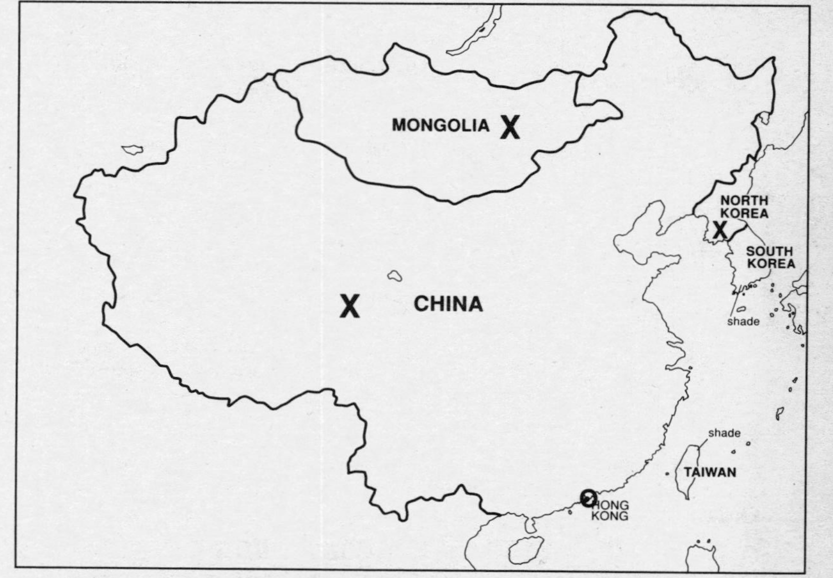

Reading Political Cartoons

The political cartoon below might have appeared in a newspaper during the time of the Korean War. Study the cartoon. Then answer the questions that follow. For help, you can refer to page 535 in your textbook.

1. What is the political cartoon about? **the Korean War**
2. What are four symbols in the cartoon? What do they stand for?
   a. **Uncle Sam is a symbol for United States forces and democracy.**
   b. **The Asian soldier is a symbol for communist forces.**
   c. **The torn shape of Korea is a symbol of the division of the country into North and South Korea.**
   d. **The trampled people is a symbol for the casualties of war.**
3. What point do you think the cartoonist was trying to make in the cartoon?
   Answers may vary, but student responses should indicate that the cartoon depicts the Korean War as a struggle between opposing forces with little regard for the people of the country.

Arts and Recreation in East Asia

Study the pictures and answer the questions that follow. For help, you can refer to pages 536–537 in your textbook.

1. What is the form of art called that is represented by the Chinese painting above?
   socialist realism
2. What is the purpose of this form of art?
   to use the "tremendous energy of the masses" to bring about change
3. In painting, what did this form of art replace?
   landscapes and other traditional themes
4. In which parts of East Asia do traditional arts and crafts continue to thrive?
   Hong Kong, Taiwan, and South Korea
5. What is the popular form of Chinese exercise called that is shown in the picture above?
   taiji quan
6. Why did Mao Zedong urge people to exercise?
   He wanted to end the low esteem in which China's educated classes held physical activity.
7. What are three forms of the martial arts that are popular throughout East Asia?
   kung fu
   tae kwan do
   karate
8. What are two crafts that are still practiced throughout East Asia?
   paper cutouts
   paper dragons

Name _______________ Use with pages 538–539

Using New Words

Write the letter of the term that matches each description below. For help, you can refer to the lessons in Chapter 26 in your textbook.

a. autonomous region	**e.** Confucianism	**i.** Daoism
b. socialist realism	**f.** aquaculture	**j.** pinyin
c. iron rice bowl	**g.** Pacific Rim	
d. martial arts	**h.** Buddhism	

e **1.** the teachings of Confucius

j **2.** a new way of spelling Chinese words

a **3.** a self-governing area in China that is supervised by the central government in Beijing

f **4.** fish farming

c **5.** part of an economic policy in China where people are paid whether or not they work

g **6.** all the countries that border the Pacific Ocean

h **7.** a system of belief that teaches that suffering is caused by selfishness

b **8.** a form of art that depicts true-to-life views of working people or heroes performing great deeds for the nation

d **9.** ancient forms of hand-to-hand combat

i **10.** a system of belief that teaches that people should accept their fate calmly

Name _______________ Use with pages 541–543

The People of Japan

Study the illustration, and then answer the questions that follow. For help, you can refer to pages 541–543 in your textbook.

1. The picture at the right shows a samurai who may have lived in Japan one thousand years ago. Who were the samurai?

The samurai were warriors that once ruled Japan.

2. What Japanese traditions were passed down by the Samurai?

a sense of duty and honor to one's family, leaders, and country

3. In today's Japan what happens if a person doesn't fulfill his or her duties to the family?

To fail to do one's duty causes a person to "lose face." The whole family is shamed and disgraced.

4. Why are politeness and good manners important aspects of Japanese culture?

The Japanese have deep respect for authority and order and believe that everyone has a certain position in society.

5. How does the Japanese view of society and the individual differ from the Western view?

The Japanese believe that society is more important than any one person. They see themselves as members of a group, rather than as unique individuals striving to get ahead.

6. Why do you think the Japanese developed such a distinctive culture?

Answers may vary but should indicate an understanding of the impact that Japan's isolation had on the development of Japanese traditions.

Name _______________ Use with page 544

Writing a Summary

Read the selection below. Then complete the activities that follow. For help, you can refer to page 544 in your textbook.

Samurai warriors were part of a privileged military class that ruled Japan from the twelfth to the nineteenth centuries. They pledged total loyalty to their feudal lords and defended their masters' territories. At the top of the samurai class was the shogun. He was the greatest of all feudal lords. Though shoguns were appointed by the emperor, it was the shoguns themselves who were the real rulers of Japan.

The samurai warrior was an awesome fighting machine. He was highly skilled in the use of the bow and sword. To protect himself he wore an elegant but very effective suit of armor. It was designed to provide freedom of movement while offering maximum protection. Because it was lightweight and flexible, it was unmatched by any other armor in the world.

The sword symbolized all that was important to a samurai warrior. In his hands it was a fearful weapon that had required strict training to master. The sword also stood for the samurai code of honor, bravery, and respect. All disagreements and problems were resolved by the sword, and the warrior lived and died by its laws. Strict rules were observed. For example, it was an offense to touch or step over another man's weapon. To lay your own sword on the floor and kick it in someone's direction was a challenge to the death.

1. Underline the topic sentence in each of the paragraphs.
2. Write a summary of the selection in three or four sentences.

Samurai warriors were part of a privileged military class that ruled Japan from the twelfth to the nineteenth centuries. They pledged total loyalty to their feudal lords and protected their masters' territories. A samurai warrior was an awesome fighting machine. His sword symbolized all that was important to him.

Name _______________ Use with pages 545–547

Interviewing Akio Morita

Suppose you could interview Akio Morita. You might ask him questions similar to the ones below. Use the space to write the answers you think he might give. For help, you can refer to pages 545–547 in your textbook.

Interviewer: Japan has experienced remarkable growth since World War II. Yet, your country has very few natural resources. What made this growth possible?

Morita: **The hard work of the Japanese people has made it possible. We demand excellence and efficiency of ourselves. We have also been able to adapt and improve upon the technologies of other countries. And we have continued to improve our manufacturing technology. For example we now use computer-controlled robots in many factories.**

Interviewer: What are some of the products made by Japanese companies?

Morita: **We produce everything from calculators and microchips to motorcycles and grand pianos.**

Interviewer: What is it like to work in a Japanese company?

Morita: **Workers receive extensive training after they are hired. They are made to feel as if they are part of the company family. In some businesses the workday begins with group exercises and company songs. Large companies may have recreational facilities for their workers.**

Interviewer: Suppose you could give advice to the children of Japan. What would you tell them?

Morita: **An industrial economy needs skilled, educated workers. I would advise the children of Japan to study hard in school so they could qualify for one of our best high schools.**

Name Use with pages 550–551

The Japanese Government

The diagram below shows the organization of the Japanese government. Study the diagram and then answer the questions on this page. For help, you can refer to pages 550–551 in your textbook.

GOVERNMENT

Although the Emperor is nominally the head of state, the power of day-to-day government of the country lies with the Prime Minister and his Cabinet. The Diet (parliament) consists of two houses, with a total of 763 elected members.

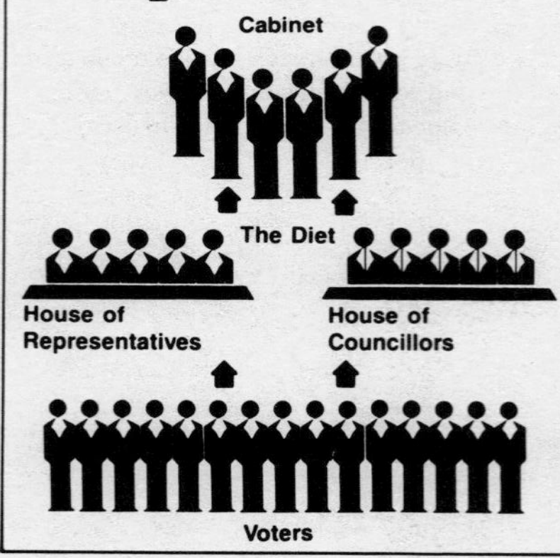

1. How did Japan's current form of government come about?
   At the end of World War II, the United States forced Japan to write a constitution forming a democracy.

2. According to the diagram, who is Japan's head of state?
   the emperor

3. Which person shown on the diagram is the head of the government?
   the prime minister

4. According to the diagram, from where are members of the cabinet selected?
   the Diet

   Who selects them?
   the prime minister

5. According to the diagram, what two Houses make up the Diet?
   House of Representatives
   House of Councillors

6. How are members of the Diet selected?
   They are elected by the voters.

7. What other country's government that you have studied is like that of Japan?
   Great Britain, Canada or other parliamentary systems

Name Use with pages 552–553

Arts and Recreation in Japan

Use the terms in the box to label each picture according to the artistic or recreational activity it represents. Then answer the question that follows. For help, you can refer to pages 552–553 in your textbook.

haiku	calligraphy	sumo wrestling
judo	flower arranging	

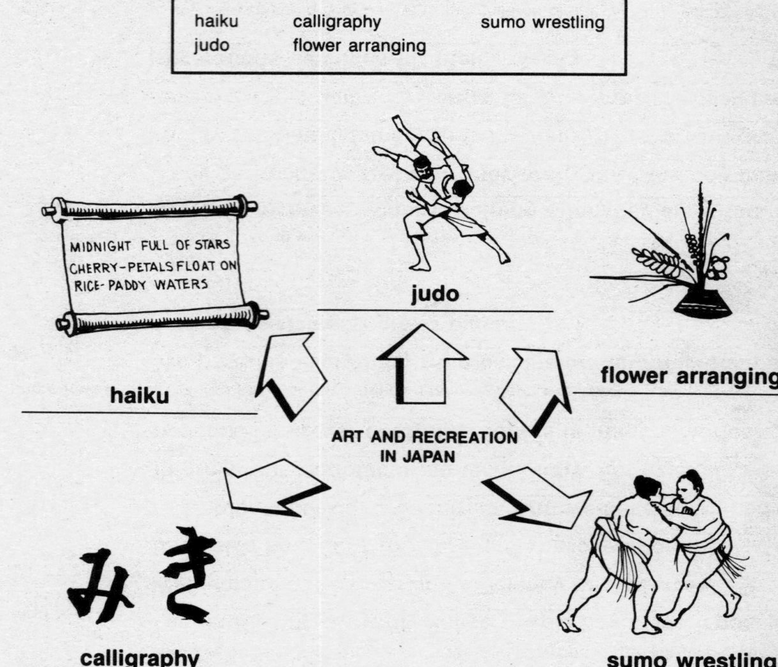

haiku **judo** **flower arranging** **calligraphy** **sumo wrestling**

Why are flower arranging, gardening, and calligraphy among admired art forms in Japan?
The Japanese believe that art should be part of everyday life, not something for special times and places. Thus flower arranging, calligraphy, and gardening are highly admired art forms.

Name Use with pages 558–559

Using New Words

Follow the directions to find each hidden term. Then, write the definition on the line below the letters. For help, you can refer to the lessons in Chapter 27 in your textbook.

1. Cross out the letters d, t, m, z, s **calligraphy**

   c d a t l l m i z g s r d a t p m h y

   the art of beautiful writing

2. Cross out the letters a, g, m, r, y **Shinto**

   a g s r h y g i n a g t r o m

   the oldest of Japan's religions

3. Cross out the letters a, c, j, k, y, x **sumo wrestling**

   c a s k u j a m o y w a c r e k s t c a l i x n g

   one of Japan's traditional sports

4. Cross out the letters c, g, o, r, u, w **Diet**

   w o d g r i c e u r g t

   the Japanese legislature

5. Cross out the letters b, d, e, h, t **samurai**

   s e b a t e m h u r d a i t

   warriors who ruled Japan hundreds of years ago

6. Cross out the letters d, i, p, r, w **homogeneous**

   h i p o m r o w i g e n r e i o d u r s

   to look and act in a similar way

Name Use with pages 561–564

The Countries and People of Southeast Asia

Use the map and follow the directions to complete the activities below. For help, you can refer to pages 561–564 in your textbook.

1. Locate and label the countries that make up Southeast Asia. List them below.

   Philippines **Laos**
   Indonesia **Brunei**
   Singapore **Cambodia**
   Malaysia **Myanmar**
   Thailand **Vietnam**

2. Locate the country that was settled by people from southwest China about 2,500 years ago. Then color it brown.

   Malaysia

3. Shade the other countries that were settled by people from southern China.

   Vietnam, Myanmar,
   Thailand, Laos

4. Draw a circle around the country in which the Dutch built canals.

   Indonesia

5. Draw a rectangle around the country into which the Spanish introduced the Roman Catholic religion.

   Philippines

6. From which two Asian countries have people immigrated to Southeast Asia during the last 100 years?

   China **India**

7. What are the two major religions in Southeast Asia today? List them below.

   Buddhism
   Islam

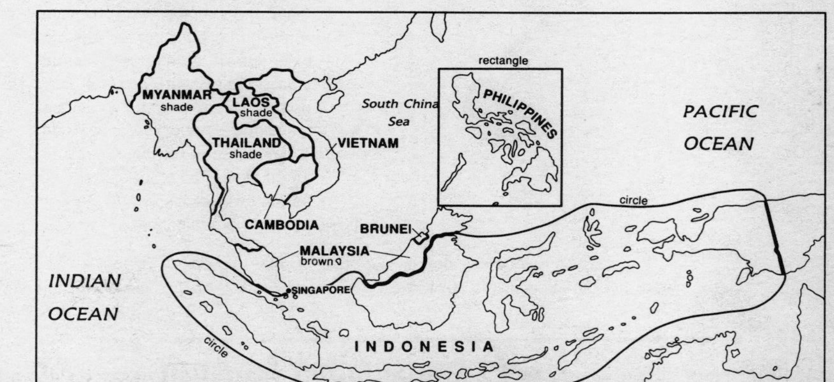

Name Use with pages 565–570

Southeast Asia: Government and Economy

Use the terms and phrases in the box to complete the chart below. You will need to use some terms and phrases more than once. For help, you can refer to pages 565–570 in your textbook.

- constitutional monarchy
- republic ruled by military leaders
- republic headed by a president
- communist
- absolute monarchy
- parliamentary system
- richest country in the region
- financial and industrial center
- making economic gains with the help of foreign companies
- poor economy due to war
- third-richest country in the region
- poor economy due to poor planning, debt, and civil unrest

THE GOVERNMENTS AND ECONOMIES OF SOUTHEAST ASIA

Country	Type of Government	Condition of Economy
Philippines	**republic headed by a president**	**making economic gains with the help of foreign countries**
Singapore	**parliamentary system**	**financial and industrial center**
Brunei	**absolute monarchy**	**richest country in the region**
Malaysia	**constitutional monarchy**	**third-richest country in the region**
Indonesia	**republic ruled by military leaders**	**making economic gains with the help of foreign countries**
Laos	**communist**	**poor economy due to war**
Myanmar	**republic ruled by military leaders**	**poor economy due to poor planning, debt, and civil unrest**
Cambodia	**communist**	**poor economy due to war**
Thailand	**constitutional monarchy**	**making economic gains with the help of foreign countries**
Vietnam	**communist**	**poor economy due to war**

Name Use with page 571

Drawing Conclusions

Read the article below. Then put an **X** next to each conclusion you can draw from the article. For help, you can refer to page 571 in your textbook.

During the Philippine elections of 1986, the Marcos government sent troops into most communities to destroy ballot boxes and votes that had been cast for Corazon Aquino. But the people of the Philippines formed human chains around the ballot boxes to protect them. Large crowds filled the streets, blocking the movement of military tanks. Soldiers put down their guns and joined the masses. Faced with such massive protests, Marcos and his followers were forced to flee the country, and Corazon Aquino became the president.

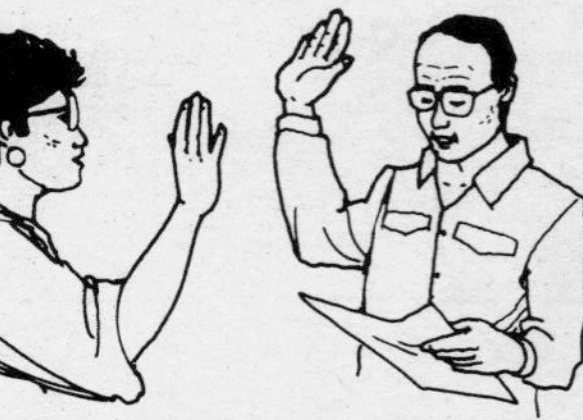

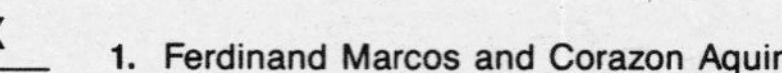

X 1. Ferdinand Marcos and Corazon Aquino were political opponents.

___ 2. Corazon Aquino disliked Marcos and his family.

X 3. Corazon Aquino had the support of the majority of the Philippine people.

X 4. The Philippine people were tired of the government of Ferdinand Marcos.

___ 5. No one supported the Marcos government.

___ 6. Marcos's high-level military generals gave their support to Aquino.

X 7. Marcos feared losing the 1986 presidential election.

X 8. Marcos did almost everything he could to keep Aquino from winning the election.

___ 9. Corazon Aquino had run for president in the previous election.

___ 10. The Philippine people based their decisions on debates between Marcos and Aquino.

Page 157

Name Use with pages 572–573

Arts and Recreation in Southeast Asia

Follow the directions to complete the activities below. For help, you can refer to pages 572–573 in your textbook.

1. a. Draw a line to the picture that shows a popular sport in Southeast Asia.
   b. In which country did this sport originate?
   Thailand
   c. How is this sport different in Asia than it is in the United States?
   In Asia boxers use their elbows and knees and make lightening-fast kicks.

2. a. Draw a line to the picture that shows a form of entertainment that is also part of the education of most Indonesian children.
   b. What kinds of stories are depicted this way?
   stories of ancient Hindu rulers, gods, and heros

3. a. Draw a line to the picture that shows one kind of traditional music being performed in Indonesia.
   b. Why does almost every village in Indonesia have this kind of orchestra?
   because the people feel that without a gamelan a village can't have a proper festival

Gamelan

Thai Boxing

Shadow Plays

Page 158

Name Use with pages 574–575

Learning New Words

Each of the words listed in the box below are hidden among the letters that follow. Draw a circle around each word you find. The words may be read forward, backward, up, down, or diagonally. For help, you can refer to the lessons in Chapter 28 in your textbook.

meditate	Vietnam War	paddy
	shadow play	gamelan
	gross national product	

A G Y E D I M T R A B C K H I K L M H P C K C Q
H I A B R O E D V T Z N C A Z P O M A Y A L A M
S I L M K U D L A L B X E A T R O K M D A Y O S
U I P M E E I S L K E F V R S L E O M D K G E D
K W W M S L T I W S O L A E A E D N O A S N O M
G O O P S O A M E N U I E Q L K A N Z P E N S A
A D D V I E T N A M W A R E O W E Q R K O A K Q
D A A K D A E T J R X Q O A K L E U I S Y E D S
S H H E E K O T E S R X A S L O B A E A C T S O
T S S E T C U D O R P L A N O I T A N S S O R G

Write each circled word in the space next to its definition.

Vietnam War 1. The longest and most damaging war in Southeast Asia

gamelan 2. An Indonesian orchestra

meditate 3. Think deeply

gross national product 4. The total amount of goods and services produced in a country during a year

shadow play 5. A form of entertainment in which puppets are used to act out well-known stories by casting shadows

paddy 6. Flooded field where rice is grown

Name Use with pages 583–587

Looking at the Geography of the Pacific

The map below shows how the Pacific Islands are divided into three main groups. Study the map. Then complete the activities on this page. For help, you can refer to pages 583–587 in your textbook.

1. Collectively, what are the Pacific Islands called that are shown on the map?
   Oceania
2. Locate and label the area known as Polynesia. Then color the area green.
3. Locate and label the area known as Micronesia. Then color the area red.
4. Locate and label the area known as Melanesia. Then color the area brown.
5. Locate and label the island country known as New Zealand. Color North Island yellow. Color South Island orange.
6. Locate and label the world's smallest and oldest continent. **Australia**
7. Which three main inland regions make up this continent?
   the Western Plateau
   the Central Plains
   the Eastern Highlands
8. What large underwater area can be found off the northeast coast of this continent?
   the Great Barrier Reef

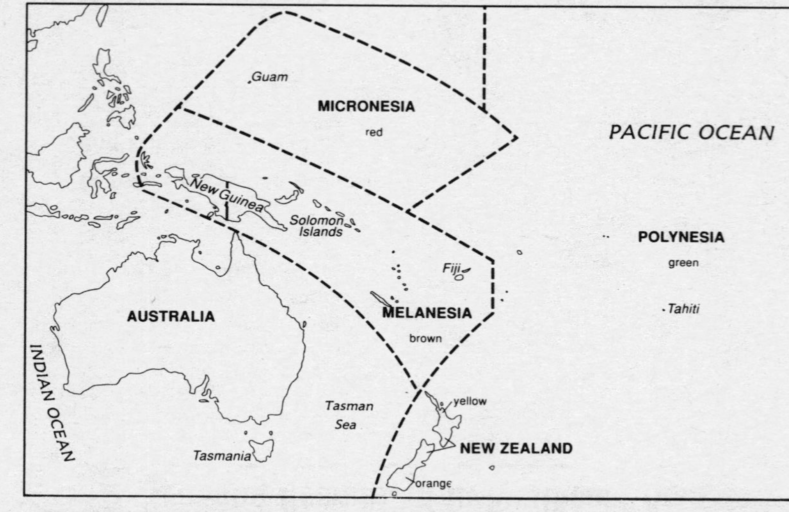

Name Use with pages 588–589

Using Maps of the Ocean Floor

The map below shows the floor of the South Pacific Ocean around the continent of Australia. Use the map to answer the questions. For help, you can refer to pages 588–589 in your textbook.

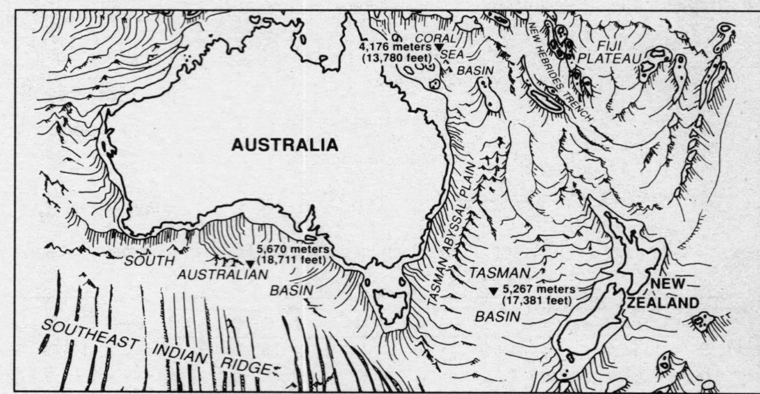

1. Is the map above a relief map or a contour map? How do you know?
   It is a relief map. It shows the features of the ocean floor without using contour lines.
2. What is the name of the mountain range that runs across the ocean floor south of Australia?
   the Southeast Indian Ridge
3. Which feature curves around the Fiji Plateau?
   the New Hebrides Trench
4. How far below sea level is the floor of the Tasman Basin?
   17,381 feet (5,267 m)
5. Would ocean ridges or ocean basins be further below sea level? Explain your answer.
   basins because they are flat areas on the ocean floor. Ridges are mountains that rise above the ocean floor.
6. How do scientists show elevations and features of the ocean floor more accurately than they are shown on the map above?
   by making contour maps

Name Use with pages 590–593

Products of Australia and the Pacific Islands

Circle the pictures that represent products from Australia. Draw a box around the pictures that represent products from New Zealand. Draw a triangle around the picture that represents an important natural resource found on many of Oceania's tropical islands. Then answer the questions that follow. For help, you can refer to pages 590–593 in your textbook.

1. Why is Australia called the "Lucky Country"?
   It is an uncrowded land with abundant natural resources.
2. What are two minerals mined in Australia that are not shown in the picture?
   bauxite, iron, copper, lead, zinc
3. Why do the ranches in Australia have to be so large?
   Because of the dry land and sparse vegetation it requires a lot of land to graze livestock.
4. What are two major natural resources that New Zealand has that are not shown in the picture?
   water
   forests
5. Why can a variety of fruits be grown by New Zealand farmers?
   New Zealand has both good soil and a variety of climates.
6. Why do the people of Oceania's tropical islands call the coconut palm the "Tree of Life"?
   It grows in poor soil and has many uses.

Name Use with pages 594–595

Using New Words

Use the code in the box to figure out each word. Then write the word on the line above its code. For help, you can refer to the lessons in Chapter 29 in your textbook.

CODE

a = ○	g = ▽	l = ◡	q = ●	v = ◠
b = □	h = ✳	m = ■	r = !	w = ⊠
c = △	i = ¿	n = ʕ	s =)	x = ∴
d = ➡	j = ◡	o = ◠	t = ◪	y = ⊠
e =)	k = ?	p = ▼	u = ¡	z = (
f = ▲				

d 1. c o p r a

b 2. t y p h o o n

e 3. i c e b e r g

a 4. a t o l l

c 5. o u t b a c k

Write the letter of each of the following definitions in the space before the above word that it matches.

a. a doughnut-shaped coral reef looped around an area of still, warm water
b. a whirling tropical hurricane of the Pacific
c. a huge, arid area of Australia
d. the dried meat of a coconut
e. a large body of ice that has broken away from a glacier

Name Use with pages 597–599

The People of Australia and the Pacific Islands

The words below were written by Louis-Antoine de Bougainville. Read what he wrote. Then answer the questions. For help, you can refer to pages 597–599 in your textbook.

1. What island was de Bougainville writing about?
   Tahiti
2. Who were the people he mentions?
   Tahitians, one group of Polynesians
3. Why have these people been called the "Vikings of the Sunrise"?
   because they were expert in both sailing and shipbuilding
4. Which group of these people sailed south to settle New Zealand?
   the Maori
5. Which group of people were the first to settle in Australia?
   the Aborigines
6. How were these people treated by the early European explorers?
   Many were attacked and killed.
7. Why did many European immigrants come to New Zealand and Australia?
   because Australia and New Zealand offered land, work, and adventure

Name Use with pages 600–601

ECONOMIES: Australia and Pacific Islands

Study the graphs. Then answer the questions. For help, you can refer to pages 600–601 in your textbook.

LEADING IRON-ORE PRODUCING COUNTRIES (millions of tons)

Soviet Union	271,100,000
Brazil	106,400,000
Australia	100,800,000
China	84,000,000

1. a. According to the bar graph on the right, which South Pacific country is one of the leading iron-ore producers in the world?
   Australia

   b. This country is a top producer of what other three mineral resources?
   copper
   nickel
   aluminum

   c. This country's developed economy includes a mixture of what economic activities?
   farming, mining, manufacturing, and service industries

LEADING WOOL-PRODUCING COUNTRIES (millions of lbs.)

Australia	1,607,000,000
Soviet Union	1,021,000,000
New Zealand	800,000,000
China	412,000,000

2. a. According to the graph on the right, which two Pacific countries are leading producers of wool?
   Australia
   New Zealand

   b. Which of these countries is the largest exporter of wool?
   New Zealand

   c. What is the most important part of this country's economy?
   farming and ranching

3. a. What is the main source of income for the many Pacific Islands not shown in the graphs? **tourism**

   b. How do the economies of these islands differ from the economies of New Zealand and Australia? **Most of the Pacific Islands have developing economies. New Zealand and Australia have developed economies.**

Name Use with page 602

Making Decisions

Sonia's teacher has given the class three choices for a field trip. Tomorrow they will vote on where the class will go. Read how Sonia decided which trip to vote for. Then answer the questions. For help, you can refer to page 602 in your textbook.

I know that I want to go to the place where I can learn the most. The first choice is going to the botanical gardens. I could learn about many different kinds of plants and it's nearby. But I've already been there several times.

Our second choice is going to the Metropolitan Museum. They have many different kinds of exhibits including some on Pacific cultures. We are learning about the people of the Pacific Islands in our social studies class. The only problem is that it takes about two hours to get to the museum. We would have to leave early in the morning.

Our third choice is taking a tour of the historic district of our town. That sounds like fun, but it's fall and it may be cold. Besides, I have been to the district several times with my family, and I already know quite a lot about the history of our area.

The more I think about it, the better the museum sounds. I can learn about something I am studying in class, and there are lots of other things to see and do, too.

1. What decision did Sonia have to make? **She had to decide which field trip to vote for.**
2. What was her goal? **to go to a place where she could learn the most**
3. Which trip did Sonia finally decide to vote for? **the museum**
4. Which two things didn't Sonia consider as she thought about her decision? Put an **X** next to each one.
   - **X** a. Each trip would cost a different amount of money.
   - ___ b. Her social studies class is studying the people of the Pacific Islands.
   - ___ c. She has been to the historical district of her town several times with her family.
   - **X** d. A long trip might not leave much time at the museum.

Name Use with pages 603–605

GOVERNMENTS: Australia and Pacific Islands

Complete the map by writing phrases from the box in the spaces provided on the map. Each space should have only one phrase, but you may use a phrase more than once. Then answer the question that follows. For help, you can refer to pages 603–605 in your textbook.

- parliamentary system of government
- trust territory of the United States
- elected legislature and a council of chiefs
- ruled by a monarch and a council
- only matai can vote for government officials

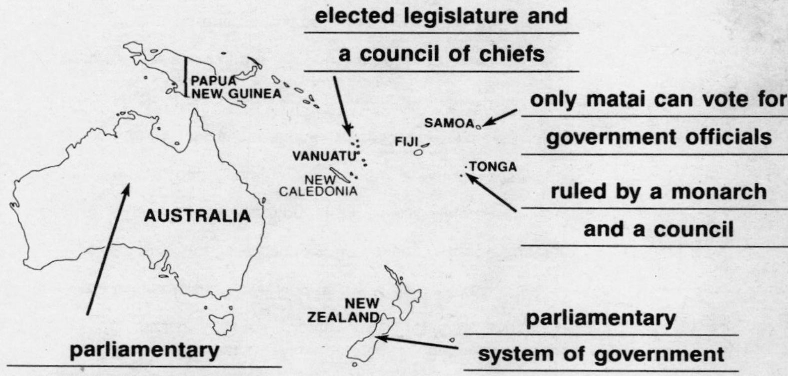

How would you describe the many forms of government in the Pacific region? **Most have representative assemblies. Australia, New Zealand, Papua New Guinea, and Fiji belong to the British Commonwealth of Nations. In most of the rest of the island nations, traditional island chiefs and elected government officials form the governments.**

Name

Use with pages 606–607

Arts and Recreation in the Pacific Region

Follow the directions to complete the activities below. For help, you can refer to pages 606–607 in your textbook.

1. a. Draw a line to the picture that shows one way the Samoans keep their cultural identity alive.
   b. What happens as warriors bend over their oars?
   They yell out chants to the beat of drums.
   c. What are some of the chants about?
   the history of families

2. a. Draw a line to the picture that shows where Australians enjoy performances of the fine arts.
   b. What did the Australians hope to show outsiders by building this structure?
   They not only appreciate the fine arts, but they also create world-class architecture.

3. a. Draw a line to the picture that shows the most popular sport in New Zealand.
   b. What are two other popular New Zealand sports?
   long-distance running
   mountain climbing

Sydney Opera House

Rugby

Samoan Canoe

Name

Use with pages 612–613

Using New Words

Complete each of the activities below. For help, you can refer to the lessons in Chapter 30 in your textbook.

1. Put an **X** next to each statement that correctly describes a *trust territory*.

____ a. A trust territory controls its own government.
__X__ b. A trust territory does not belong to an outside power.
__X__ c. The government of a trust territory is controlled by another country until that country decides the trust territory is ready to govern itself.
____ d. A trust territory is a kind of economic system.
____ e. An outside power controls the government of a trust territory permanently.
__X__ f. Guam is a trust territory of the United States.

2. Put an **X** next to each statement that is true about *stations*.

__X__ a. Stations are huge ranches where sheep and cattle are raised.
__X__ b. Much of the world's wool is made from sheep on New Zealand stations.
____ c. Sheep stations are the only kind of farm found in New Zealand.
____ d. Stations are large fruit orchards in Australia and New Zealand.
__X__ e. Only 6 percent of Australians work on farms or stations.
____ f. Stations are a form of government in the Pacific islands.